1933

A CENTURY
OF PROGRESS
CHICAGO

It is a real pleasure to welcome
this literary contribution of the
egg and poultry industries as a
permanent record of the achievements in the production and preparation of two foods universally
used.

—A. W. BITTING

Foods and Agricultural Section
Department of Exhibits

It is a real pleasure to welcome
this literary contribution of the
egg and poultry industries as a
permanent record of the achievements to the production and preparation of two foods universally
used.

A. W. BITTING
Foods and Accessories Service
Department of Exhibits

eggs

General Editor
PAUL MANDEVILLE

 The Authors

MARY ENGLE PENNINGTON
Consultant in the handling
of perishable foods

FRANK L. PLATT
Editor, American Poultry
Journal

CLARA GEBHARD SNYDER
Director of foods and nutrition,
Institute of American Poultry
Industries

Chapters and paragraphs by
the editor and an assisting staff

Art editor and book designer
RAYMOND HEER

Sponsored by the
INSTITUTE of AMERICAN POULTRY INDUSTRIES

PROGRESS PUBLICATIONS
1530 Merchandise Mart   Chicago, U. S. A.

D<small>edicated to all</small>
those people, near and far,
who find pleasure, profit or health
in the lowly hen and her product.

AN ACKNOWLEDGMENT

The egg and poultry industries have afforded us an unique opportunity to realize one phase of our original exhibition program, namely a book which sketches the evolution of the industries and describes their present state of development.

We have been greatly pleased with the poultry exhibit at this Exposition, which represented in the most practical manner the application of science to the breeding, incubating, rearing, housing and feeding of poultry on the farm. The display was in itself an accomplishment worthy of the highest praise, and helped to emphasize in many minds the advance in a phase of farm production whereby today the value of the chickens and eggs produced in the United States is exceeded by only three other farm products—dairy, cotton and corn.

A book which serves to record not only the progress made in the production of eggs and poultry, but which carries the story forward to include their processing, marketing and uses as food in America is an admirable monument to the Exposition which has called it forth.

Rufus C. Dawes
President

A Century of Progress
International Exposition Chicago 1933

WHO
AND
HOW

THIS book has been done by collective artistic enterprise. A part of the editor's work was planning and arranging the subject matter so that it would appear to the general reader—as it does to those whose daily work is producing or marketing eggs and poultry—a changing, living and colorful drama important to the happiness of many.

The ones who conceived the Century of Progress Exposition had in view three complete pictures of each major industry—first, an exhibit of scientific progress; second, a collective exhibit of how the products are made, distributed and used; third, a permanent contribution of literature to the history and present state of each industry. The egg and poultry industry is one of a few to respond to this third idea.

The conditions prescribed for entering "Eggs" at A Century of Progress, Chicago Centennial Exposition, as an exhibit and not as a concession were that it should be educational in character, contain no advertising and be sold at cost. These conditions have been fulfilled. The editor and the authors join in expressing first their gratitude to Frederick S. Brandenburg of Madison, Wisconsin, and to L. B. Kilbourne of Chicago, Illinois, for meeting the conditions of publication and sale.

The editor wishes to thank the authors for their cooperation and support. They have written the story without thought of profit, for the glory of an industry in which they themselves are taking an active part. The generous assistance of many friends of the industry brought to a fuller realization a book of exceptional artistic qualities, of scientific value to those within the industry and of general educational interest to those without. The various members of the Institute of American Poultry Industries, who have aided and sponsored the project, have the editor's sincere appreciation.

Henry J. Wright of the Great Atlantic and Pacific Tea Company, himself a distinguished editor, counseled us, as did also Gove Hambidge who wrote the preface, thus adding to the professional excellence of the work. Edward N. Wentworth, Director of Armour's Live Stock Bureau, and his son, Edward N. Jr., graciously contributed a chapter on the biology of egg and chick formation.

Special mention should also be made of Dr. A. W. Bitting of a Century of Progress Exposition, a nutritionist of international fame, who inspired the thought and often made smooth the way that our industry might contribute a literary exhibit as part of the Exposition's program. Luella Haney Russell, an anthropologist, reviewed the manuscript for accuracy and unity and supplied paragraphs containing ethnological material, some of which is new to the literature of our industry. She was unceasing in her researches, assisting the editor and the artist in this work.

The editor wishes to thank Mr. Raymond Heer for his loyalty and his understanding cooperation with the authors. He gave unstintingly of his service, and diligently prepared each separate page layout to reflect the pleasing beauty of studied design. In securing many valuable illustrations, Mr. Heer had the assistance of the staff of the Institute of American Poultry Industries, of Swift and Company, Armour and Company, various poultry publications and household journals, The National Geographic Magazine, The Prince George Hotel of New York, the United States Department of Agriculture, Harvey C. Wood, manager of the International Egg Laying Contest at A Century of Progress, the Field Museum of Natural History, the American Museum of Natural History, 8 and the Art Institute of Chicago.

The editor joins the author of the cook book in acknowledging the individuals and the publications, notably the leading women's publications that have furnished recipes and ideas for recipes. Appreciation is expressed to all who contributed in this manner, for without such help the collection of recipes would have been difficult to obtain.

Included in this acknowledgment are, also, the following who loaned unusually fine photographs: American Medical Association; American Poultry Association; Larro Research Farm; Nela Park Laboratories of the General Electric Company; American Poultry Journal; The Poultry Tribune; Grit and Steel; The U. S. Egg and Poultry Magazine; McCall's Magazine; Delineator Magazine; Good House-keeping; Ladies' Home Journal; Woman's Home Companion; Standard Brands, Inc.; The Borden Company; Kraft–Phenix Cheese Corporation; Martin Cantine Company; National Biscuit Company; Palace Live Poultry Car Company; New York Central Lines; Peat Import Corporation; Quaker Oats Company; The Smith Incubator Company; Priebe & Sons; Herman Folkman; William A. Hendrickson; Mrs. F. C. King; Miriam W. Stuart; L. P. Graham; George B. Means; Louis Stahmer.

—PAUL MANDEVILLE

June 1, 1933

B O O K   I

Whence come our
eggs and poultry?

C O N T E N T S

LIST OF ILLUSTRATIONS—BOOK I

THE EGG CAME FIRST

INTRODUCTION

What the Book is About
Time and Change
What is an Egg

A domestic
flock that
adds beauty
to the rural
estate.

WHAT THE BOOK
IS ABOUT

GOVE HAMBIDGE

A BAREFOOT boy and a clucking hen are the symbols of country life. Biddy has won a lasting place in the affections of mankind, and throughout the length and breadth of America few things are more closely associated with farming than chickens.

For that reason, this book on eggs and poultry should have a wide appeal. As a one-time editor, seeing manuscripts piled a foot deep on top of a huge desk, I used to think that everyone in the world must be afflicted with the itch to write. I am not sure but that the itch to keep a few chickens is almost as universal.

It is a pervasive dream. The first ambition of the country boy is to have a small flock all his own, and perhaps some pigeons. That same boy, when he gets a little older, may be helped through school or college by the pin-money his mother earns from her hens. And as for the city man—his castles in the air, as often as not, bear a queer resemblance to a chicken house. It is on a little place in the country, to which he will be able to retire some day and do what he pleases, his living secured by an unceasing flow of eggs.

19

This book is not calculated to encourage that last dream. Indeed, it should not be encouraged. To burn one's bridges and start out with the idea of making a tidy fortune from eggs, as so many do, is to follow a road that too often leads to bitterness and shattered hopes. It is wise to be hard-boiled about eggs—to absorb into the soul some of that flinty economic wisdom outlined by Frank L. Platt in the pages that follow.

On the other hand, to consider the small flock as a contribution to subsistence, on the farm or the country place, is a very different matter. I have never been able to see why any farmer should be content with poor fare at his own table. He, the producer of food, should eat like a prince, though there be holes in his shoes and patches in his overalls. Yet I have seen farmers in a dairy country buy canned milk from the store to use in their coffee. To say the least, this shows a lack of imagination. By the same token, for the expenditure of a little extra trouble, delicious broiled, fried and roasted chicken, not to mention fresh eggs, might be commonplace items in the fare of many farm families who now content themselves with far less agreeable foods.

If, after providing lordly meals for himself, the farmer is then able to sell some poultry products to add to his cash income, well and good. Thousands of small flocks peppered all over the Middle West indicate what can be done in this direction. Indeed, America gets a great deal of its egg supply from just this source. And it is significant, as Paul Mandeville points out, that most of these small flocks are run by womenfolk who already have plenty to do, but who take on the care of chickens because they are determined to make their contribution to the family income.

WHAT THE
BOOK IS
ABOUT

It is not at all unlikely that the egg you eat for breakfast has been all tangled up with the dreams and ambitions of some young housewife back on the farm.

This book, then, is not limited in its appeal to men. It should be useful to all who are interested in poultry, whether as a major economic project, a supplement to other farming operations, a contribution to the home food supply, or a hobby second to none in fascinations. Whatever you do, do it well—a commonplace aphorism, but it applies as much to poultry-keeping as to anything else, and to the little hen house in the back yard as much as to the great specialized poultry plant. This book will help you to do it well.

But those who keep chickens are not by any means the only people who are, or should be, interested in poultry and eggs. For every one who keep them, there are twenty-five who eat chickens, or their eggs. This book is written for them too. Where Mrs. Snyder managed to dig up 800 recipes for cooking eggs and poultry I have no idea, but she either dug them up or made them up, and they are a rich store for the housewife.

To this same housewife I commend the clear account of just what eggs do in various kinds of cookery. Getting three meals a day year in and year out is no small matter. The more thoroughly one understands just what happens at certain points, and the reasons for it, the more intelligently the job can be done, with fewer disappointments and less guesswork. And I believe the modern housewife likes to use her brains in cookery.

Then there is the question of the place of eggs in nutrition, which is also discussed in these pages. On millions of breakfast tables the golden egg looks up and greets the morning with cheerful eye. There is reason for that universal use of eggs for breakfast, as you will here discover. Some of the best things foods do for these flesh-and-blood contraptions, our bodies, eggs do—building up tissues, helping to keep us in top-notch health, bolstering our resistance against disease, and contributing to our happiness—for happiness depends very considerably on health and good nourishment, though we are seldom aware of it until we begin to feel under the weather.

All this is what might be expected of the egg. It was, after all, devised by nature to nourish young living things and to give them the best possible send-off for a long and useful life. When nature does a job like that, she is not likely to do it halfway. So, to take a single example, we find the egg rather unique among every-day foods in being well stored with vitamin D. It really is what it looks like—a bit of materialized sunshine.

With literally hundreds of ways to cook eggs, they can be given their proper permanent place in the diet without any danger that they will ever grow tiresome.

As for poultry—I will not dwell on its nutritive value, but rather on its singular deliciousness. Just consider Southern hospitality, for instance, and how inextricably it is bound up with fried chicken. When I travel in the South, my path is marked by a broad swath of fried chicken, so I travel there as often as possible. There is no man so hard that he does not soften a little when fried chicken is served. As for turkey, duck and goose—the mere mention of them makes the mouth water.

The point is that of all foods relished by man, the bird can lay fair claim to being the most noble. This was true long before the peacock was brought in with high ceremony at the medieval feast, decked out in the glory of spread tail feathers. Wild or domesticated, the bird has always been associated with feasts; indeed, a roast chicken at any meal makes it a feast automatically. When that doughty adventurer, D'Artagnan of the Three Musketeers, sat down in the inn and demanded a forthright dinner, what did mine host bring him? A hot bird and a cold bottle, forsooth.

But there are still others besides poultrymen and ultimate consumers interested in this business of poultry and eggs. WHAT THE BOOK IS ABOUT There are the men who deal in these products at wholesale and retail, who transport them in trucks and railroad cars, who keep them in mighty cold-storage warehouses.

These branches of the industry have been dealt with by Dr. Mary E. Pennington, who has devoted many years to the patient scientific study of cold-storage processes and problems. The transportation, handling and storage of eggs and poultry is a matter that concerns not only those who do this work, but the producer and the consumer as well, for on it depends the quality and wholesomeness of the product, the adequacy of distribution, and to no little extent, the price. If eggs and poultry, with all their food values and deliciousness, are not luxuries available only at certain times of the year, we can to a large extent thank those who occupy this middle position between the producer and the consumer.

Their story is one of vast commercial development and constant hammering away at technical problems. For that matter, so is the story of the producer, as Frank Platt makes clear. The poultry industry as a whole, starting from a few backyard hens, has grown to the point where it produces 35 billion eggs a year and distributes them to every home in America. This is almost talking in the astronomical figures of an Einstein. So great a growth has necessitated new and sometimes revolutionary developments at every step—developments for hatching eggs wholesale, for feeding broilers wholesale, for storing eggs wholesale, and what not.

Yet eggs, curiously enough, must still be candled one by one and graded by the human eye, just as coffee and tea must still be tested by the human palate.

There are mistakes, there are shortcomings, but by and large the achievements of the industry have been extraordinary. And it is still growing, still changing, still dreaming and planning new things. Therefore it is still exciting to those who are in the game.

All of these things have been told in this book. Here, cheek by jowl, you will find the romantic, the practical, the dramatic, the scientific, the commercial. Each writer is a specialist in his or her field, each has seasoned knowledge and enthusiasm. The purpose has been to reach widely differing audiences—the producer, the processor, the dealer, the teacher, the scientist, the consumer. I think no reader will fail to find in each section something surprising, interesting, new and worth-while.

These things I can say because I did not write the book. My part has been a minor one. I lay no claim to being an expert on eggs or poultry. But on the other hand, I doubt if anyone has a more expert enjoyment of the exquisiteness of an omelet or the succulent richness of a second joint. I am glad I can underline my gratitude to the producers of these good things by being associated with so worth-while a project.

—GOVE HAMBIDGE.

June 14, 1933

Malay sooth-sayer preparing a fowl for reading the future.

TIME AND CHANGE

PAUL MANDEVILLE

THIS is a book about change. It suggests that more changes are to come. It is concerned with living things, with potential beings and with food. It is concerned with an industry developing in time out of ceremony, fun and feasting.

Romantic Beginnings of Poultry Keeping

Poultry is raised for other purposes than food. It is raised for ornament and sport. Birds which now are grown chiefly for meat and eggs have been, and still are, prized for their plumage and for their gameness in a fight. From primitive until very recent times, the beautiful cock was the cherished possession of every household; and the fighting cock was the subject of many early drawings. But beyond this, in remote antiquity, the cock was first captured to serve as a timekeeper. The primitive Malaysian today employs the cock to count his days in the dark recesses of the jungle just as the pre-Malays carried the ancestors of our domesticated fowls, for the same purpose, as they migrated down the great river gorges of southeastern Asia. The regularity with which the cock told certain periods of the night and day linked him with the moti- 25

Trap for w i l d fowls. T a m e d cocks are staked. Wild cocks hear the c r o w i n g, c o m e to fight, and are caught in t h e running k n o t s. Several may be captured in a single day.

Malay boy carry-ing s n a r e and tamed cock to be used as a decoy.

vating powers of the universe. The dependability of his alarm as he sensed danger or something strange, and his ability to portend approaching catastrophe were uncanny. So the first tamed cock was not only a timekeeper but also an invaluable watchdog for the primitive traveler and his family—and he was easily portable and easily fed.

A series of rituals developed around the cock because of his mysterious abilities. In the beginning cocks and only cocks were wanted. The Malay tribesman stole baby chicks or a nest of eggs in the jungle; and as the chicks developed, the cocks were kept and the pullets were returned to the wilds. Some of the birds were offered in sacrifice to ward off evil, and present-day chants of the East Indian indicate that these sacrifices often took the place of human sacrifice. The sport of cock-fighting, too, arose as a substitution for human battle. Omens, divinations, proverbs and ceremonial customs grew up

Old Roman wall mosaic. Cocks were domesticated for sport before they were valued for meat.

around the cock and were in time catalogued. Throughout the Malay world these things are recorded and are still practiced by primitive groups.

The early Malay (just like some of his kindred tribes today) did not eat the chickens or their eggs, but had them only for time-keeping and recreational purposes. When the demand for ritual flocks grew, and the pullets were saved for convenience, the eggs were either broken or given away to the Chinese, who preserved them in mud and ash. The breaking of the eggs, too, became a ceremony and a means of augury.

The part played by the early Malay woman in sparing birds and eggs for food is not recorded; but as far back as we are able to trace the habits of pioneer groups in all countries, we find the womenfolk taking an interest in hens for the sake of their meat and the eggs they laid. So as time went on and poultry was carried from one country to another, the women mated birds for one purpose and the men for another.

"Here may be emphasized", says an English authority, Sir Edward Brown, "a point frequently forgotten . . . that, except where the fowl has been bred for its sportive qualities, and in modern times for exhibition, both of which are mainly the relaxation and pleasure of men, the control and breeding of

Women of all countries have taken an interest in chickens for their food value in meat and eggs.

poultry have been, throughout the ages, and still are, almost entirely in the hands of women, the home makers, the food purveyors . . . The birds fitted into homestead conditions, provided a more or less regular supply of food, and upon a sudden emergency, could be killed and quickly cooked, which could not be said of any other class of stock, and certainly not of the regular crops, almost all of which are seasonal."

The interest of women and of children on the farm in poultry raising depends in these days on another fact—the cash value of eggs and chickens which provides spending money and often the means of education. No other industry offers so many people a supplementary livelihood. A business for millions, there are excellent earnings in eggs and poultry when handled as a side line to general farming, or in combination with fruit or dairy products, or some other branch of farming.

The Lure of Eggs

Eggs are fascinating. They present occasional opportunities for good profit but the hazards are many, both for the flock owners who at times may suffer devastating losses from disease or the elements, and for the dealers who take the risks of creat-

American women see cash value in hens and their eggs as a means of supplementing the family income.

ing a daily market for flock owners and a daily supply for consumers. Eggs are sensitive to changes; the yield and quality vary. The markets are extremely variable. But the dangers and the occasional profits account for their lure. "Once an egg man always an egg man" applies alike to producers and dealers who have served their apprenticeship.

35 Billion Eggs a Year

In the aggregate, the poultry business is an immense business, comparing favorably with wheat, beef or pork, often exceeding them in volume. The annual value of eggs and poultry consumed exceeds a good round billion dollars even at their present low prices. Only three agricultural products consistently exceed eggs and poultry in the United States in economic importance—dairy products, corn and cotton. Comparatively little corn leaves the farm, and it might be noted that a great deal of it is fed to poultry.

Eggs and poultry are end products of agriculture and bring

food to consumers in concentrated and, for most people, easily digestible form. Of livestock products, eggs and poultry are among those which will survive when the ranges are gone.

Egg production in the United States reaches the astonishing total of approximately 35 billion eggs a year, or 280 eggs per capita. Measured in standard cases of 30 dozen each, it is variously estimated at 90 to 100 million cases. Both production and consumption vary with place, season and cost, but on the whole they are fairly constant, varying probably not more than five per cent from year to year. Exports and imports are relatively small. The egg business is a domestic business.

Of the total number of eggs laid, about 60 per cent are consumed on the farms or nearby, so that they do not enter into any organized marketing operation. Also, about 60 per cent of all the eggs produced come from flocks so small that commonly they are given no special care, the eggs not being intended primarily for market.

This means that less than half, or about 40 per cent, of our American eggs are either produced or marketed on what might be called an industrial or organized basis. But this 40 per cent is very important; together with the service of marketing them, they account for probably 60 per cent of the total billion-dollar value of eggs and poultry consumed.

If you are a flock owner, or if you are a city dweller and take interest in the food you eat, these are important facts to know. In the latter case, bearing in mind your reliance on organized industry for the good eggs and good poultry which come to your table, you will read with greater interest the amazing things that so few people really know about eggs and poultry. It is important also that you should be able to distinguish between intelligent and unintelligent handling of these highly sensitive products which, with right handling, are among the most dependable of foods. Therein rests a condition of progress. Intelligent buying, to which must be added intelligent cooking and use, are a great stimulus to intelligent production and handling. They help to give the producer and the dealer a goal worth striving for.

Is There Profit in Eggs

That question—is there profit in eggs?—is probably uppermost in the minds of most people who dream of owning a flock of hens. It may be said at the outset that egg production for profit is both a hazardous and a highly competitive business. As a sole source of income it has serious pitfalls. Comparatively few have succeeded after expanding to a point where the care of poultry has got beyond their immediate personal control. Even as a one-man business, studies by the New Jersey College of Agriculture show, the mortality of investment in poultry-producing plants is high. The exceptionally successful investors nearly all had five or ten years' experience behind them. It is a business that will yield to experience, and some encouraging fortunes have been made by flock owners.

In the egg and poultry packing trades a similar degree of competition is found, and the glamour soon fades for most of those who enter with grandiose ideas of easy profit. All dealers take serious losses at intervals because the movement of eggs is obscure, a large proportion do not appear in the market, market demands are hard to anticipate and eggs are perishable, so that they cannot be held indefinitely like some farm products. On the other hand, eggs and poultry have been the sole source of a comfortable livelihood and even of a fair fortune for some dealers. Here again experience and close personal attention to management are conditions of success.

From the foregoing one may with reason conclude that in eggs and poultry there are business opportunities for people of ability who are familiar with either production or marketing, or both. Possibly there is a major fortune yet to be made in eggs, or in eggs and poultry, by some genius with honesty of thinking, and with courage to live through the pioneering stages of elevating so extensive an industry to the status of big busi-

ness, able to stand on its own earnings and capable of indefinite expansion under single control in the modern manner. With few exceptions, eggs and poultry are now handled in a really large way only in combination with dairy or meat businesses that share or carry the overhead, or at retail by chain stores. From the standpoint of poultry farming, no operation on a very large scale has survived long; which is to say, it has never been mastered as a large business under one management.

From Trader to Merchant

We all know the story of the covered wagon era in America, but we may not perceive at once the effect of migration upon trade. With every advance into the land of promise, a trader followed the settler. Lines of communication and supply had to be kept open from post to post and from city to city. With each move to a new location it was natural for the trader to look to someone at the last point of departure for his supplies. He traded where he was acquainted and he often went out as an agent of a former employer. And so the number of traders

Hollanders often transport eggs and chickens in bicycle baskets. This was a common method in some of our rural districts 30 years ago.

and of marketing centers multiplied. Little wonder we are a nation of traders.

The motive of trade is gain, but the results are creative to a high degree, especially in a new country. As the population increases and the number of dealers multiply, trade becomes more competitive. Trading considered alone and without any of the services which attend production or marketing in its distributive and merchandising phases, is warfare. It is often conducted with good-will toward competitors, but always there is a zest for possession, and material wastes accompany any free competitive system of business. To eliminate the chances of trade is to make of a warrior a man of industry.

Our national destiny depends upon the ability of Americans, and among them those engaged in agricultural industries, to achieve a business shorn of the material losses which accompany wasteful competition; to enjoy a business wherein all or most of the fighting shall be done in laboratories, in factories, on farms and where not; to cooperate in an effort to reduce and control the wastes of production and distribution; to utilize for worth-while purposes the wealth created by their enterprise.

To a high degree the ability to do these things has, during recent years, marked the course of progress in the production and marketing of eggs and poultry.

The story of marketing eggs well illustrates the way America developed its marketing system and brought to the American table the greatest year-round variety of foods the world has ever known. The eggs which move annually out of the Mississippi Valley alone into the industrial areas of the northeastern states would make a train reaching from New York to Washington and return. Fifty thousand American carloads*, or about 150 thousand carloads of European measure, are required to move these eggs. The South sends to the North eggs to supply its shortage during early spring, and later on the North supplies the South with part of its surplus of spring and summer eggs held in storage for autumn needs. This system of exchange came about by reason of the facilities built up during a time when exchange of food for machinery, clothing, books and what-not was necessary to the life and growth of new agricultural communities. A successful method of handling perishables was created to meet the needs of this exchange and eggs became one of the heavy-tonnage farm products handled by railroads.

The egg and poultry marketing industries are slowly but steadily yielding to a new economic order which seeks to minimize hazards and to prevent any inefficient and wasteful methods of distribution that may have grown up under a system of free competitive trading. The economies to be effected were spoken of by Herbert Hoover, when he was Secretary of Commerce and he listed the wastes to be attacked. These wastes, which apply to many foods, have already yielded in many respects to orderly methods in handling the products of the hen. They are worth mentioning because the war on waste

---

* Not including movement by truck. The total movement in all directions through organized marketing channels, it has been shown, is about 40 per cent of all eggs laid—equivalent to about 100 thousand carloads of 400 cases each.

Eggs have become one
of the heavy tonnage
farm products handled
by railroads.

is still going on. They are: An unnecessary number of purchase and sale transactions. Transportation of inferior and un-
salable products. Delayed movements and repeated handling.
Inadequate facilities for expeditious handling. Unnecessary
cross-hauls in search of consumers. Uncontrolled distribution
by which local gluts and famines are created. Destruction of
agricultural capital by crowding the market in periods of slight
over-production. The cost of speculation and hazards produced
by all of the above.

These wastes, all of them, are to be conquered in time; but
it must be remembered that if we are to preserve variety for the
American table, especially the variety obtained from out-of-
season foods and foods not indigenous to our home localities, it
will be by further building up our American system of handling
perishables, a system which is recognized as the best in the
world.

Waste is, as a rule, synonymous with want of knowledge. It is caused by no one factor. The activities of flock owner, buyer, packer, shipper or distributor are no more to blame for waste than is our failure to inform consumers to the end that they will buy more intelligently. With these aims in view, this book deals with common facts about eggs and poultry of interest to all. It is concerned with poultry keeping as an art, a science and an industry; with the mystery of the egg and the chick; with the new era of cold and cleanliness in the handling of delicate food; with consumer, flock owner and market man; and finally it is concerned with the best of foods, eggs and poultry, and how to prepare them for the table.

WHAT IS AN EGG?

MARY ENGLE PENNINGTON

W HAT a noise in the chicken yard! *Clack-clack-alack!*
Clack-alack! over and over as a proud hen tells of her
achievement. Why shouldn't she be proud? To have
produced so wonderful an object as an egg is something to be
proud of. All the makings of life lie within it, awaiting only
warmth to differentiate and build nerves, muscles, blood-vessels
and the pulsing rhythm that, from birth to death, is the evidence
of life.

Put your hand, gently, around the warm, velvety shell as the
new-laid egg lies in the nest. What a pleasant sensation is
gives! There is a "bloom" on the shell which makes it soft
and smooth, but it does not shine. This is one of the ear-
marks of a fresh egg. Much handling and poor surroundings
destroy the bloom of a new-laid egg, so that it loses its velvet
dullness and acquires a gloss which is easily recognized by the
well informed and interpreted as an indication of staleness.

If the bloom on the shell means something to us who eat the
egg, it means something also to Mother Nature, who is not
concerned with the egg as an article of food but is much interested in obtaining from it another chick. So, over the shell,
before the egg is laid, the hen spreads a thin layer of an
albumen-like substance which lightly covers the pores through
which, later, air will pass to the developing chick. As long
as this layer of albumen is dry it is almost impossible for mold 37

spores or bacteria to enter the egg through these air holes—a wise provision, since either molds or bacteria would ultimately so destroy the egg that it would be useless for either chick or food.

When mother hen sits on the egg, warming it to about 103°, and moistening it with her damp feathers, she rubs off the thin shell cover and so opens the air holes fully to the young chicks. Then the egg is no longer velvety and dull but smooth and glossy, and we see at once from its appearance that it is a stale egg and not desirable for food—except food for growth of the developing chick within.

Fashions in Shells

Many people go no further in their contemplation of the shell of an egg than to distinguish its color—whether white or brownish or creamy white. This, as a matter of fact, is of small importance since the color of the shell bears no relation to the quality or character of the egg itself. It simply means that certain breeds of chickens put into the outer layers of the shell more or less of a brownish pigment, while other breeds do not secrete that pigment in the oviduct where the eggs are formed; hence the shells of the eggs they produce are white. Such ideas as that an egg with a white shell has a milder flavor than an egg with a brown shell, or that the content of the brown shell is "stronger" and beats to a lighter foam than does that of a white shell are totally without foundation. They arise, probably, from the preferences in certain markets for eggs with brown shells and in other markets for eggs with white shells, preferences based on fashions rather than on facts and often upon reasons very remote from the obvious, such as territorial preferences for certain breeds.

Of course, if you have been brought up in New York City or in San Francisco and so have been accustomed to pay more for eggs with white shells you will find it difficult to believe that eggs with brown shells are quite as good. On the other

White, cream colored and brown shells enclose the eggs we eat.

hand, if you have lived in Boston or some other New England city, where the browner the shell the better you like the egg within it, you will take what I say about eggs with white shells with reservations. But if you are a good observer and keep track of facts accurately, you will find that I am right—weight for weight and quality for quality, white eggs and brown eggs are equally good and should bring the same price on the market. When you pay a premium for one or the other, you are paying a price to be in fashion, and whether that fact gives you your money's worth only you can decide.

What the Shell Is Made of

Far more interesting than the color of the shell, and of real importance also, are its structural characteristics, for upon these largely depend not only the making of another chick but also the getting of the egg to market in such good condition that you and I will find it a desirable food.

The shell of the egg is almost pure calcium carbonate, a substance found widely in nature, as for example, in white marble and in oyster shells. Tiny glands in certain portions of the oviduct of the hen secrete calcium carbonate, and as the egg works its downward way with a rotary motion through the duct the shell is deposited around the yolk and white, as though it were a package being slowly and carefully wrapped. Whether it be a thick or thin shell, or smooth or rough, or

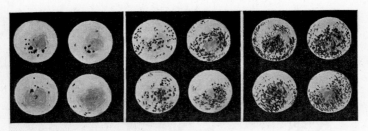

Showing wide differences in the number of large or open pores in the shells of hen's eggs. Each dot indicates an open pore. Both the large and the small end of each egg is shown.—After Almquist.

long and slender, or round and short—these things depend partly upon inherited characteristics and partly upon the food the hen receives. Since the shell of the egg commonly averages 12 per cent of the total weight, we see that the hen must provide about a quarter of an ounce of calcium carbonate (or lime as we may call it because everyone else does) every time she lays an egg. Obviously a hen must not only eat a large amount of lime but she must apportion it properly throughout herself—so much for bones, so much for muscle protoplasm, so much for eggshells, and so on. Therefore, scientists have found it profitable to study the utilization of the calcium that a hen eats and what will help her to make it into good bones, good eggshells, and, indeed, into a good hen! From such studies have come some of the facts which have helped us with problems of human nutrition, such as giving children codliver oil when bones are growing so fast that a great deal of lime must be sent to just the right places if the youngsters are to be straight and strong. Codliver oil is equally good for young hens—and older ones, too, for that matter. It results in thicker, better shells on the eggs the hens lay.

Nevertheless, there must be here and there little holes through the shells—pores, they are called—through which air can pass to the developing chick. These pores are of two sizes—large ones, which are not numerous, and many smaller ones.

WHAT IS
AN EGG?

40

The hen and the hatchery man are much more interested in these pores than I am, because I am not hatching eggs—I am getting them to market fresh and sweet and altogether good, and my concern is to keep the layer of bloom over the pores, especially the larger ones, and so keep molds and bacteria from entering the egg to spoil it.

The Inside Wrapping or Membrane

When she has an important job on her hands, such as turning an egg into a chick, Mother Nature likes to make assurance doubly sure. So, to reinforce the protection which the shell gives, she has lined it with a rather thin but very tough membrane which sticks close against the shell and covers all the pore openings on the inside. This membrane is made of chiten, which is very similar in its chemical nature to horns and hoofs and finger nails. Indeed, the chemists say it is one of the most difficult substances among organic compounds to decompose. So, if a mold spore does drop through a big pore and land on the chitenous shell membrane, it is still a long way from the luscious dinner that lies beyond. To make the matter still worse for the mold spore, the shell membrane is not one continuous film but is made of a multitude of tiny fibers crisscrossing and interweaving so that a mold filament will find what might seem to it a thick forest where it constantly would bump into trees and have to find new lanes—all very time-consuming and difficult for a mold mycelium to negotiate.

One thing, however, would help the mold spore or the bacterium enormously—a drop of water! If the eggshell gets wet the bloom layer is dissolved and comes off. Then, when the water rests against the shell membrane it seeps between the fibers, fills those tiny spaces and makes a stream whereon the mold filament or bacterium can float or swim right through. When this happens the chances are against the egg or the chick—especially if many of the pores get wet. But there is still one more barrier—a second membrane, much thinner and more delicate than the shell membrane, which makes a sack in which the egg white is completely enclosed. Many times we find a mold colony developing between the two membranes, but not yet through the second and into the egg substance.

The Air Cell

When the egg is laid and at the body temperature of the hen, the shell is completely filled. But as it cools to atmospheric temperature the egg substance contracts and leaves a space, generally at the blunt end. This space is between the two membranes, the thin, or egg membrane, forming a cover for the egg white which pushes against it. It is called the air cell, and as the egg ages, especially if it is being held in a warm dry place, this air cell grows larger and larger. Thus it is an index of the quality of the egg and one of which we will have more to say in the chapter on grading eggs.*

Two Kinds of White

Within these elaborate defences are the white and the yolk, both constructed by nature to nourish the developing chick. By the same token, they are excellent food for man. When we remove the contents of the shell we see surrounding the yolk a mass of thick, gelatinous egg white, or egg albumen as many call it, which hugs the yolk closely and spreads well beyond it. This we call the "thick white." A second circle is formed of a less gelatinous material called the "thin white." In an egg of high quality, from well bred and well fed hens, we usually find a greater amount of thick white, by volume, than of thin white. We are of the general opinion, also, that a large proportion of thick white is indicative of high quality. We know that such eggs poach and fry acceptably to our present standards, but even those who know most about eggs still have much to learn not only of the quantity and quality of the thick and thin white but of the relation to them of breed and feed.

* How eggs are tested. Page 189.

This shows that the thick white is a jelly and the thin white is rather sirupy. One can see right through the shell of the egg when it is held before an electrically lighted candle.

Chemically speaking, egg white is a high-grade protein. Egg albumen was one of the first proteins to be separated from other substances and obtained in a pure or crystalline form, and we still use it to illustrate the properties of proteins in general. We heat it in a test tube to see it coagulate to form what we so well know as hard-boiled egg. We put it into a parchment paper bag suspended in water to show that it will *not* dialyse—that is, it will not pass through a membrane, a common property of high-grade proteins and a mighty important one; and we beat air into it to see it increase its bulk and become a white foam.

This latter property egg white has to a marked degree, as every housewife and cook well knows. Upon it much of the usefulness of egg white in cookery depends. It is a distinguishing characteristic of hen's eggs as compared with duck eggs, the white of which will not beat to a foam. The laboratory has not yet given us the primary reasons for the high foaming ability of egg white. One reason, however, may be what we call its structure. That is, if we treat egg white appropriately and examine it under a microscope, we see masses of fibers, soft, to be sure, and not very well formed, but on their way, at least, to a truly organized form. Within the meshwork made by these fibers is entangled the egg albumen and egg globulin and the three or four other proteins which compose egg white. There are few such fibers in the thin white, but many of them in the thick white. If we cut through egg white with scissors—cutting and cutting and cutting—we destroy its thicker portion and the whole mass assumes the characteristics of the thinner portion. The thick white is quite iridescent, the thin but slightly so. The thin white is transparent, the thick is on its way to translucency. A fibrous structure within the thick white would partially account for both appearances.

The Heart of the Egg—the Yolk

When the egg is laid, the yolk is approximately in its center. It is a spherical mass, varying in color from pale yellow to deep orange, held within a gossamer film known as the vitelline membrane. The name vitelline comes from the Latin *vitellus,* the yolk of an egg. Upon this membrane lies the blastoderm, in which is the vital cell capable of becoming a chick. At the two poles or ends of the membrane are twisted white threads which serve to stabilize the position of the yolk—a fact of importance to us because the position of the yolk helps us to determine the freshness of the egg, but of much more importance to the hen and the hatchery man. The reason for this, to me, is one of the fascinating examples of nature's carefulness from which I always get a thrill.

The germinal spot, with the potential new chick is, as I said above, supported on the vitelline or yolk membrane, where, as development proceeds, it can draw for sustenance upon both yolk substance and the enveloping white. But one thing is an absolute necessity if the cells are to divide and redivide, namely, heat. The closer the germinal spot to the body of the hen, the more evenly and perfectly it is warmed and the better the chance for the chick to reach perfection. So the chalazae, as the white threads are called (from a Greek word meaning a hailstone or a little tuber, and pronounced as though *ch* were a *k*), balance the yolk so that the germ placed on the yolk's equator is always uppermost and therefore as close as possible to the warm hen. No matter which way we turn the egg, the germinal spot floats upward, to be kept warm until hatching time. Isn't that a fascinatingly clever trick? How we, in determining the freshness of the egg, use the position of the yolk and the degree of visibility of the germinal area I will tell you in the chapter on candling.* Now we will get on with our story of the egg yolk from the food viewpoint.

Within the thin membrane is a mixture of proteins, fats and certain rather rare but important substances known as cholesterols and lecithins, good food for both chicks and children. The protein and fat are in what is known as an emulsion—that is, the fat, although it cannot be actually dissolved in the mixture, is prevented from separating out as a layer of oil by the thin films of protein which coat the fat droplets and so prevent them from touching each other. Cream is also an emulsion, which we break up in order to separate the fat and thereby make butter. It is relatively easy to split a cream emulsion, but it is very difficult to break down an egg yolk emulsion—for which we should be duly thankful when we consider the long distances that eggs must travel to reach their market and the many jolts and jars they must undergo on the way.

When you get right down to it, we really know very little about the structure of egg white, but we know still less of the structure within the yolk substance. Certain facts about the behavior of the yolk lead us to believe that there is some definite placement of the various components. For example, if a yolk in place within the shell is frozen, it is found, after thawing, to have acquired a rubbery consistency and has quite lost its liquid character. If, however, the yolk membrane is broken and the yolk substance permitted to flow out before it is

* How eggs are tested. Page 189.

frozen, it will be almost as liquid when it thaws as it was before freezing. We are all acquainted with the effect on an egg of freezing within the shell, and how useless that makes it. In the chapter on frozen egg* we will read of just the opposite, namely, an egg product whose great usefulness is due primarily to the fact that it is frozen hard and can be held for many months in that condition with but very little change. In the one case, the various components of the yolk are as nature placed them and accidental freezing makes them useless. In the other, man disturbs the placement and disorganizes the arrangement—though we do not know what the arrangement is—by breaking the yolk before freezing it.

A large part of the charm of an opened egg is the color of the yolk. We are accustomed to see the golden ball drop into the egg cup or mount the layer of coagulating white as the frying pan does its classic job. Perhaps we have noticed that eggs laid in the winter or very early spring have yolks lighter in color than do summer eggs. Not because of the cold weather or the small amount of sunshine but simply because the hens ordinarily get less green food—especially grass—in the winter-time. And it is upon an abundance of such green food in the diet of the hen that the color of the yolk very largely depends. If we withhold green stuff from the hen— grass, alfalfa, cabbage and the like, and certain grains, most notably yellow corn—the yolk color of the eggs she lays day after day will gradually become more and more pale, until finally it is an unpleasant grayish white. Having got the egg to this colorless point we can return it to its normal sunny shade simply by again feeding the hen greens and yellow corn.

The cow and the hen are alike in this respect—both require green feed to give color to their products. But from her feed the cow selects a yellow substance called *carotin* and transfers that to the fat of her milk, while the hen, to color the egg yolk, uses mostly very complex substances derived from plant chloro-

46   * Freezing the freshness of eggs.   Page 222.

1. Germ cell
2. Shell
3. Outer shell membrane
4. Inner shell membrane
*5. Chalaza (p l u r a l chalazae)
6. Outer thin albumen
7. M i d d l e t h i c k albumen
8. Inner thin albumen
9. Thick albumen surrounding the yolk
10. Air space
11. White yolk stalk
12. White yolk plate
13. Dark yolk plate
14. Vitelline membrane

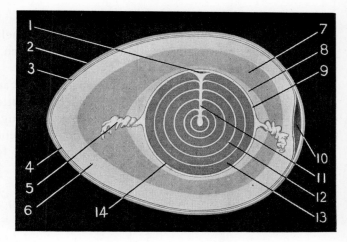

* Sometimes called the "lower" chalaza to distinguish it from the opposite or "upper" chalaza—a distinction used when alluding to the position of the egg as it is held in the hand for candling.

phyl (which means "leaf green") and termed xanthophyl (which means "leaf yellow"), with just a little carotin. Carotin is the forerunner of vitamin A, and, as we know, butterfat is rich in vitamin A. Vitamin D we find in plant cells green with chlorophyl—and thence the hen, by making use of the chlorophyl transfers the vitamin to the egg. This accounts for the richness of the sunshine vitamin D in egg yolk. Recently egg yolk has been shown to be one of the best sources of Vitamin A also—this comes probably from the carotin portion of the coloring matter.

The presence of so much vitamin D as we find in the yolks of eggs—and this is a recent discovery of science—makes them unique among animal foods as a source of this very important item in the diet of all of us. Office workers, city dwellers, those working at night and sleeping in the daytime, and young children, are especially in need of vitamin D. Even those of us who get our share of unfiltered sunshine may well remember that the little cackling hen, talking so loudly out in the chicken yard, has imprisoned within that velvety shell a veritable ball of sun's rays ready to add to our supply when next we breakfast, or lunch, or dine.

On page 47 is a diagrammatic sketch of an egg whereon you can locate the various parts as I have written of them. And, because you may be interested in knowing something of the quantities of the more important constituents contained in the egg, I have given that information in the following table:

COMPOSITION OF EGG

	Water Per cent	Total Solids Per cent	Ether Extract (Fats)	Ash (Mineral Substances)	Total Nitrogen	Protein Nitrogen	Lipoid Phosphorus	Total Phosphorus	Carbon Dioxide mg. per c.c.	pH	Ammonia Nitrogen Per cent
Egg Yolk entirely free of white___	47.8	51.97	32.70	1.77	2.79	------	0.155	0.23	------	------	------
Egg White	88.00	12.00	0.02	0.65	1.67	10.44	------	------	1.3	8 to 8.6	------
Egg Magma in Commerce___	------	26 to 28	10 to 12	------	------	------	------	------	0.7 to 0.9	7 to 7.5	0.0011 to 0.003

Approximate proportion of whole egg, shell 10%, yolk 30%, white 60%.

POULTRY KEEPING AN ART, A SCIENCE AN INDUSTRY

FRANK L. PLATT

Jungle Fowl To Egg Machine.
The Royal Succession of Breeders.
The Breeder's Magic.
Mechanical Mothers.
The Microscope Brings Health.
The Private House of the Hen.
Revolution in Poultry Feeding.
Festive Birds and Some Hard
Common Sense.

White Plymouth Rock. A combination of beauty and utility finally a c h i e v e d through many phases of the breeder's art.

JUNGLE FOWL TO
EGG MACHINE

The Frontierman's Axe is Silenced

THE century that is past has crowded the years with progress. So rapid and vast have been the changes that many who have come to view the Chicago Centennial Exposition of 1933 have stood amazed as they looked upon a metropolis in the fullness of its maturity, realizing that here, one hundred years ago, an infant city was born; a city that within so short a time has become so great and beautiful. It is as though a mighty magician had stood upon the shores of Lake Michigan and poured out his giant cornucopia of knowledge and invention, of science, the arts, and the wealth necessary to pursue them.

The frontierman's ax is silenced, the stockade that protected early settlers from warring natives is gone, and on this same site a city of four million people raises its spires. It is a city that ever faces eastward to the promise of the rising sun. Its streets lead to the rich and fertile lands of the west. And back and forth in the busy streets are men and women and children treading out their destiny. Among them are students, and artists and workers; there are inventors, and financiers and those who man the vehicles of transportation; there are editors, and preachers and musicians; there are teachers, and merchants and those who investigate the sciences; and there are men of

business who buy and store the surplus grain of the farms, and packers who process the fatted live stock into edible meat foods. This is a city where there are factories turning out manufactured goods; acres of presses running off their printed pages for eager eyes to read; broadcasting stations filling the air with music; boats that ply the waters; "through" trains to Atlantic and Pacific Coast ports; ships of the air with mail and passengers; and a thousand other activities which engage the mind and heart of an immense, intelligent population.

It was not always thus in the history of our nation. When the United States were young, ninety per cent of the people lived in the country. It then was inconceivable that a single city should grow so large that it would house and support more people than the entire remainder of the state, yet this is the relation Chicago bears to Illinois; and this situation is so general today that sixty per cent of the nation's total population is classified as urban and forty per cent as rural. In other words, where formerly there were nine people out of every ten engaged in producing farm products, today there are only four people out of every ten. Back of this change, there is a vast and swift-moving drama of agricultural and industrial progress.

When our English forefathers came to this continent they found here some half-million natives whose simple tools of agriculture were sufficient to maintain their race in its semi-nomadic state. But the colonists were not used to this type of life and many of them perished for want of food until the Indian taught them how to cultivate corn, potatoes, beans, squash (and the recreative tobacco) with the dibble stick and the stone hoe; with the horn pick and the shoulder-blade spade. But such slow methods as these were not suited to a pioneering people whose very adventure to the new world was impelled by a desire for a better life, for greater security for themselves and their children. Add to this the white man's belief in the rights of private property and his zeal for competitive enterprise, his concern for the welfare of the individual—in contrast to the Indian's collective enterprise, collective property, and concern for tribal welfare—and we can readily understand how the early hardships of farming were a direct challenge to the inventive genius of the white man. So a new nation was founded, dedicated to the pursuit of happiness. To the American this meant the pursuit of wealth; to the Indian it meant the pursuit of nature. To produce wealth, nature had to be harnessed, broken and driven by the white man; and this harnessing necessitated the development of many machines.

Thus with the growth of plantations came many technological advances; and as life became more complex and population tended to concentrate in cities, the well-being of our people became more and more dependent upon progress in the manufacturing facilities of our farms. The job of feeding the cities became the business of agriculture. It is a business that has called for organization of distribution, for technique in production, for the application of scientific methods in handling agricultural products, and for many labor-saving devices to take the place of the hands that left the farms. Thus the output per man of those who remained gradually increased. Many men of genius made their contributions. From the invention of the reaper to the combined harvester, from the simple spade to the use of a tractor drawing a gang plow, the history of American agriculture has been replete with epoch-making advances.

Machines—Some of Them Alive

This has been an era of machines in agriculture as truly as in any other industry. But all machines on the farm are not of iron and steel. Some of the most efficient are of flesh and blood. The cow, for example, takes the raw material of the fields and transforms it into milk and butterfat. And the little hen is also an animal machine of great power in processing the food she eats into meat and eggs.

All machinery requires attention and care and some knowledge of its construction and purpose. This is especially true of the animal-machine which is more intricate in design and more wonderful in its functions than any machines built by man. The loom takes the threads of cotton from the spools and weaves them into cotton cloth. Into the milling machine the miller pours wheat and brings out flour; or he grinds corn into corn-meal or corn-flakes. But Nature builds a hen-machine which utilizes wheat and corn and green grasses as raw material, and within twenty-four hours they are fabricated into something altogether different—a delicious egg, with its proteins, fats, vitamins and minerals, all done up in a package that has a hard lime-rock shell.

JUNGLE FOWL TO EGG MA-CHINE

Under good management the hen-machine will carry on this processing of raw material into a finished product day after day. It is rather common for a hen weighing not over four pounds to produce 160 eggs in one year, each egg weighing an average of two ounces. That means 320 ounces or twenty

The "egg machine". White Leghorn bred specifically for egg production. A Mediterranean type.

pounds of eggs produced by one hen in one year. Thus this little feathered creature, the hen, produces five times her own weight in one year of laying. And there are many cases of individual hens laying over 300 eggs in one year; that is, they go to the nest and in the course of 365 days deposit from nine to ten times their own body weight in eggs.

Hen machines are not cast in a mold. They break their way out of the egg-shell and grow. When hatched, the chick weighs about 1½ ounces; this is less than the egg from which it came. When twelve weeks old, it may weigh forty ounces. This is an increase of twenty-six times the original weight. How is that for efficiency? If a Holstein calf, weighing 100 pounds at birth, should grow at the same rate it would weigh 2,600 pounds when twelve weeks old—obviously a monstrosity.

Not being built and replaced in the same way as ordinary machinery, not being cast and fitted together, but being bred, with each hen-machine carrying something of the traits and capacities of its ancestors, the question of heredity is a matter of first importance in getting a good flock. Hens are not stamped out in a die, all alike, all with the same capabilities. Their capacity to make rapid and profitable growth and their ability to lay many eggs depends very largely on their inheritance. Lack of care and poor management would, of course, ruin the finest stock ever bred; but the best of care and management will not transform poorly bred stock into good producers of poultry meat or eggs. Good breeding, therefore, becomes a question of first-rate importance. Where did it come from, and just what does it mean?

The Rise of The Hen

Travelers to Asia report that there are still to be heard the rural sounds of civilization and domestication in the vast solitude of the jungle—the crow of the cock and the cackle of the hen. No game is more difficult to reach. Before the stealthiest human foot can approach, they flit into covert like quail and find refuge in the dense foliage of the jungle. These are the wild fowls, the Gallus Bankiva of India, from which the ancient fowls of Persia, Egypt, Greece and Rome descended.

The first poultry in the United States was from this primitive European stock. It had been carried with civilization across Europe and thence to the shores of North America by the early colonists. The turkey was discovered in America and it was introduced to Europe and the rest of the world by the first explorers; but chickens came from Europe, and before that from Asia.

This early American poultry was not of large size. It was well adapted, however, to the pioneer stage of America. It could forage for its living, and would always come home to roost.

JUNGLE FOWL TO EGG MACHINE

The chicken is a home bird, a family fowl. It has a special adaptability to domestication. This is one of the rarest qualities possessed by animals. After thousands of years in capturing, subduing and taming hundreds of different species, man has been able to domesticate only about fifty of them. Many species will not willingly accept the company of man, his care and protection, in exchange for their own life in the wild; but

Gallus Bankiva. The wild fowl of India, progenitor of the domesticated fowls of the world.

fowls, even young birds trapped in the jungle, have become quite tame when reared in confinement.

Because of their willingness to associate with man, fowls have entered very intimately into the lives of humans, and being so universally kept they have claimed the interest of more groups of people than any other bird or animal.

Fowls have followed man wherever he went because of another quality too—they have had the ability to spread over the earth, that is, they have shown adaptability to practically all latitudes and altitudes. You find them prospering along the frozen shores of Alaska, as well as under the heat of the equator in Africa. Large flocks of layers are found at sea-level in New Jersey, and at the same time in the mountain-high altitudes of Utah and Colorado, where a very large poultry industry has developed. It was quite natural, therefore, that pioneers moving into all the new parts of America should travel with their horses, their cows and their hens. One may see in the panorama of the past the caravans of covered wagons slowly moving across the prairies, through the tall, undulating prairie grass, to new homes in the Prairie State.

The Origin of New Breeds in America

It is recorded that settlers coming from the East, who were to inherit and people the nation westward, were to be seen in

Malays. Among the first oriental fowls brought to America. They influenced the rise of new breeds, especially the Rhode Island Reds.

those days slowly polling their rafts down the Ohio river, with their family, a team, a cow, a jag of hay—and some hens that were to find their roosting place on the limb of a tree, at the edge of a clearing, in the wilderness of the West.

The writer's grandmother was one of the pioneers who had come as a little girl, from Culpeper, Virginia, across the mountains into Ohio; and later after marriage had moved on, with her husband and two sons, to a farm at Sedalia, Missouri. She often told about "a flock of a hundred hens," of swapping roosters, and always choosing "an odd or especially pretty one."

Strange as it may seem, the choice of novelty in this respect has its biological value. The rooster that is outstanding because he is different, because he shows a turning out of line, is often the most vigorous. It was not without practical significance, therefore, that the early poultry keepers were attracted

Silver Grey Dorking. An English fowl transported to this country by the colonists. One of the ancestors of the early Plymouth Rock.

by the individuality of some new type and color of bird that showed up in their flocks.

It was on this fertile soil of ready acceptance that the new breeds of poultry which soon made their appearance were to flourish, rapidly spreading from farm to farm until they covered the West. This new stock completely changed the poultry of America in a comparatively short period. Our modern American breeds, the Plymouth Rock, Rhode Island Red and Wyandotte, find their origin in these forces of change.

New oriental blood had a direct bearing on the rise of these breeds. It came from two sources—from the Malays and from the Shanghais, or Asiatics.

It was in 1843 that the British Government opened five principal ports of China, including Shanghai, to commerce. Thence the Shanghais came. Stately sailing vessels brought these strange breeds across the seas, and there was seen in England and the United States a new type of fowl, now known as Cochins and Brahmas. We now call them the Asiatics, but originally they were known as Shanghais. Some of the cocks

Partridge Cochin. One of the Asiatics. An oriental fowl that took America by storm about 1847. It gave size to the American breeds.

were enormous, weighing twelve to fifteen pounds, and because of the heavy plumage that extended clear down their shanks to their toes, they looked even larger than they were. Nothing like these great, shaggy-legged birds had been seen before, and they created a sensation on both sides of the Atlantic. The roosters were said to be "big enough to eat off the top of a barrel." The hens were said to "take to petting like kittens, and they were unable to fly over a three-foot fence." In England, the people from Queen Victoria and the nobility down were taken with "a Cochin mania." In America, spurred on by the prosperity following the discovery of gold in California in 1848, a surprisingly large number of people bought these new fowls, paying high prices because they were far different from the early American stock. Henry Clay acknowledged the "valuable addition" of a pen of these huge birds, with the assurance that if he succeeded with them he would "take care

Dark Brahma. Another Asiatic that improved the common stock of America and influenced the rise of new breeds, especially the Wyandotte.

not to monopolize the benefit of them." Daniel Webster was pleased to acknowledge the arrival of a coop of chickens that he described as "noble specimens of the Chinese breed."

These Asiatics were bred in increasing numbers, and their blood was diffused into the common stock of the country. "They, more than any other race," wrote John Robinson, "had the size which degenerate native stock everywhere lacks." The same authority added that as a result of the infusion of the Asiatic blood, "the average size of the fowls brought to the Boston market was doubled within a few years."

From the crossing of the Asiatic stock on the early poultry a large number of new breeds arose, most of which have passed into oblivion; but one, the Plymouth Rock, emerged as not only an intermediate type but as a family that possessed distinctive character, with dominant points that are readily transmitted with pronounced uniformity. This modern Barred Plymouth Rock made its first appearance at the Worcester, Massachusetts poultry show in 1869. It was a cross between the Cochin and the common Dominique male. Its originator,

Light Brahmas. Recent prize winning flock. America's first all-purpose fowls, imported from the Orient.

the Reverend D. A. Upham, took orders for 100 sittings of eggs at two dollars a sitting. By 1882, the author of "The Complete Poultry Book" referred to the Plymouth Rock as "the most popular breed of fowls in the United States"; and thus thirteen years after its introduction as a distinct variety, it had become the accepted and common type of farm fowl from the Maine woods to the prairies of Nebraska.

The Wyandotte likewise resulted from combining the Asiatic stock with the old home stock. Its body characteristics, including size, disclose Asiatic blood; but the details of the crosses that entered into its origin are unknown. The name Wyandotte was first definitely assigned to it in 1883. Before that time it was variously known as the American Sebright, the Hambletonian, the Eureka, the Sebright Cochin et cetera. Since then a number of varieties of the Wyandotte breed have been produced by crossings with Cochins and with Brahmas.

The Wyandotte has a rounded body like the Asiatics but it is not as large and its shanks are free from feathers.

The Rhode Island Red sprang from the farm fowls of Rhode Island, where the red color had remained uppermost from the old days of sailing ships when Red Malay Game cocks from the Orient, had been brought into Fall River and New Bedford.

The early stock of the Little Compton, Rhode Island district

Barred Plymouth Rock champion egg-layer. A favorite dual-purpose fowl, and the oldest American breed standardized.

represented the blood of the Brown Leghorn, the Malay, and the Cochin. The breed was exhibited at Madison Square Garden, as the Rhode Island Red, in 1892; and it was given official recognition as a standardbred in 1904.

The Black Giant, grown extensively in New Jersey (therefore called the Jersey Black Giant) is another American breed. It originated in crosses of the Partridge Cochin, Dark Brahmas, Dark Cornish and Barred Plymouth Rock. The modern improved breed carries the blood of the Black Langshan, Black Orpington and Black Java. The Black Java is itself an American breed, although there has been much controversy over this fact. It undoubtedly arose from breeding black sports of the Barred Plymouth Rock with Cochins and other black fowls. The Java and the Giant have not enjoyed the wide popularity accorded the Plymouth Rock, the Wyandotte and the Rhode Island Red.

In each case it was cross-breeding with Asiatic fowls that led to the production of the American breeds. Their yellow skin,

Silver-laced Wyandotte. The second officially recognized American breed, and the first of many beautiful and useful varieties. A popular meat and egg fowl.

their brown-shelled eggs, their red earlobes are typically Asiatic. In Europe and England today the old native races have a predisposition toward white skin and white-shelled eggs, and such were the tendencies of the early American stock. The points which some present-day American consumers most prize—the rich butter-colored carcass and the brown egg—are inherited from the Shanghais and Malays.

After these new American breeds swept across the country, the farms of the Middle West began to grow them quite extensively. Other breeds are also grown, but the American breeds outnumber the others. On January 1, 1930, fifty per cent of the chickens of the United States were on the farms of Illinois, Indiana, Ohio, Michigan, Wisconsin, Minnesota, Iowa, Missouri, the Dakotas, Nebraska and Kansas. These twelve states had a combined poultry population of 243,000,000 head. Their egg production in 1929 amounted to 1,330,034,000 dozens, or about one-half the entire egg production of the nation.

Barred Plymouth Rock Cock. A choice bird for the meat packer and for the production farmer of the Middle West. A fine pencil-barred specimen.

Poultry-keeping in this area received a tremendous impetus during the World War. The idea of increased poultry efficiency swept the country. Hens on almost every farm were culled on the basis of a big capacious abdomen, widespread pelvic arch, and faded pigment—that is, the fading of pigment in beak and legs—all indications of good laying ability. The watchword at farmers' meetings was "Cull out the drones." That there is a distinctive and individual difference in hens was plainly demonstrated. Immediately the demand sprang up for increasing stock that had been specifically bred to meet the problems of efficient production and show a profit. Instead of being merely a by-product of farming, poultry assumed the importance of a livestock industry, and appreciative thought was accorded to the accomplishments of poultry breeders.

There have been three distinct classes of
poultry breeders, developing traits and
qualities within their fowls. The first of
these was the gamecock breeder; then the
fancier; and lastly, the production breeder.

The Golden Age of the Cocker

L ET us look at the first of these historical groups, the cocker,
as he was called. He was a skillful breeder. He developed type and temperament in his strains. He knew the
importance of constitutional vigor and ranked it foremost. He
produced strength of limb, and alertness of step, beyond anything we have today. He was the first to consider the size and
texture of the feathers. He went beyond his day and developed
a type that was not only apparent to the eye but a type that was
actual when you took the bird in your hands.

These birds were bred to fight, and we owe much to their
masters. The high valor and defiant deeds of those monarchs
of battle are what originally led to the wide distribution of
chickens. The sport of cock-fighting was chiefly instrumental
in introducing chickens into Europe in the first place—from
India into Persia, into Phoenicia, into ancient Greece, into
Rome, across the Alps and through the straits of Gibraltar into
the land of the Gauls and Britons. When Caesar invaded
Gaul and the British Isles, he found the fighting cock there
ahead of him. In fact, some historians claim the term *Gallus,*
applied to a Gaul by the Romans, was a pun on the original
term Gael because those people were reported by Caesar as
fighting under the standard of a cock. Similarly the term

Pyle Games. Exhibition variety of the type bred by George Washington. Games added strength to the common stock and led the way to scientific breeding.

Danen (Danes) was recorded as being derived from *de hahnen*—referring to those people whose soldiers carried two cocks to war, one to tell the hours and another to excite the men to battle by an exhibition of cock fights just before military engagement. In the same manner the ancient Carians received their name from the Persians. The Roman historian, Plutarch, said the people of Caria used to carry cocks on the ends of their lances; and the Greek historian, Herodotus, said the inhabitants of Caria wore cock-crested helmets, and so the Persians called them cocks. Thus we see how love for the game cock resulted in disseminating fowls throughout Europe.

Game cocks in America arrived from several directions. The first group came from the British Isles. The colonists brought their favorite fighters with them. Lord Fairfax had several hundred on his estate in Virginia. American Breeders still

The set-to. This and other terms of the pugilist's vocabulary are borrowed from the cock-pit.

raise this variety, and advertise them as "pure Old English pit games."

The second group came from French and Spanish importations to the new world, some direct from Europe and some from Mexico, South America, and the West Indies. These, too, are still bred as pure strains in our southern states, and especially famous are the Red Cuban games.

A third group came from a new English infusion. The old English game had been mixed with the Asiatic game, adding new vigor to the old stock.

The fourth group came direct from the Orient. American traders brought them into many ports. A heavier bird was the result of this new oriental blood. It was preferred by some, but disdained by lovers of the Old English "light-weights."

Because poultry breeding owes so much to the game fowl, the skill of the cocker in breeding and training his birds is

The clinch. Trainers clipped Old English Games before entering them in the pit. Van Dyck painted Charles I at a tournament like this.

Taking the count. A cock knows when his adversary is licked and crows. Pit Games were fed a "cock bread", the first packaged food for poultry.

worthy of comment. Many years before horses or cattle were bred along pedigree lines, this system was used by the game fowl breeder. The great feudal estates kept breeding pens and family records of the birds that occupied them. During the period 1200 to 1400, cock-fighting had increased so rap- 69

"When cock
meets cock
Then comes
the tug of
war!"

"Each tug-
ging to be
victor breast
to breast
Yet neither
conqueror nor
conquered."

idly in England that we read of several attempts were made to
have it outlawed because of its interference with archery and
other necessary forms of recreation. In the next two hundred
years it had assumed such prominence that it became the
"sport of kings." It kept its reputation as the most popular

Artificial spurs even the chances, and it takes the better cock to win. This is a throat pass.

Steel fighters depend upon speed, quickness of eyesight, and wing power.

recreation in the Three Kingdoms until Queen Victoria ascended the throne (1837). Then the growth of the humanitarian principle, and the increasing popularity of horse racing, resulted in a second Act of Parliament outlawing the game pit.

During these seven hundred years of raising pedigreed stock

Strategy and deceit are often used. One will feint and duck, then pirouette and strike a deadly blow.

"The main is fought and passed
And the pit is empty now—
Some cocks have crowed their last
While some more loudly crow".

for fighting the cocker learned much about selective breeding, and the experience thus gained was applied to the improvement of the common stock of the country. A glance at Gervase Markham's book *Cheape and Good Husbandry* (1614) will show us some of the methods practiced in those days:

72   "To speak then first of the choyce of the Fighting-Cock, you

Mexican on way to the pit with fighting cocks securely snuggled in baskets so as not to become unduly excited before battle.

shall understand that the best characters that you can observe in him is the shape, colour, courage and sharp heel; for his shape the middle and different size is ever accounted best, because they be ever most matchable, strong, nimble, and ready for your pleasure in his battel; and too the exceeding little cock is as hard to match, and is commonly weak and tedious in his manner of fighting. He would be of a proud and upright shape, with a small head, like until a sparhawk, a quick large eye, and a strong back, crookt and bigge at the setting on, and in colour suitable to the plume of his feathers, as black, yellow, or reddish. The beam of his legge would be very strong, and according to his plume, blew, gray or yellow; his spurres long, rough, and sharpe, and little bending and looking inward."

"Now for the breeding of these cocks for the battel it is much differing from those of the dunghill, for they are like Birds of Prey, in which the female is ever to be preferred and esteemed before the Male, and so in the breed of these Birds, you must be sure your Hen is right, that is to say, she must be of a right plume (feather), as grey, grissel, speckt, or yellowish, black or brown is not amiss; she must be kindly to her young and of a large body, well poaked behind for large egges and well tufted on the crown, which shows courage; if she have weapons (spurs) she is better, but for her valour it must be excellent, for if there be any sort of cowardice in her, the chickens cannot be true.

"And it is a note among the best breeders, that the perfect hen from a Dunghill cock, will bring a good chicken, but the best Cock from a Dunghill Hen can never get a good bird."

Thus the breeder of cocks for the pit produced a fowl of alertness, graceful poise and stately walk. He was the first true breeder of poultry. From generation to generation, from century to century, the boldest and most symmetrical birds, and those of purest fighting blood lines, were kept, while the weak, ill-formed or poor-conditioned specimens were set aside. Some of the defects that the cocker considered serious were crooked breast, imperfect eye, short feet, unhealthfulness.

Constructive breeding, and breeding in line, first came into play in perpetuating strains of pit games that were stout and sure. The old cockers bred a bright and beautiful bird, bold, with enduring courage, vigorous, healthy, strong. In order to accomplish this he not only mated his birds carefully but also put the cocks through a thorough training. The training rules were borrowed by the British from the Hindoos and Malaysians who regarded such rules as magic formulae. Birds were conditioned by exercise, diet, sparring, and a regular daily program.

Choice cockerels were exercised by long walks. "Quarrelsome" pullets, too, were exercised, in order to strengthen the breed.

A cock-ale was a special part of the game cock's diet. This became corrupted into the popular cocktail in America. If the ale was good for the cock, it was good for the cocker.

Sparring was perfected by covering the spurs with leather muffs. The idea of boxing-gloves, for pugilists was borrowed from this. Boxers also borrowed many other things from the cock-pit, such as their rules and fighting-language. All of us use some daily expressions that had their origin in the great fighting mains several centuries ago, namely, such terms as: sulky, plucky, gritty, clean-cut, rattled, cuts his own throat, pink of condition, et cetera.

Old Engish Dorking. The oldest of all English breeds. Five toes distinguish it from other early fowls. Possibly descended f r o m early Roman 5-toed fowl.

The Supremacy of the Fancier

When cock-fighting was abruptly outlawed in England as that nation was passing into an industrial era, "back-lot fanciers" made their appearance. They met with their friends at the tavern and compared birds. Perhaps the innkeeper offered a pewter mug or a copper kettle for the best. Slowly, gradually, beautiful feather patterns developed out of the confused mass of hereditary material in the stock. Such charming and wonderful varieties as the Penciled Hamburgs, White Crested Black Polish, Sebright Bantams, and Silver Grey Dorkings came into full glory.

The cocker was a specialist. He carried his hobby so far that even the hens of his breeding were cruel and pugnacious to one another. Then came the dawn of the fancy. The fancier also scrutinized every bird that went into his breeding

THE ROYAL SUCCES- SION OF BREEDERS

White-crested Black Polish. An early fowl claimed by both the Dutch and the Italians. The name Polish refers to poll or crest.

pen, and a specimen that was foul grown or disproportioned was rejected.

We owe much to these fanciers just as we do to the earlier pit game breeders. The beauty standards they fixed to appeal to the eye and gratify the senses command admiration. The thought and care they bestowed upon their birds rivaled the keenness of interest displayed by their predecessors, the cockers. Money might purchase their finest birds, but only a fancier in love with his work could produce them. He patiently studied many details of his birds, that many niceties might fulfill the dictates of the eye. The fancier was a breeder-artist, and greater than the sculptor-artist who makes a model in cold, dumb stone. The breeder-artist put into a living thing the bright and beautiful colors of the painter, and working with the invisible and none too well understood laws of transmission

Old English Houdan. Created by crossing original F r e n c h Houdans with Dorkings for size, and with White-crested Black Polish for fullness of crest and comb. It carries the Dorking 5-toe, and has a triple leaf comb.

and inheritance, shaped the plastic material with which he worked into his ideal.

The cocker bred primarily for body-shape, speed and internal qualities with little thought of external characters until the popularity of cock-fighting began to wane. Then his interest in plumage resulted in separating his birds into distinct varieties according to color and markings. So the poultryman's maxim became "Shape makes the breed, color the variety."

In place of the cock-pit, the fancier's assemblage for competition was the *exhibition*.

The bird for the show, like the bird for the pit, must have special care and training to fit him for the competition. Proper grooming just before the show consists of brushing the legs, polishing the shanks, freshening the comb and wattles, and, in the case of white birds, washing the plumage.

We have learned much from the fancier. The first lesson

Mottled Houdan. Modern breed with v-comb and uniform patterned plumage as preferred by American fanciers.

was a recognition of the dominant traits of different breeds. The second lesson was a recognition of variety characteristics and the ability of man to create a large number of beautiful birds fixed in type. A third lesson was that maintaining a standard of excellence for standardbred poultry led naturally to improvement in the common stock of the country. It is this last point that has been particularly emphasized in America, as has been said of us "The American does not despise beauty but he worships utility." The three great American breeds are ample testimony—the Plymouth Rock, the Wyandotte, and the Rhode Island Red—all good layers, good meat birds, and beautiful fowls.

THE ROYAL SUCCESSION OF BREEDERS

The Enlightened Age of the Utilitarian

The cocker was a warrior. Then came the artist, the fancier. And third, the worker. He is the breeder of today. His hens are not bred for the pit, nor for the show pen, but for production; they are the workers. First it was battle, and then art, and now science. This new type of poultry breeder must be

Creve-coeur. First standard bred fowl of France. Crossed with Houdans in America to give v-comb and mottled plumage to the modern Houdan.

recognized as a constructive improver of one of the most important and valuable forms of livestock in the whole system of animal husbandry. He has essayed for himself the job of taking the breeds and varieties, and after preserving the health and vigor (which were the aims of the old cocker) and, after preserving the racial character of the breeds (which was the fundamental aim of the fancier) adding to these things his own contribution of usefulness.

That chickens can be bred to grow faster, and feather earlier, and lay more eggs, and larger eggs, and begin to lay younger, is not an opinion; it is a fact, amply proven. And that birds bred to possess these superior qualities can transmit them, in liberal measure, to their offspring is again a matter of record. The inheritance of egg-laying ability was forcefully brought to the attention of farm poultry keepers by Professor William A. Lippincott, Kansas State College of Agriculture. He

Egg-laying contest at A Century of Progress International Exposition, 1933.

started his test by going to the public market and buying ten mongrel hens, which were then mated to a cockerel whose dam had a high egg record, and who had come from a whole line of heavy-laying females. This mating was made in 1914. The ten mongrels laid an average of 72 eggs each in that year. Their daughters laid 156 eggs each in their first year. These half mongrel, half high-production bred pullets were then mated to another well bred male, and the pullets from this mating, carrying three-quarters high egg blood, laid an average of 189 eggs each in one year. These three-quarter blood pullets whose grandmothers were mongrels with an egg average of 72, were mated to still another production-bred cockerel, and their offspring averaged 193 eggs each. The males used in this grading-up work were of the same breed and from the same breeder, the late Douglas Tancred. They were males of

a powerful, vigorous type. They had been bred from hens that had been trapnested and whose production was known to be high. The authorities in charge of the Kansas Agricultural Experiment Station were so impressed with the indisputable and overwhelming value of the experiment that they published in bulletin form Professor Lippincott's complete figures on

the experiment.

Thus with the advent of the production breeder, the arena of competition becomes the *egg-laying contest* in place of the cock-pit or the exhibition.

England instituted egg-laying trials in 1897. At those trials or egg tests, the basis of award was averages rather than the actual count of the production of individual hens. Some valuable lessons were learned, nevertheless, chiefly in relation to seasonal facts.

Hens that gave the highest winter average had the highest yearly average. Laying ability in autumn or winter was determined largely by the hatching period. The knowledge of this last fact has been of practical value in the business of egg production. By hatching early, and by selecting pullets for laying and for mating from these early hatches, the farm producer has been able to increase egg yield in the season of scarcity and high prices.

The first American egg-laying contest, as we know it to-day, was held at Storrs, Connecticut, in 1911. It was staged by Professor F. H. Stoneburn of the Connecticut State College, in conjunction with F. V. L. Turner of Philadelphia. It was soon followed in the Middle West by an egg-laying contest under the direction of T. E. Quisenberry at Missouri State Poultry Experiment Station, Mountain Grove. There are now forty or more contests held annually in different parts of the United States.

A contest pen of Rhode Island Reds. Ten typical fast laying hens. Compare dual-purpose Red p. 285.

It was worthy of notice, that although there were certain individuals and pens that made exceptional records, the production of the contests as a whole was higher than that on the home farms. The result was that the methods of feeding, housing and general management employed at the contests were adopted at home, and the production on the home farms was increased. This was true not only on the farms of breeders, but also on the farms of other poultry raisers who did not aspire to be breeders.

But the breeders who entered birds in these contests went further. Contest rules required contestants to have birds at the contest at a definite date, November 1st—more recently changed to October 1st in many contests. Naturally, the birds that were in just the right condition to start laying as soon as they arrived at the contest and had the stamina to maintain production throughout the year were at a considerable advantage. This conditioning process requires the selection of a suitable hatching date so that pullets will arrive at maturity at just the right time, as for example, February or March for the

In any breed qualities of flesh and feathers will yield to the one purpose, egg production.

heavy breeds and April 1 to 15 for Leghorns to be ready for contests starting October 1. It involves, also, skillful feeding during the growing period so that steady growth will be made and yet sexual maturity not reached before it is desired; this means a judicious use of grain in addition to a good growing mash so there will be a sufficient amount of body weight obtained to enable them to go through a heavy laying season in good condition. Another step in this conditioning process is the gradual changing during the last couple of weeks before the birds are sent to the contest to the feed that is to be used at the contest, so there will be no possibility of a setback due to a sudden variation or too complete a change in diet. Breeders make it a point to find out well in advance complete details of the management of the contest to which they send their birds, and guide themselves accordingly. The feeding system commands first attention; another point of equal importance is whether or not lights are used in the houses to induce egg production. If lights are used, it is possible to allow pullets to come into production at least a month before they are sent to the contest and have little or no setback because of the change.

Contests originally paid little attention to the size of the eggs laid other than to discard all extremely small, unmarketable eggs known as "peewees", and not record them. In recent years, however, size has been considered along with the number of eggs produced, so that now at most contests awards are made according to the number of points a bird earns, each full point representing the number of 2-oz. eggs she lays. The system of recording points decided upon by a number of the contests is as follows:

Egg Wt. in Oz. per Dozen	Points Allowed
18	.70
19	.75
20	.80
21	.85
22	.90
23	.95
24	1.00
25	1.05
26 and over	1.10

Eggs are weighed each day. This has stimulated breeders to pay more attention to egg size in their breeding work.

The changing of the contest rules some years ago to forbid the replacement of birds that died undoubtedly helped to emphasize the importance of livability and vitality in breeding.

Since egg laying contests have offered exceptional opportunities to gather complete data on the various phases of egg production, such as, date of first egg, cycle of laying, broodiness, molting, intensity of production, gain and loss in weight, amount and kind of feed consumed, and costs, much valuable information has been obtained that commercial poultrymen and breeders have used to advantage.

Egg laying contests are undoubtedly responsible to a large extent for impressing on utility breeders the importance and necessity of trapnesting for flock improvement. It has only

White and Dark Cornish. An English fowl bred for meat.

been possible within comparatively recent years to buy high quality trapnested stock in any quantity. Until this time, many breeders who were not equipped to do much if any trapnesting used to enter birds in these contests for the sole purpose of getting their birds trapped; these birds, with official trapnest records were then returned to the home farm and were used as breeders from whom they could obtain stock with which to build up the rest of the flock. The desire of these men in entering birds was not to make exceptional records or to win the contest, but to have as many of their birds as possible lay at least 200 eggs in a year, in order to have a strong nucleus for a breeding flock.

The effect of the egg laying contest has been far reaching, for it has made it possible for a larger number of people to enjoy added profits and better living conditions because its lessons have made possible the dissemination of higher quality stock, from a production standpoint, throughout the farms of the country. It has undoubtedly done more than any one thing to stimulate the present day breeders to study the real fine points in breeding, especially the factors and principles of heredity.

THE ROYAL SUCCESSION OF BREEDERS

85

THERE are so many variations in nature that of the countless leaves of a tree no two are ever exactly alike. This diversity runs through all living things, and the art of breeding begins with the principle that no two are alike, and the best shall be selected for reproduction. Breeding in itself is very old. All primitive peoples practiced selective breeding of both plant and animal life for purposes of ceremony, adornment, and food. The Chinese practiced selection for the perfection of the lotus and the peony tree for fourteen hundred years; they also improved the rice seed. Two thousand years ago and since, the American Indian raised corn in colors to match the colors he assigned to the Powers of the Six Directions. We have yet to learn the secret as to how he achieved these varieties. The same keen sense of purpose that actuated the first primitive breeder to select and classify his specimens, characterizes the modern breeder, who brings to his aid the accumulated knowledge of the past together with the more recent contributions of scientific research.

Variations in poultry have occurred because of both natural and artificial selection. Artificial selection is the result of the breeder's art. Natural selection is the result of climate, geography, accidental matings, and fitness to survive.

The domesticated fowl spread from India in every direction, and in every part of the world special types evolved in harmony with the people's particular temperaments and interests in so far as environment and human ability to change nature permitted the new breed of fowl to flourish. In Japan the artistic sense was accentuated, and the fancy breeds dominated;

Silkie. Japanese fowl of ancient origin. Sometimes called "negro fowl" because of its black skin.

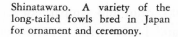

Shinatawaro. A variety of the long-tailed fowls bred in Japan for ornament and ceremony.

so we have the Silkies and the long-tailed varieties—the colored Shinotawaro and the White Yokohama that often achieve tail or saddle feathers twelve to twenty feet in length. Malaysia preferred to perpetuate the fighting breeds and these were eagerly accepted by Spain. During the period of conquest cock-fighting became a paramount interest in Spain, and so the sporting bloods were exhibited and raised in every land touched by her famous galleons. Thus Mexico inherited a Malaysian institution, and preferred therefore to rear and promote the game breeds.

Italy and the other Mediterranean countries developed small-

Malay Game. A Philippine variety. Contrast long legs and upright carriage of other Games and other Malays, see pp. 58 and 67.

bodied birds with agile and nervous dispositions. China, on the other hand, developed the huge-bodied kind with feathers down their shanks, calm and sympathetic in disposition.

Ancient England began with a paramount interest in the game cock, to be followed with the idea of fowls for the production of food as an integral part of agriculture. The table poultry of old Sussex, Surrey and Kent has been recognized for centuries for its delicacy and succulence. The Dorking is one of England's superior table breeds. In the development of these breeds, poultry was, and has remained, a part of pastoral agriculture.

The limitations of environment must be recognized. The Philippines offer a good example. Many attempts have been made to introduce the American and Australian breeds into the Philippines. The stock becomes dwarfed after a second or third generation; some die out. All Philippine breeds have a tendency toward smallness of size in spite of breeders' efforts to lengthen the leg or raise the body. Whether this is a problem of climate or food or both, has not been fully deter-

Silver Sebright Bantams. A creation that astonished the poultry world and stimulated fancy breeding.

mined. Climate and feed undoubtedly have a bearing on type, within which natural limits the breeder works.

There appear to be biological limits beyond which production cannot be increased. Extraordinary hens with 350-egg records or better may help to raise the average ability of a breeder's laying stock; but there is a natural time element in the fabrication of an egg that man may not be able to change.* Therefore hens with the power to lay two eggs per day as a regular performance would seem to be quite beyond the range of the breeder's magic to achieve.

Sebright's Wondrous Birds

The secret of the breeder's magic is selection. This principle of selective mating enabled Sir John Sebright to produce a breed of bantams bearing his name, Sebright bantams, which are a classical example of the distinctive and beautiful in poultry. Even Sir John's own friends are reported to have doubted his ability to produce such wondrous lilliputians of the feathered tribe, and to have openly stated that "he must have

* See page 178; also pages 99 and 284.

La Fleche. A French breed of obscure origin, showing antler or v-comb. Originally crested like Sultans. English and American fanciers removed the top-knot by selective breeding.

imported them from some foreign land." Silver and Golden Sebright bantams are bred today with a beauty of feather that is matchless in the whole array of breeds. These pigmies of the poultry yard have the pert bearing and fine appearance of aristocrats among fowls.

About 1800, when the Sebright bantam was being fashioned and the first matings were being made, another English breeder whose name has become a part of livestock history, Thomas Bates, purchased his first Shorthorn cattle. Bates' aim in breeding was utilitarian. Already the Colling brothers, through the fortunate selection of a sire, had succeeded in overcoming the features of late maturity and coarseness which had been common in the cows. Bates now proceeded to give attention to the milking qualities of his cows. He measured the quantity of milk given by each cow and kept detailed records of the

Sultan. A rare breed introduced into Europe from Turkey, but has many characteristics of the Feather Footed Siberian. Note the full crest and v-comb.

feed consumed in relation to the milk produced. He selected his breeding stock with a view to the capabilities of his cows to produce, this being quite a different course from that pursued by Sebright, who was selecting altogether for external points of appearance without regard to internal qualifications for economic production. Both were distinguished breeders.

For many years the work of Sebright was the model which poultry fanciers strove to emulate. The beauty standards that he set in the Sebright bantam influenced judges at the shows and fairs to award prizes on the basis of those externals that could be seen by the eye. Only in more recent years has the appreciation of points so broadened that the internal capacity to produce is a fundamental consideration in the selection of breeding stock in the leading poultry breeds. There is notice-able a characteristic style and finish about these utility or "production-bred" birds, just as there was about Bates' Short-horns, and a flock of such fowls is a fine-looking sight.

The Value of Inbreeding

Progress in recent years has been rapid. Breeders like Sebright and Bates were quick to take advantage of an exceptional specimen which gave promise of improving their lines, and they inbred their stock to intensify the blood of the select individuals. The idea, however, that a cow or a hen is the mass sum of a number of different units, each unit representing a certain characteristic, and that these units are transmitted to the offspring as rather independent factors, was only dimly perceived by early breeders. They sought to get certain points, and a sire or dam that would transmit them was given a high rating as "prepotent"—that is, potent to pass on the characteristics of the parent to the offspring; but the knowledge that the germ cells actually carry different factors is a more modern interpretation of the physical basis of inheritance.

The Significance of Mendel's Studies

The papers of Gregor Johann Mendel, an Austrian monk who made a close study of the mode of inheritance, have provided the basis for analysis of the mechanics of heredity and variation. His experiments, first reported in 1865, when they went unheeded, were rediscovered in 1900, and today both the practice and the principles of breeding are thoroughly Mendelian. Genetics is the term applied to this study of the fulfillment of the possibilities wrapped up in the germ cells.

Mendel explains the results of heredity and variation on a mathematical or statistical basis. He worked with plants, which have the advantage of making large numbers for observation possible. He limited himself to simple and prominent features, such as long stem vs short stem in peas, and found that this characteristic behaved as a separate unit and followed a definite law of inheritance.

Gregor Johann Mendel. The man who established laws of inheritance applicable to both plant and animal life. His work inspired poultrymen to study the factors of heredity in fowls as a basis for scientific breeding.

He crossed tall peas that measured six feet with short peas one foot high. One might expect a blend with all the offspring medium-sized, or one might anticipate that half of them would be tall and half short. But no; all the plants from this cross were tall. These tall hybrids were then bred together, and there was another surprise; the offspring were not all tall; of 1,000 plants grown, an average of 3 out of every 4 were tall and 1 was short.

Then these short-stemmed peas, averaging 1 out of every 4, were self-fertilized—that is, the pollen of a flower was placed on the pistil of the same flower; they proved to be purebred for the factor of dwarfness. The factor of shortness had proven to be a definite something; it was a unit that had not become lost, and had segregated itself out as pure. This was the essential discovery that Mendel made, that is, segregation, and the regularity with which differences are transmitted.

Mendel's experiments were not confined to the one character of height. He patiently followed up other factors, such as the color of the unripe pod, whether a shade of green or bright yellow; the shape of the seeds, whether rounded or wrinkled; in fact, his observations covered seven distinct features in peas. He studied them as separate units, the shape of the pod for example, being independent from the distribution of flowers on the stem. The whole plant represented the sum total of a number of separate units.

Mendel's Experiment Applied to Animals

In repeating these pea experiments for comparable results, a test was made on rose-comb and single-comb chickens. The Wyandottes have rose combs, the Plymouth Rocks have single combs. The results are identical with those in the case of tall and short peas. All the hybrids are rose-combed. When these rose-combed chickens are bred together, they produce 3 rose to 1 single. If the single-combs are then interbred, they produce all single-combs, showing that they are pure for this factor. The cross-bred rose-combs segregate out according to Mendel's law.

Horns on cattle are a unit in the Mendelian sense, and man has been able to produce a polled breed of cattle in a single decade; something that nature had not done in all the centuries. Such features as comb and horns suggest that a hen or a cow is not an indivisible whole; rather, it is the fulfillment of a whole group of rather definite factors. Each of these units is represented in the germ cells of the reproductive system, and each young generation in turn is but the elaboration of the hereditary material that it receives at birth.

Important Factors in Chicken Breeding

This clear conception of an individual as a combination of factors has resulted in tremendous progress in breeding, in poultry as elsewhere. It is patent that if we want large fowls, the factor for this character, largeness, must be present in the germ plasm of the eggs from which the birds are hatched.

And if the size of the birds, or the type of comb, or some other

Rose and single-comb crossbreeding produces 3 rose to 1 single in the second generation. The first generation are all rose-combs.

external character is inherited as a factor, why not the internal qualities that specifically relate to production?

It has been found that there are several different factors that have a direct bearing on the productive value of a hen. In breeding for production, therefore, these factors are taken into consideration. One is the age at which a pullet starts to lay. If a Leghorn is not sufficiently precocious to begin laying at five to five and one-half months of age, and a Plymouth Rock or Rhode Island Red at six to six and one-half months, it counts against her.

Another consideration is the moult. As long as a hen continues to lay, she retains her old feathers. This, then, is a sign of persistence of production, which is a genetic factor. In addition to persistence, it is desirable that a pullet shall lay at a good rate. There is a big difference between a pullet that lays a dozen eggs in her first month of laying, and one that lays twenty or twenty-two eggs. This is called "intensity of production." Both intensity and persistence are important points in breeding for increased egg production.

Some hens sit and rear their own young. In breeding for eggs, however, this tendency, which is called broodiness, is deemed undesirable. A hen that becomes broody two, three or four times in a year would be devoting an excessive amount of time to this maternal instinct, and it would be impossible

Vigorous males necessary to maintain vitality in heavy-laying stock.

Upper:
White Wyandotte
White Plymouth Rock

Lower:
Buff Orpington
Jersey Black Giant

for her to make a good laying record. Broodiness is a genetic factor.

Size of egg is important. In the New York and Boston markets especially, it is not uncommon in the winter months to see a difference of eight cents to twelve cents a dozen on the quoted prices of eggs, due altogether to the difference in the size. It is not profitable, therefore, to breed small-egg stock. Egg size is an hereditary trait. It is another unit in the make-up of our bird.

The Fascinating Duties of Scientific Breeding

On general farms and on large commercial poultry farms, mass matings of 100 or more fowls are often made. One male

Releasing a hen from trap-nest. Her egg is marked with name and date, and is recorded on the score board.

to about fifteen females is used in the case of the larger breeds, and one male to about twenty females in the case of Leghorns. For pen matings, however, one male is mated to a selected number of females, possibly ten or a dozen. These females may be trap-nested daily—that is, the hen lays in a nest that traps her until she can be released, which enables the poultry-man to identify her egg and keep a perfect score of her production. Eggs from the trap nests are marked with a pencil, indicating the hen that laid them, and the date they were laid. These eggs can then be set in pedigree trays, each hen's eggs in a separate tray, and the chicks hatched separately. A band stamped with a number that corresponds to the number of the hen that laid the egg can be clamped around the wing of the chick that hatches, and it is thus wing-banded for life.

This is the first step in pedigree hatching and pedigree breeding. The other steps relate to the poultryman's observations and his record keeping, a work that is thoroughly carried on by a number of poultry breeders. They record the number

Marked eggs are set in incubator p e d i g r e e trays, each hen's eggs in a separate tray so that her chicks can be identified.

of eggs set from each hen, and the number of chicks that hatch. If there is poor hatchability, not only the fact, but the exact percentage of hatchability is recorded against the dam.

Of the chicks that are started in the brooders, an exact count is made of those that reach maturity in the fall. The percentage of mortality and the reason for each loss as it occurs is recorded, because the death of a bird may be due to an inherited trait of poor livability.

When the pullet starts to lay, she begins her own trap-nest career. Her eggs are weighed. She is weighed. It is expected that her eggs will increase in size, and that she will hold her body weight. The color of her egg is observed and recorded. Tinted egg stock is not wanted in the white-egg breeds.

At the end of a year, her trap-nest record and other data are available for scrutiny; and if the pullet has made good, she is suitable for use as a breeder. If she has done unusually well,

A chick wing-banded for life with a number that corresponds to the number of the hen that laid the egg.

Leg-banding is another method of identification. The wire cage is another type of incubator pedigree tray.

and her sisters likewise, it is a mark of credit to her sire, and he is singled out as a stud bird for the coming year.

This procedure seems rather involved, yet it is the most fascinating part of poultry work. It is the sure road to flock improvement. The breeder who follows such practices must be fitted temperamentally and morally to be methodical and honest in his record keeping. He will put more overhead expense into his birds and can command higher prices for his stock. He can sell cockerels for breeding accompanied by pedigrees which show the egg record of the bird's dam, grandam, great grandam, and so on. Many of these pedigree records are rich in 250-egg blood, and birds of such breeding command good prices. Some breeders have pedigreed stock showing 300-egg yield through several generations, and they are mating birds with still higher laying records. Since the innovation of the egg laying contest in America, eleven varieties (representing seven breeds) have produced individual birds which have laid between 300 and 358 eggs in a year. These are the Barred Plymouth Rock, the S. C. Rhode Island Red, the Buff Orpington, the White Leghorn, the Australorp, the Rhode Island White, the White Wyandotte, Jersey Black Giant, R. C. Rhode Island Red, White Plymouth Rock and White Orpington. The average has risen from 145 eggs per bird at the first contest in 1911, to 213.18 per bird in the Hunterdon, New Jersey contest of 1932. Trap-nest, records and selection have made this increase possible.

Thus the breeder's magic becomes science. By being faithful to his knowledge and ideals he has been able to transform the color of fowls, and to modify the texture and the fulness of their feathers, at will. He has been able to change their body shape and size, and to multiply the types of combs. He has been able to add a toe or a top-knot, or to take them off. But more than these, he has been able to change the disposition of fowls and to increase their reproductive powers so that they might yield more abundantly, which means in the end that he has been able to increase man's wealth and man's food supply.

MECHANICAL
MOTHERS

THE reproduction of the species is always a matter of much importance, and in this, the hen, unlike animals that give birth to their young, lays eggs that are hatched outside her body. It requires three weeks to incubate a hen's egg and give life to a chirping, bright-eyed chick. This is the same miracle of nature witnessed in the planted seed which, succored by the earth, bursts its envelope and ushers forth with the beauty of new life.

Early Types of Incubators

The fact that the hen does produce eggs that develop into young outside her body has given rise to very ingenious methods for the incubation of those eggs. Devices by which hens' eggs are artificially hatched are not new. Chinese writers refer to the operation of incubators as early as 500 B. C., and they claim to have borrowed the custom from the Malays. The early Malay, according to tradition hatched eggs of the jungle fowl without the help of the feathered mother, and all pullets were returned to the jungle as only cocks were wanted. Some Malay groups to-day incubate eggs in bamboo or reed cylinders set in a bin filled with rice hulls for insulation. An incubating temperature is maintained by bags of heated rice alternating bags of eggs within each cylinder.

The Chinese method to-day is probably a modification of this early type. The Chinese use a series of units (jars or 101

11-day Chinese incubator, showing inner basket from which eggs are removed to finishing trays.

mudplastered baskets). Professor F. H. King of Madison, Wisconsin, visited a hatchery in China in 1909. He observed thirty of these unit incubators in one room. A bowl-shaped basket holding about 1200 eggs, just fit into the top of an earthen jar which was placed inside another jar encased in basketry. Heat was supplied by charcoal smothered with ashes; it was put through an opening in the side of the outer jar. Each unit was covered with a close-fitting lid. The eggs were removed from the basket after the eleventh day. Then they were placed in finishing trays, which were padded with cotton and covered with quilts and hung above the basketed jars so as to utilize the rising warm air.

The Egyptians have developed huge hatcheries with a capacity of 70,000 or more eggs. Archaeological investigation reveals that practically the same style has been in use in the valley of the Nile for over two thousand years. These incubators are really great ovens made of sun-dried brick and mud; they are divided into a number of compartments each carrying several thousand eggs; and they are heated by burning camel dung or finely chopped straw. Some ancient models used a type of lamp. Both in Egypt and in Asia temperature was determined by the operator holding an egg to his eyelid where

10-day incubator finishing t r a y s kept warm on a Chinese bunk.

sensitive nerves told him whether the temperature was too hot or too cold; the profession was hereditary.

Early Greek and Roman writers recorded other methods used by the Egyptians which were more simple. The eggs were said to be incubated in warm beds of straw or in warm earth. Modern writers have questioned these statements and say there is little probability as to their truth; but such hatchings are quite possible under certain climatic conditions. Before irrigation reclaimed the semi-arid San Joaquin Valley of California it was not at all unusual to find chicks hatched in sand where the sunlight filtered through a partial shade.

About fifty years ago the first American factory-made incubators appeared on the market. They applied the thermosbottle principle. Thermometers were used to test the heat, but they were not self-regulating. The *Hammonton* was simply a wooden box kept warm by a hot-water tank insulated in sawdust. The *Eureka* added an alarm clock so that the operator could be awakened during the night to watch the temperature.

Standard Lamp Incubators

The fact that temperature could be applied to eggs and that chicks could be hatched artificially, meant that after the inven-

The Eureka. One of America's first incubators. The alarm clock warned operators when temperature of the hot-water tank dropped.

tion of the kerosene lamp, one of its first practical applications in industry was the lamp-heated incubator, which rapidly gravitated to the farms of America. Since one incubator can do the work of an indefinite number of hens, artificial incubation has been one of the big factors in the development of the modern poultry industry.

In the 1890's George Stahl, of Quincy, Illinois, manufactured a *Wooden Hen* that was heated by a kerosene lamp, had a regulator to control the temperature, and produced good hatches for careful operators. Within another decade, the Cyphers incubator and the Prairie State incubator were transforming the poultry business in the East; and in the West, such names as Reliable, Sure Hatch, Successful, Old Trusty, and Miller's Ideal were soon to become household words, with one or more of these machines on almost every farm that possessed a poultry flock.

These were the incubators upon which we pinned our hopes in the early years of the twentieth century. They ranged in

Standard L a m p Incubators, regulated automatically by thermometers connected w i t h kerosene lamps.

capacity from 60 to 360 eggs (five to thirty dozen). Some machines were larger, but the larger types usually employed two lamps for heating. They were equipped with thermometers and were self-regulating to maintain an even temperature in the egg chamber; and they were of two types. In the Eastern machines the air was heated directly by the lamp, while in the Western type, the lamp heated water, which was circulated through tubes. On the whole, these incubators were dependable hatchers, producing good chicks; thus the foundation was laid for the transformation of poultry culture from a home art to an organized industry.

How great it was to become, no one then foresaw. In 1912, the Cyphers Incubator Company of Buffalo, with its branches in New York, Boston, Chicago, Kansas City, Oakland (California), and London (England), did a million dollars' worth of business. That winter at the Boston Poultry Show, D. C. R. Hoff, special representative of the Prairie State Incubator Company, sold three carloads of Prairie State incubators during the week of the show in the booth of Joseph Breck & Sons. Two things had already happened, however, that were changing the course of events.

MECHAN-
I C A L
MOTHERS

Enter the Mammoth Incubator

Joseph D. Wilson, of Stockton, New Jersey, had successfully made the first shipment of baby chicks to a distant point. And

Early long-pipe Mammoth, applied the hot-water heating system then developing for homes. Water pipes heated from a central coal stove ran the full length of the incubators.

up in New York State a successful poultryman, W. P. Hall, of Pembroke, had built a successful long-pipe, hot-water mammoth incubator, more than forty feet in length and with a capacity of 6,000 eggs, with a coal stove to furnish the heat. Thus the baby chick business and the mammoth incubator came forward, hand in hand. Both were practical. Baby chicks can be shipped successfully because the embryo chick develops largely from the white of the egg, and the yolk serves as its first food. It is therefore equipped with the very finest and best of food nutrients to nourish it for the first 24 to 72 hours after hatching, and it can go on a journey without any other food. For some years, the advice was not to feed too soon after hatching, but to allow time for the yolk to be digested. Nowadays feeding is done much earlier, as incubation has been perfected to the point where the yolk is not hardened

Triple-deck Mammoth. The Hall incubators copied Nature's method and warmed the eggs from above.

during the incubating period, it is easily and more quickly assimilated, and the chicks are ready for early feeding. As a consequence, long-distance shipping of baby chicks is less popular today and there is a pronounced tendency to buy nearer home. The chicks can then be placed under hovers which serve as foster mothers, and feeding the brood for growth starts without much delay.

The big incubators, heated by hot water and burning coal for fuel, rapidly superseded the lamp type. They produced splendid chicks. Hot-water pipes ran the length of the machine above the eggs. The heat of these pipes radiated downward to the top of the eggs. The germ of life floats on a germinal disk in the upper part of the egg. The hen, sitting on a clutch of eggs, applies the warmth of her body to the tops of the eggs. Mr. Hall followed this principle in the development of the Hall mammoth. He went a step further in copying nature. The hen, building her nest on the ground, attracts some moisture upward through her porous nest; and the Hall mammoth incubator had a slatted bottom so that moisture, even water, on the floor under the incubator, might rise into the egg chamber and increase the humidity of the air surrounding the eggs. Fresh air could enter the egg chamber

Single cabinet incubator invented by Dr. S. B. Smith of Cleveland, Ohio. Originally steam heated, now electrically heated.

through this slatted bottom, and the air in the incubator room was never vitiated by the fumes of burning kerosene lamps, as was sometimes the case where ten or a dozen small lamp machines were being operated in a single incubator cellar.

A Poultry Boom

The mammoth incubator was a big step in advance. It was patterned after the hen, and it applied in a practical way those three essentials for successful incubation—heat, fresh air and moisture. No attempt at scientific incubation was made by Mr. Hall. He was a practical poultryman, and his invention was just the simple outgrowth of his practical experience. It came upon the scene at a strategic time, and was taken up and adopted by poultrymen with surprising speed. In 1908, a total of nine new Hall 6,000-egg machines were installed. One of them went to the Lakewood Poultry Farm, New Jersey, later owned by Park and Tilford, one went to the Pittsfield Poultry Farm, Maine; one was installed on the farm of Otto

MECHAN-
I C A L
MOTHERS

Modern single cabinet wherein the temperature is evenly distributed by hanging the trays to a revolving drum.

Arens, Plainfield, New Jersey; and several went into operation in New York State. The next year, 1909, there were thirty-two of these machines sold. Three of them went into Massachusetts. In 1910, more than 100 Hall mammoths were installed, and for several years there was a tremendous increase in incubator capacity, with improved models of the long-type, hot-water mammoths being introduced by other manufacturers.

What were the conditions that brought on that sudden, almost dramatic period of expansion?

In the five-year period, 1909–1914, figures of the Department of Labor show that farm prices were 44 per cent above what they had been in 1900. Wholesale prices of *all* commodities, including farm prices, had increased to 23 per cent above 1900. Farm prices had risen much higher and much faster than the prices of industrial products, and there was complaint in the urban districts of the high cost of living. There was an economic reason for a back to the land movement. Bolton Hall, wrote a book on "Three Acres and Lib-

47,000-egg capacity single cabinets in series. These incubator units placed in batteries form hatcheries of a million eggs or more.

erty." The job of agriculture was to gear itself up to greater production. Prices for farm products were out of line with city prices. There was need for a 6,000-egg Hall mammoth incubator, with its potential capacity for increasing the production of food; and the adoption of such equipment by poultry growers was accelerated by the ratio existing in the price structure. Those who took orders for big machines in those days thought themselves good salesmen, but actually behind the orders, there were forces they did not see.

Hatching 1,000,000 Chicks at a Time

The World War was both deflationary and inflationary in the matter of poultry production. In the East, the rising cost of grain seriously crippled poultry feeders. In the West, the demand was for more food products, including poultry and

eggs. What had been up until 1915 largely a development of

100,000-egg hall in a million-egg room incubator developed in California.

big poultry farm operations in the East, now turned to the West, and the sale of baby chicks and the installation of mammoth incubators gave a boom to poultry as a business all the way from Minnesota to Texas and east to the Alleghenies. But the biggest boom was yet to come, after the war.

Dr. S. B. Smith of Cleveland, Ohio, converted an old church into a hatching chamber, and, in 1922 offered to the public a forced-draft closet-type machine. The Buckeye Incubator Company undertook the manufacture of this machine in limited sizes; other sizes with such an astonishing capacity as 47,000 eggs per machine retained the name Smith. Originally they were steam-heated. Now they are electrically operated, and the rated capacity has been increased to 52,000 eggs per machine. Machines of such magnitude were destined to revolutionize large-scale production of baby chicks.

The first Smith incubator was exhibited at the seventh annual convention of the International Baby Chick Association in 1922. It was sold to the Calkins Poultry Farm, Salem, Ohio, where its first hatches in April and May averaged 68 per cent of all eggs set. This was an improvement in results over the hatches in the long-type mammoths, whose operators figured on about two eggs to make one chick. It is estimated today that the forced-draft type of incubator will give a minimum of four per cent better hatches than the old Hall types. By

1932, hatcheries that had installed these machines to the extent of being able to set at least one million eggs every three weeks were to be found in Illinois, Iowa, Missouri, Minnesota, and Ohio. Upon visiting one of these hatcheries, Grant M. Curtis remarked:

"It seemed unbelievable, but at Cleveland, Ohio, in an immense hatchery this form of incubating equipment had been operated with success a number of years on a commercial basis, with a capacity of 1,034,000 eggs at one filling (prior to that time an unheard-of total) and had turned out 22,000 to 30,000 chicks per day, every day of the hatching season, Sundays and holidays included. What such a hatching machine would or could mean to the then well started baby chick branch of the poultry industry, may well be imagined."

Other cabinet machines have proved popular with poultry-men. Such well known makes as the Buckeye, the Petersime, the Robbins, the Bundy, the Lauer and others are to be found in some of the leading quality hatcheries of the United States and foreign countries. One chief advantage of these electric machines is the perfection of control. Electric heat is much more easily regulated than the heat that comes from a coal fire; and the ventilation is more constant and complete, being secured by an electric fan. The principle of electric incubation has also been brought down into the range of smaller capacity machines, from 100 to 2000 eggs, for home hatching, or for breeder-farm work.

An achievement of the West Coast was the million-egg room-type incubator, developed in California. The whole room is the incubator. Operators can walk freely up and down long aisles where 100,000 or more eggs are hatching in open trays. There are several aisles to a room.

The Methods of the Hen

All of the marvelous progress in the mechanics of artificial incubation has been possible because of the biological fact that

Taking off a hatch in a battery of 52,000-egg single cabinet units. An average of 25,000 chicks every day in the hatching season.

hens lay eggs from which their young are hatched. To get good hatches requires, of course, not only that the incubator be efficient, but that the egg contain a strong living cell. That means that the eggs must be from a healthy, vigorous flock, well fed and well managed. Given such eggs, the modern incubator will hatch, on the average, more chicks than mother hens.

In only one respect have modern incubators dispensed with the functions of the broody hen, and that is in the matter of cooling the eggs. Daily the setting hen leaves her nest in search of food and drink, and during her absence of perhaps twenty minutes, the eggs in her nest cool. When incubators were first developed, the practice of cooling the eggs was considered important, and in the operation of the Cyphers and Prairie State lamp incubators, the operator was instructed to

MECHAN-
I C A L
MOTHERS

Battery brooder. Storage cages for baby chicks. Long pipes furnish "top heat".

take out the tray of eggs daily and place it on top of the machine for cooling. With the advent of the Hall, cooling went out of vogue, and it is not practiced in the new electric machines. On this subject, Alexis L. Romanoff, of New York Agricultural College, Cornell University, states: "It has never been proved satisfactorily that cooling is necessary for the developing embryo . . . Moderate cooling of eggs should not do any harm, but would likely stimulate the growth and harden the embryo, that is, might remove predisposition to disease after hatching."

Turning the eggs is practiced in all types of incubators. The hen, sitting on eggs, turns them with her beak and moves them with her body. It has been assumed that this turning is a form of exercise that stimulates the growth of the embryo.

Taking Care of the Babies

MECHAN-
I C A L
MOTHERS

After hatching, chicks cannot be thrown out on a cold world, any more than children. They need protection, and above all, access to warmth. This is called brooding. With mechanical mothers to hatch the chicks, there had to be mechanical nurses to take care of them.

Thus the development of brooding closely paralleled the advances in incubation. With the lamp-heated 60-egg incubator

Broiler plant, where thousands of broilers are grown out-of-season.

came the lamp-heated 50-chick brooder. The chief feature in brooding is to apply the heat to the top of the chick, that is, to warm its back, but this point was not grasped at first. The hen applies warmth to the backs of her chicks. They run under her warm body, and tuck themselves in her feathers, and thus get protection from the wind, rain or cold; but their feet remain on the ground, however cold and damp it may be. Transferring incubator-hatched chicks to brooders with bottom heat proved disastrous. It was essential that the heat be applied from above. One poultryman remarked: "If you hold a chick in the palm of your hand, it will peep and peep. Put your other hand over its back, and it will nestle down and be contented."

The adoption of nature's method of "top heat" made possible as rapid changes in brooding and as great increases in the capacity of brooder houses, as had distinguished the advance in incubators; and at each step the brooders followed the incubators in design. First was the kerosene-burning incubator and the small oil-burning brooder. Then came the coal-burning mammoth incubator, with its long pipe system radiating warmth over the tops of the eggs; and similar hot-water stoves with manifolds and long pipes were installed in brooder houses, and proved very successful. Lastly, the development of the forced-draft incubator has its counter-part in the develop-

MECHAN-
I C A L
MOTHERS

115

ment of cage-type brooders, in which moisture, circulating air and heat are furnished. This is called battery brooding.

A battery brooding room, approximately twelve feet square, holds about six batteries with a rated capacity of 600 chicks each. Battery brooding is rearing chicks in cages with wire floors, set in tiers one on top of another. Some batteries are heated electrically, with a bulb or heating unit in each tray. It is a compact way to carry chicks, and it first came into use in the large hatcheries.

When the baby chick business was young, people ordered their chicks in advance and awaited delivery. Competition developed to the point where "prompt shipment" was promised to buyers. This necessitated hatching chicks in expectation of orders, and frequently resulted in surplus chicks on hand, especially as the spring season advanced and hatchability of eggs ran ahead of expectations. To carry these surplus chicks in the hatchery for a period of a week or two weeks, or until they could be sold to local poultry keepers, necessitated the use of a storage brooder, now known as the battery brooder. Storage capacity became an indispensable part of every hatcheryman's equipment. The battery brooder requires a small amount of floor space, and since the chicks are penned in a compact unit, it is easy to take care of them.

It was thought that three weeks was long enough to carry chicks in battery brooders, after which they should be transferred to floor brooders (that is, placed under brooder stoves set on the floor), or put in long-type brooder houses. But improved feeds proved efficient in growing chicks to broiler size right in the batteries. A number of broiler plants are

growing chicks to a weight of 2½ pounds in ten weeks, in batteries. Thousands of broilers are thus being produced out-of-season for the markets. As spring advances, at many plants the broilers are finished off outdoors, in what are called Jersey Economy Coops. This coop was developed by H. B. Steckel,

of New Jersey, and is simply a small coop with a slatted front

Brooder hover for every 500 chicks in brooder houses. Heated by coal, oil, or electricity.

and a slatted floor, in which the finishing broilers can get the benefits of the outdoor air and outdoor sunshine. Here they can be carried four weeks longer, to a weight of 3 to 3½ pounds and an age of about fourteen weeks; and this last pound of weight is more profitable to the grower than the first pound that he puts on the chick.

In the development of brooding, another important type of brooder was designed for rearing chicks from the time they left the incubator until they no longer required heat, and it is a type of brooder which is still in general use. Commonly called the coal-stove brooder, brooders of the same type may burn oil or gas. Over the stove there is a canopy which deflects the heat downward onto the chicks. These brooder stoves, with canopy, will brood lots of 300 to 500 chicks, and one such stove gives the farmer a uniform flock of chickens. This is very different from the old method by which he might hatch 300 chicks under hens, with hens and their chicks running around the farmyard, the chicks of all sizes and ages, with countless dangers from sudden rainstorms or attacks by rats or weasels.

A coal-stove brooder can be placed in a colony house; or a series of such brooder stoves can be installed the length of a long brooder house—one stove in each pen. Electric hovers are used in the same way, and are increasing in popularity.

117

THE MICROSCOPE
BRINGS HEALTH

EGGS are being produced today under conditions that represent a high state of cleanliness. The thoroughness with which modern poultry buildings are cleaned and disinfected would prove surprising to farmers of an earlier age. In the development of this system of management, less and less reliance has been placed on medication for the purpose of maintaining health in the flock, and more and more has been put upon sanitation. Clean surroundings, and clean feed and water, are recognized as of first importance. Disregard of them would prove costly, for uncleanliness and health do not long exist together, and every poultryman knows that the fullest return for feed and labor is procurable only from a vigorous flock in health. As a matter of good business, therefore, cleanliness and health are foundation stones upon which the modern poultry industry and its products have been built.

The principles of sanitation upon which modern poultry practices rest were measurably advanced by Dr. George Byron Morse, who was a powerful propagandist for cleanliness. As an official of the United States Department of Agriculture, speaking of cleanliness in the poultry yard, he said:

"The eye with the microscope has a larger apprehension of dirt than the unaided eye."

If man had been endowed with eyes like the ordinary house fly, with their powerful magnifying lenses, he would not have been so slow in arriving at an understanding of dirt. It was

after 1840 that the microscope became an instrument used to

Louis Pasteur. By experiments on chickens he discovered the principle of vaccination, established the germ theory of diseases, and proved the value of cleanliness to health.

serious purpose in scientific research, bringing to the view of the human eye the infinitely little. A new world was opened up, and a new conception of nature has followed, with the result that old ideas about hens and their welfare have long since been replaced by more precise knowledge of life and health. As we look back upon this Century of Progress, science is to be seen advancing uniformly to reduce losses to producers of eggs and poultry and to safeguard the consumers of these great health foods.

The Discoveries of Pasteur

The hen has contributed to our welfare in many ways. Poultry problems were among the first studied by modern medical science. It was in his study of fowl cholera, a disease now almost non-existent, that Louis Pasteur found the principle for making a vaccine. The first practical result of utilizing this principle and method was to save the cattle and sheep of Europe from the ravages of anthrax. From his work, Pasteur firmly established the "germ theory" in the latter part of the nineteenth century, and it is the accepted principle of medical science today that some particular kind of microscopic organism is always associated with each particular disease. This great truth has tremendously advanced the knowledge of sanitation and safeguarded the health of human beings. From the water we drink to the ventilation of our buildings, and to the matter of surgical instruments in a hospital, cleanliness and sanitation are constantly considered. The victory of man over the infinitesimally small is not complete, because some germs pass through a porcelain filter and thus defy detection; but men of science pursue their quest, patiently, confidently, untiringly. Their aim is that man shall have health, and have it more abundantly.

Having been seen under the microscope, the minute causative agents of disease could be studied, and plans worked out to attack them. This opened up a whole new field of operations, and rather revolutionary ideas were advanced. Pasteur, for example, in 1882, taxed the credulity of some of his friends by suggesting that germs from animals that had died might be brought to the surface of the ground by earthworms. That was the beginning of the wise practice of burning or burying deep the carcasses of dead animals. It was first warning against the dangers of contaminated soil.

Clean ground is not today a new subject to poultry keepers. It is only one of the stones in the arch of cleanliness. Frequently the ground is limed, or it is plowed and a green crop grown on it, and thus the soil is freshened and cleaned.

These methods of management, which require a complete housecleaning and plowing up of the yards, or, in the case of portable houses, moving them to a fresh pasture, are a part of the work on every poultry farm; indeed, it is more than mere work. It is a part of a battle that is being fought on a wide front, in every field of agriculture, in plants, and fruit trees, and animals. Just as the big red luscious apple, perfectly

Clean ground is first insurance for healthy flocks. Plowing is one method.

sound to the core, is grown on a tree that was sprayed, so is the best poultry grown where natural enemies are held in check.

Let us see how this is done, thus following the great leaders of the scientific advance. It was Pasteur's fervent hope that "his followers step into the road that he had marked out."

The Work of a Great American

A disease that was proving quickly fatal among young turkeys threatened the continued existence of this feast bird upon American farms. Growers were discouraged. It seemed hopeless to attempt to raise young turkeys. They died of what was being commonly called "blackhead."

Today it is a very different story. A sick or ailing bird is the exception. There are single farms where hundreds or even thousands of turkeys are grown, and such turkey farms are to be seen not only in New Jersey, Pennsylvania and Maryland, but also in Iowa, Minnesota and the wheat country of the Dakotas. Tons and tons of prime turkeys are dressed every fall and winter for the Thanksgiving and Christmas markets.

The mass production of turkeys dates back to a modest man, recognized as one of the greatest animal pathologists, Dr. Theobald Smith, retired director of the animal pathology division of the Rockefeller Medical Foundation. Earlier, when he was associated with the United States Bureau of Animal Industry, the problem of blackhead in turkeys was referred to him. Mr. Cushman of the Rhode Island Experiment Station had requested the aid of the government specialists, and shortly thereafter (in 1895), the United States Department of Agriculture published a bulletin in which Dr. Smith attributed this infectious disease to a germ which he had isolated and which he described as one twenty-five-hundredth of an inch in diameter. He had found this parasitic protozoan imbedded in the wall of the ceca; and it was here that it began its work and produced the first effects of the disease.

This discovery laid the foundation for a study of blackhead and led to control of the disease. With the specific organism isolated, a study of that organism, its life cycle, how it reproduced itself, and how to control it, followed in rapid succession. The conclusion was that an effort should be made to grow turkeys in confinement, that they might be reared in freedom from infection. To grow what had long been considered to be a semi-wild fowl within a limited enclosure was a radical departure from old methods.

Scientific men are often criticised for their "theories." When Pasteur started out in his endeavor to save the silkworm industry of France, he was told point-blank that he was only a laboratory man and knew nothing of the practical aspects of silkworm culture. It is hard to realize now how radical and extreme a departure was the idea of growing turkeys in confinement; but Dr. Smith determined to try it. He had watched through a field-glass the movements of proud and majestic turkeys as they foraged in the grain fields and pastures. He had studied their behavior. From birds that had died, he took the viscera and examined them microscopically. His plans had more scientific foundation and were less of an experiment than they seemed.

While living in Boston, engaged as Professor of Comparative Pathology at the Harvard Medical School, he hatched some

Turkeys on range require clean ground not occupied by other fowls.

turkey eggs in an incubator and started to grow the poults, as young turkeys are called, in his back yard. His neighbors knew that the turkeys were there and they knew what he was trying to do, yet one day when he was away from home, someone broke in and stole one of them. In spite of difficulties, however, he established the principle that turkeys could be grown free of blackhead by (a) cleaning the shells, (b) hatching in an incubator, and (c) growing the poults at a distance from other fowls and on ground not recently occupied by other fowls. By following these simple precepts, turkey growing has assumed a magnitude that is almost unbelievable.

There are still farmers who look upon turkey growing as very difficult, although admitting that their neighbors are wholly successful. The difference is in the degree of sanitation. Each of the three points enumerated above is a sanitary measure. Some growers take the added precaution of not starting their poults on the ground, but construct a wire enclosure, a little above the ground, with a wire or slatted floor; and thus protected from the possibility of outside contamina-

Spraying eggs in incubator trays is a preventative against harmful bacteria.

tion, the baby poults run out into the sunshine on this "front porch" type of yardway.

The White Death That Took Half of Our Chicks

It was believed by several prominent investigators that white diarrhea, so destructive to young chicks, was caused by the same organism as blackhead. The coccidial type of white diarrhea known as coccidiosis, is caused by coccidia, a single cell type of animal organism, just as bacteria are the lowest type of plant organism. Coccidiosis attacked young chicks at two to eight weeks of age. Its chosen sites were the ceca and duodenum. In this respect the trouble was similar to that of blackhead in turkeys, with the further similarity that it was caused by microscopic protozoa.

As in the case of turkey growing, it was apparent that the aim of the chicken grower must be to attain a high degree of cleanliness. In the Year Book of the United States Department of Agriculture, 1911, Dr. Morse put it *Cleanliness the One Foundation,* and he went on to say: "This fundamental doctrine of cleanliness as applied to the well-being of poultry may be expressed in three general principles, (1) clean intake, (2) clean output, (3) clean surroundings." To attain this

Spraying baby chicks is a control measure against insects and germs.

high state of cleanliness, he enumerated seven primary points, which he expressed "In mandatory form, since nature in her sovereignty over animal life, demands cleanliness under the penalty of disease and death." These seven points in poultry management, as given by Dr. Morse, were:

(1) Clean out
(2) Clean up
(3) Clean the water supply
(4) Clean the food
(5) Clean the eggs
(6) Clean the incubators and brooders
(7) Clean the breeding

Today sees the practical application of the points in that seven-fold program, and through the application of these sanitary measures, poultry practice has gained steadily in certainty of results. Thousands of birds are grown each year on many, many poultry farms; and the finest of poultry meat and eggs are available to consumers in any good market.

With the years, there have been developed infinitely better *methods* for securing that cleanliness on which modern poultry practice rests. Morse's procedure for cleaning a brooder was to do the job with old-fashioned kitchen soap. Today some poultrymen use a disinfecting gun that shoots a flame of fire against the walls and floor. Dr. W. L. Chandler of the Michigan Agricultural College has formulated a new type of iodine, colloidal in form, which will destroy the microscopic hard-shelled balls known as the oocysts of coccidia; this iodine penetrates them as though they had an affinity for it. Another method of disinfecting is a chemical treatment of litter as recommended by Dr. Justin Andrews, of the Johns Hopkins University. In addition, wire or slatted floors, as employed in the construction of runways for young turkeys, are favored by some growers; and this principle may take the form of cages or batteries, with their wire floors. Another practice, quite common, is to run a cement slab out from the brooder house and put fresh sand on it, thus providing clean ground for each brood.

The principle is that rigid sanitation is the best preventative measure, and cleanliness is the important control factor.

An important aspect of the white diarrhea problem was the view taken of it by Dr. Leo F. Rettger, of Sheffield Scientific School, Yale University, whose work resulted in the discovery of *bacterium pullorum,* and led to the complete control of what is called pullorum disease, or bacillary white diarrhea. This control is so perfect and gives such tremendously successful results that it is not uncommon now to grow chicks with a loss of only one-half of one per cent, and seldom in excess of three per cent, during the entire period of babyhood—which might be defined as that period from the time a chick is hatched until a mother hen would wean her chicks; and these results are obtained in chicks hatched in incubators and reared in brooders, making possible artificial rearing in large numbers, with extraordinarily low mortality.

When Dr. Rettger was doing his research work, the situation was very different. Pearl, Surface and Curtis, of the Maine Agricultural Experiment Station, stated: "The loss of chicks ascribed to this cause varies in different years and in different places from 10 to 90 per cent. It is perhaps not too much to say that more than 50 per cent of the chicks hatched throughout the country are lost from white diarrhea in its various forms."

The prevailing opinion was that chicks hatched in incubators were the more likely to break down with the disease, and some farms that had installed good equipment for hatching and rearing were unable to grow a sufficiency of poultry to make their investment profitable. It was a serious situation, and the more so because large-scale machinery, in the form of mammoth incubators and coal-burning brooders, was being introduced and held promise of making a "man's business" of poultry keeping. Whereas the maturing of 800 pullets was considered a good season's work on a one-man poultry farm, the new large-scale incubators and brooding systems could increase this production 300 to 400 per cent. The question was, were the hen and her chicks equal to the opportunities ahead?

Fruit growers, some years before, had been threatened and discouraged by the ravages of scale, blight and coddling moth, and control measures had been introduced by which they overcame these losses and grew more perfect fruit than before. The poultry business, likewise, was to emerge with a new degree of security. When the present is spoken of as a day of surplus, the increase in production may be attributed at first thought to the invention and perfection of machinery, such as the mammoth incubator and brooder; but science also has done her part that there may be "fullness in the earth."

Dr. Rettger spent his summers at the Connecticut Agricultural College, where, in cooperation with Professor Frederick H. Stoneburn, he carried on a careful search for the cause of bacillary white diarrhea in chicks, hatching eggs in different kinds of incubators and under hens, trying different systems of brooding and methods of feeding. But not in these things did they find the fundamental cause of the trouble. They did find, however, that in a certain flock of thirty breeding hens, it

Screen porches
offer light and
fresh air to hens
in crowded
houses.

was impossible to raise the chicks. From that point began the principle now so widely practiced, of "cleaning up" the breeding stock. And equally important was the recommendation of Rettger and Stoneburn to discriminate in the purchase of eggs for hatching, purchasing only from stock known to be healthy.

When that advice was first given in 1910, there was no baby chick business as we know it today. Eggs were purchased for hatching. Operators of large incubators did custom hatching as an accommodation at such profit as they could make on a charge of about one cent an egg. The idea of setting eggs from only stock known to be healthy was full of possibilities. Many people who operate big incubators nowadays would not put an egg in their machines unless it were from an accredited flock. It is not uncommon for large hatcheries to have from 10,000 to as many as 50,000 breeding birds tested, that the entire egg supply for their incubators may come from what are known as tested flocks.

Tests for Egg Laying Contests

It is no small job to test this enormous number of birds individually. The great step forward in the work of testing was begun in 1915 by Dr. G. E. Gage when he tested a number

Wire floors bring cleanliness to pullets and poults, and are protection against vermin.

of flocks in Massachusetts, examining a sample of the blood of each hen. A sensitive stained antigen is now prepared for a rapid test. The color reactions develop in about three minutes, and Dr. Robert Graham of the University of Illinois reports that this is a practical procedure for diagnosis.

This method of diagnosis and precaution against pullorum has become a pre-requisite for modern contest pen birds. At Chicago's Century of Progress International Egg Laying Contest, where there were 122 pens from 26 states and Canada, the hens and cock of each pen were tested individually by an expert on the grounds before they were admitted to the competition. If a bird showed an unfavorable reaction, it was rejected, and opportunity for replacement was given its owner. This insured competition between only birds in the best of health, was a guarantee against spread of infection, and was a safeguard for pedigree chicks hatched and sold at the exposition.

The continued blood-testing of the breeding stock leads to 100 per cent freedom from pullorum, with the result that chicks are grown with no measurable loss from bacillary white diarrhea. This is particularly true in those states where long-tube testing has been carried on over a series of years; and a number of flocks have not had a single reactor in them for ten or a dozen years.

From such sources of supply of eggs ready to be transformed into bright-eyed, chirping day-old chicks, it is not uncommon for the purchaser to report growing as many chicks as he paid for, the entire mortality being no more than the extra chicks included by the hatchery, which usually amounts to four chicks per hundred (forty extra chicks to the thousand).

The mother hen that steps on one chick of her brood of twelve, and loses it, has twice the mortality of the big grower whose losses do not exceed forty per thousand; and if a mother hen gets caught in a rainstorm, and from the drenching of her brood loses another chick, the mortality record of that brood stands: alive 10, dead 2. That is a mortality of one-sixth. On the basis of 1,000 chicks, it would mean a loss of 167 chicks. Such a figure is in striking contrast to the results of modern methods which turn the capabilities of modern equipment to competent and efficient production. This equipment would be barren and its capacity as zero without the researches of modern science which have increased the ability of the mechanism to produce maximum results. To the appreciation of this fact this chapter is dedicated.

THE PRIVATE HOUSE
OF THE HEN

THE poultry house is the hens' workshop and their home. It is an inspiring sight, upon opening the door of a modern hen dwelling, to see an active, productive flock of layers. They know where the feed hopper is and after taking a few mouthfuls of mash, they go to the drinking fountain; and they move back and forth—over to the windows where there is sunlight and fresh air, up into the nests to deposit their eggs—and later in the afternoon they are scratching in the litter on the floor for their grain feed, and then as darkness falls they take their place on the roosts with full crops, contented. On the morrow they will rise, singing and happy hens, to enjoy again the privacy and comfort of their home. Even the caretaker will knock on their door before entering, that they may not be unduly alarmed and disturbed.

Early writers on poultry housing stressed the fact that dryness and pure air were of first importance. They also dwelt on the hardiness and delicacy of different flocks or strains. That there is a marked difference in the stamina and constitutional vigor of different flocks is true, and it is also true that without a dry poultry house, and one that admits fresh outdoor air so that there is adequate ventilation, no flock of poultry can remain in health. This is the case with the growing chickens as well as with the laying flock.

Poultry is a species of birds. And where do birds roost? In the open air, with a movement of air over them and below them. Nature gave them wings to soar through the air. For every 34 pounds of air breathed by a man, an equal weight of

A good hen house. Dryness, plenty of outdoor air and sunlight indicate a hardy flock.

chicken would require 64 pounds, or nearly twice as much. The oxygen contained in fresh air is taken into the lungs, where it combines with the iron in the blood, and is carried to all parts of the body. One of the important functions of oxygen is the building up of proteins within the body cells.

A chicken, with a normal temperature of approximately 106 degrees, has a high requirement for fresh air. Those who have dressed a chicken know that the lungs are relatively small and imbedded in the ribs, but unlike man, a bird breathes all the way through its lungs, not carrying a large amount of residual air, and therefore the lungs of the fowl, though small, are unusually efficient.

The exhaled breath of a fowl contains some carbon dioxide and considerable moisture. The impurities in air once breathed would soon vitiate the air in the poultry house if ventilation were not provided to bring in fresh air and carry out the air that has been breathed. A movement of outdoor air to the inside, and inside air to the outside, also prevents the moisture thrown off by the fowls from accumulating on the walls, ceiling and floor of the poultry house and making it damp. In cold

Artificial light insures a dry house when the sun is not shining, and increases egg production. Ultra-violet lamps add nutritional advantage — compare pages 157–8.

weather this moisture takes the form of frost on the walls, later to melt and trickle down. Ventilation will carry off this water vapor.

How the House Controls Production

It is unnecessary to describe the early hen house that had one small window, a dirt floor, and roosting poles, and served principally to get the chickens through the winter.

Progress was associated with a more elaborate type of poultry house. It was a substantial building, with windows in front, a board floor, adequate head room, and it was more or less ornamental in architecture. Its chief weakness was lack of ventilation and dampness inside, with resulting colds and swollen eyes for the chickens. Considering the size of such a house, its carrying capacity was limited, because a large flock could not be herded together in such close quarters. An oft-tried experiment was to increase the amount of glass, but while heat radiation through the glass increased the moisture-carrying capacity of the air inside during the day, the plan offered no

The first big hen houses were horizontal. Now they are vertical, often four stories.

solution of the moisture problem during the night or on days when the sun was not shining.

It was about this time of trial and error in house construction that James E. Rice, Professor of Poultry Husbandry at the New York State College of Agriculture, went to Ohio to give a talk on poultry. One of the other speakers at the farmers' institute said to Professor Rice that evening: "I saw something today that astonished me. People would never dream of it. A muslin front in a poultry house! You would think the chickens would freeze to death." Up to that time it had been overlooked that nature had given to chickens, in the form of plumage, one of the most effective insulators of body heat that she had given to any animal.

The next report was that A. F. Hunter, editor of Farm Poultry in Boston, had developed on his poultry farm a scratching shed type of house. It had two compartments, a roosting compartment which had a muslin front through which fresh air could diffuse into the house, but winds could not blow in, and a scratching compartment, into which the fowls could come in the daytime; it had a sand floor and a wire-covered window through which not only outdoor air but direct sunlight could enter. The properties of sunlight were not then known, and all the benefits of this new house were attributed to the fresh air. We now recognize the importance of both.

Three story hen house with a sun-parlor annex. One way of eliminating colds.

Looking back at this development, Professor Rice has said: "I have seen it all, and the interesting thing is that today every type of poultry house is still in existence for all to see. Go into the country and you will see the steps in poultry house evolution, from merely the trees and the tool shed, and the ordinary outbuilding insulated with straw, perhaps with a straw loft, and birds laying in haymows, under the barn, with eggs merely a by-product. The first big poultry houses were horizontal, but now there is a tendency to build them vertical. Three and four story hen houses are quite common. I remember the first laying house of this kind that I ever saw. It was a four-story building, built as such, and erected especially to house a large flock of layers. That was in the first decade of the present century, twenty-five years ago, at Green, in Chenango county, just north of Binghamton, New York. Even before this, however, the idea of using electric lights on birds had been advanced. Today it is quite common to see poultry houses lighted up at night.

"I remember," continued Professor Rice, "making a talk at Sushan, New York, thirty-five years ago, and a man in the audience who had a poultry farm at Cambridge, gave his experience in putting electric lights on birds. The idea of wiring poultry houses has been carried on, with one man adding to another's knowledge by experience and experiment, until at the present time I feel that artificial illumination is the most definite control of production that we have. You can turn on a switch or turn it off. It is a case of start and stop, with every other factor remaining the same."

This "control of production" is fundamental to poultry housing. That is why houses are built—to give the poultry-man control. First, control against wind and rain and snow; and secondly, control of feeding, length of day, sanitation and so on. As the vicissitudes of the environment are neutralized and the factors are brought under control, production of eggs becomes more of a regular business with the hens, and the peaks and valleys of the laying year are leveled. There are no longer, for example, short days and long nights; rather with lights, the feeding day is lengthened, just as the sun would lengthen it in the spring, and somewhat of the stimulus of spring laying is secured in November and December.

The House That Eliminated Colds

In the process of developing a controlled environment through housing, mistakes were made. Some points were gained, and others were lost. It was not always easy to main-tain the flock in health. One chief difficulty was colds. Joseph Tolman was experiencing just such a set-back in his flocks, on his farm at Rockland, Massachusetts, and he called in Dr. Prince T. Woods, who suggested isolating the sick birds, putting them in an open-front house in the pine woods on the farm. Shortly thereafter they got well, their heads cleared, and they came into heavy production. Mr. Tolman at once wisely concluded that: "if fresh air is good for sick chickens, it is good for well ones," and he immediately began to provide open fronts for all his breeding houses. The style was unique and soon became known as the Tolman Fresh Air Poultry

House. These houses were about eight feet wide and twelve feet deep, with a low roof and with a completely open front, covered only by mesh wire. The results from this kind of housing were so satisfactory that the plans and specifications were published, and open-front houses of this type came into use all over the country.

The results in the Middle West were disappointing. With the thermometer twenty below zero in northern Illinois, and the wind blowing, it was found that the houses were not deep enough. While it is true that one cannot blow into a bottle, an open-front house twelve feet deep was not bottle-shaped. The plans were at once changed to suit exposed locations, calling for the construction of a house sixteen to twenty feet deep. This enabled the birds to roost farther back from the open front, with improved results. Today most poultry houses in the North Central states are built twenty feet from front to rear. The shallow house is not in favor. Furthermore, with less moisture in the air than is the case along the Atlantic seaboard, and with the winters more severe, there is more recourse to the use of muslin fronts in the Middle West. These can be lifted in the daytime to allow the sunlight to enter.

In 1913, Mr. Tolman carried the idea of the open-front house into the construction of a summer shelter for the growing chickens. This summer shelter has an A-shaped roof which can be constructed of two sheets of wallboard. The four sides are open and covered with mesh wire. The bottom is wire-covered. Thus the chickens are protected during the night, yet are in the open air. The droppings pass through the wire floor, and the quarters are always clean. No vermin, such as rats, skunks or weasels can enter. A shelter of this type, 9 x 10 feet in size, weighs about 350 pounds, and is easily moved. After chickens are feathered it will carry them up to laying age, and it is a cheap supplement to the more expensive type of brooder house equipment. A shelter of this kind has a capacity of 150 pullets; it is not easily crowded, as fresh air is

Digging peat moss in Germany for litter on American hen house floors. Peat acts as a sanitary absorbent and deodorant.

circulating around the birds all the time they are on the roosts during the night, and at daybreak they are off the roosts and out on the range.

Concerning Floors and New Ideas

The idea of the wire floor was carried into the laying houses on the Tolman plant. Instead of the conventional droppings board that was regularly scraped and cleaned, a frame covered with wire was hung under the roosts and the droppings fell through the wire into a pit, which could be periodically cleaned out. This arrangement prevents the hen's feet from ever coming into contact with droppings that fall during the night, and is a great labor-saver in the house-cleaning processes.

Some excrement does fall on the floor, and for this reason poultry-house floors are covered with litter. Wheat and oat straw are especially favored as bedding, although shavings can be used when available. In England and on the continent of Europe, peat moss is esteemed for this purpose. The peat acts as an absorbant and deodorant. When Wm. Cook & Sons, of St. Marys Cray, England, established their poultry plant at

Scotch Plains, New Jersey, following their introduction of the Orpington breed of fowls into America, they used peat moss as litter. Atkins & Durbrow, Inc., New York City, importers of peat from the German beds, had a large market amongst those who used the product as stable bedding. When horses in the city began to decline in numbers, they naturally looked for new outlets. A member of this firm took a bale home and threw it on the floor of his poultry house in Brooklyn, and it worked so well that he was persuaded to advertise it for poultry use. In the ensuing years, from 1912 to 1915, this firm received 40,000 inquiries from poultry keepers for peat-moss litter. The war then put an end to importations, which were resumed at the close of hostilities.

As an instance of the magnitude of poultry keeping, it is interesting to take the sales of peat for the years 1924 to 1930. A bale of peat litter weighs 150 to 170 pounds, and in 1924 the one firm of New York importers sold 12,184 bales. By 1930 the sales had increased to 116,694 bales. Including the other importers of peat in United States, the total sales of peat moss probably amounted to three or four hundred thousand bales in the one year, 1930. An important part of this output went to gardeners as well as poultry keepers. However, expansion in the use of a single product in the poultry field significantly illustrates the readiness with which new methods were adopted and the expansion of the poultry industry itself in the post-war period. The condition which favored this expansion and development was the favorable "feed-egg" ratio. Feed was relatively cheap in price. Grain growers were depressed, following the decline in prices in 1921. On the other hand there was prosperity in the cities. Weekly earnings of factory workers were high, and on the whole, city consumers had unusual buying power. The poultryman, as a processor of grain into eggs and poultry meat, had the advantage of buying grain in a relatively low-priced market, and this cheap raw material his hens fabricated into eggs which sold on a relatively high-price level.

His margin was wide, and he could afford not only to make substantial capital investments in poultry buildings, but also in the operation of the plant he could well afford to purchase many supplementary items.

Following 1930, grain prices receded further, but city buying power also fell, with the result that both the volume of consumption and the prices paid by consumers gradually became less favorable to the specialized poultry producer. It is plain to be seen, therefore, that what is termed progress is not always a matter of invention, or of devising ways and means of doing old jobs better, but depends also on the price structure. When prices are unfavorable, progress halts. When they are out of adjustment, and a farmer can get more money for a crate of hens than he can for a wagon load of corn, he becomes an attentive listener to poultry doctrine, and a ready customer of new poultry ideas.

Sunlight for Healthy Hens

Early poultry writers emphasized the importance of pure air and dry air in the poultry house. Professor James E. Rice was probably the first to call attention to the importance of sunshine. Thirty years ago he said that "there is value in birds getting into the sunshine." He had seen them bunched in open-front houses, right up in front, in the sunshine. No one knew about vitamins, and that the hens in the sunlight were putting vitamin D into their bodies and in turn into their eggs. It was years later that man found this fact and the reasons for it.

There were ancients who worshipped the sun. There is sound reason why we, too, should have an exalted opinion of the sun and the value of its rays. What we see is only a part of the sunshine. The spectrum, with all the colors of the rainbow, is the visible part. In this range of colors, at one end is red, and at the other end is violet, with all the other colors between them. Each of these colors has a certain band of light waves—just as radio-sending stations have certain wave

Glass substitutes admit ultra-violet rays necessary for growing chicks and laying hens.

lengths for their programs. Each of the colors that we can see with the human eye is found somewhere in the range of light rays that is described mathematically as 4,000 to 7,800 Angstrom units (an Angstrom unit is a measure of length, abbreviated A. U.). Below the violet light there is a narrow band of ultra-violet light—from 3,020 to 3,200 A. U. It is not visible to the human eye but the value of this ultra-violet light has been an absorbing subject for the researches of nutrition specialists.

It used to be believed that little chicks should be put out on the ground as soon as possible, because there was "something in the ground" that they needed. Now we know that what they needed was ultra-violet light. It prevents rickets (or soft bones) by increasing the assimilation of the calcium or lime contained in their feed. Strange as it may seem, ordinary window-glass filters out a large part of the ultra-violet rays. Bethke and Kennard at the Ohio Agricultural Experiment Station, Wooster, ran a test in 1924, using three lots of chicks. One was in a sun court where the chicks had the beneficial rays of direct sunlight not under glass. The second lot was

Movable outdoor bat-
teries for chicks furnish
fresh air and light, and
are protection against
dampness.

under ordinary window-glass. The third was under a substitute for ordinary glass which admitted a healthful amount of
all the sun's rays. The experiment broke down and had to be
given up at the end of the seventh week because all the chicks
under the window-glass had died. Quartz glass admits ultra-
violet, and has been available to hospitals but was prohibitive
in price for poultry-house construction, however, in recent years,
a type of glass has been developed which serves the purpose
and can be sold at a moderate price.

In the meantime several substitutes for window-glass have
become very popular for poultry-house use. Not only do chicks
require ultra-violet light, but laying hens also need this calcify-
ing agent to encase their eggs with the lime shell; and so glass
substitutes which admit a healthful amount of the ultra-violet
rays are used in both laying houses and brooder houses. From
1923 to 1928, the sales of one of these products increased 1600
per cent. This material was originated by Dr. A. Zimmerli,
who made greenhouse tests first but soon learned that his
formula was not suitable for greenhouse construction. When
he read about the value of ultra-violet light in preventing
rickets, he conceived the idea of using the material for build-

Portable houses w i t h portable runs m e a n clean ground, a requisite for pullets and turkey poults.

ings (such as brooder houses) in which there were growing animals.

With the newer knowledge in nutrition and improved equipment, it is possible to grow much larger flocks of young chicks than in former years. One difficulty, however, in confining large flocks is the rapid development of bad habits and vices such as feather-eating, toe-picking, and even cannibalism. Various methods to counteract these habits have been employed, such as a darkening of the room, reducing the temperature in the room, and using red glass or blue glass in the windows. Lewis I. Fox, of Metuchen, New Jersey, conceived the ingenious notion of painting the windows with a stain that would filter out the red rays and thus neutralize the light on the inside of the poultry house. The chicks then could not see the red combs or a drop of blood, and therefore would not start picking. This stain on the windows does not darken the room, and black or a blue color can be seen, but red is filtered out. It is an application of the principle that the colors have different wave lengths. The use of this stain has become quite extensive, and if you drive through the country and see a brooder house with red windows, do not be surprised. Science and practice have joined hands to make of poultry culture a real business.

Other valuable properties may be found in sunshine. But thus far, the discovery of ultra-violet light and its relation to poultry practices is of fundamental importance. It increases the strength of the egg shell. Layers producing fragile eggs that cannot be handled to any extent without breaking, need sunshine. Breeders producing eggs that are low in fertility and hatchability may need the antirachitic rays of sunshine, or ultra-violet light. This light factor is the vitamin D factor found also in cod-liver oil. Where direct sunlight is not available, the addition of a little cod-liver oil in the feed serves the same purpose. Since this is a feeding matter, it will be discussed in the following chapter.

THE REVOLUTION
IN POULTRY FEEDING

IT REQUIRES approximately four ounces of feed a day to supply the nutritional requirements of a laying hen, or ninety pounds of feed a year. This applies to the larger, dual-purpose breeds, such as Plymouth Rocks, Wyandottes, Rhode Island Reds and Orpingtons. A flock of Leghorns, representing four-pound birds, will consume somewhat less. Such a flock, giving an egg yield of 175 to 180 eggs per bird during the year, will eat about eighty pounds of feed on the average, but a very high producing flock of Leghorns, giving an annual egg yield of 200 eggs per hen, will consume nearer ninety pounds of feed per bird. Considering the additional oyster shell and grit that the layers require, a basis for roughly estimating the cost of feeding one hen one year, particularly in the case of large breeds, is the cost of a 100-pound bag of feed.

In growing chickens, the feed consumption is related to growth. During the first two weeks after hatching, it takes about three pounds of feed to produce one pound of gain in a flock of chicks. At the age of ten to twelve weeks, it takes about five and one-half pounds of feed to produce one pound of gain in weight. At from twenty to twenty-two weeks, the growth impulse has diminished still further, and it requires approximately eleven pounds of feed to make a one-pound gain in weight.

In an experimental test conducted at the New York State College of Agriculture, Cornell University, it required 2,378 pounds of feed to grow 100 White Leghorn pullets to the age

Mother hen scratched for her
brood in the uncontaminated
virgin soil. They found a
complete diet of worms, grit,
grass, and seeds.

of twenty-six weeks, or an average feed consumption of nearly
twenty-four pounds per bird. At the age of twenty-six weeks,
a White Leghorn pullet should weigh about three and one-
fourth pounds. It has then reached sexual maturity, and is
ready to lay. A similar test in growing 100 pullets of the
American breeds, which make larger fowls, heavier in weight,
showed that it required 2,882 pounds of feed to grow them up
to twenty-six weeks of age. They are then about six months
old, a time at which their combs should be red in color; they
should be in complete feather, of good size and body weight,
and about ready for egg production.

Pullets begin to lay before they have reached maximum
weight, and good feeders give special thought to the matter of
holding body weight. They weigh a few selected birds regularly, and if the business of producing eggs is tending to
diminish body weight, they increase the amount of grain. At
the same time they may reduce the amount of animal food, in
the form of meat scrap, that the birds are getting in the mash.
In other words, the pullets must not be forced at the start.

Man works for this flock. They have a complete diet of machine-manufactured feed.

When these females are two and three years old, they have a tendency to become slightly heavier, and at the same time less prolific in egg production, and therefore will stand more forcing. These older hens also lay larger eggs than young pullets. The poultryman, however, likes to go into the season with a large flock of well grown pullets, for he knows that their body weight and egg size will come up, and they will give him a long and profitable period of heavy egg production.

Fundamentals of Feeding

The feeding of poultry has been greatly simplified as a result of the manufacture of commercial-mixed mashes by the large mills. These mash feeds are composed of ground grain, such as finely ground corn and oats, together with wheat bran and middlings. A mash could be composed of twenty pounds of each of these four feed stuffs, to which could be added twenty pounds of meat scraps, making a 100-pound bag of mash feed.

The large mills with their powerful buying resources and

THE REVO-
LUTION IN
POULTRY
FEEDING

In houses mash
feed is put in
hoppers, scratch
feed on the floor.

elaborate mixing machinery have more complex and delicately balanced formulae than the home-mixer could compound; and their splendid manufactured feeds develop the maximum of those specialized capacities for growth and egg production which the breeder has developed in his fowls through long years of selective breeding. Well grown fowls are now the order of the day, each feed manufacturer vying with his competitors to produce the best results.

This question of quality in feeds is a business matter to the feeder. His fowls are far removed from primitive warfare with nature. They are housed and fed so as to render them very valuable for food-producing purposes. No longer, like wild fowls in the primeval forest, do they seek shelter from the storm by tucking their heads under their wings, while the wind and the rain drive on, nor do they subsist on wild herbage and weed seeds. The intelligence of man has taken this creature of nature, housed it and fed it, supplied its special requirements, studied its disposition and its fitness, and in the course of years the fowl of nature has become the fowl of civilization, paying tribute to the higher intelligence that developed it, and that now protects it and feeds it.

THE REVO-
LUTION IN
POULTRY
FEEDING

148

On range mash feed is put in hoppers to supplement natural scratch feed.

When the Pratt Food Company, of Philadelphia, first manufactured a starting feed for chicks, they packed it in card board boxes such as one could hold in his hand, and introduced this new product by showing it on the counter of their booth at the Madison Square Garden poultry show, where fanciers might buy what today would be considered merely a sample. To those who had been starting their chicks on Johnny-cake and clipped oats, it was something new to see offered a packaged feed that contained all the necessary ingredients for promoting the fastest growth of muscle, bone and feathers. It was offered in small packages and at the high price of eleven cents a pound, for no volume production had then been developed to bring prices down.

Sherman Edwards, of Chicago, conceived the idea of manufacturing a mash feed for growing and laying chickens, producing it in volume, pouring it into 100-pound feed bags, and selling it in carlots to feed dealers.

When he proposed the idea to his directors, the substance of their criticism was, "Let's stick to the larger animals—chickens have such small mouths."

Mr. Edwards replied, "Yes, they can't eat as much individually, but there are an awful lot of chickens in this county—have you thought of that?".

He won the day. Because of the fact that there is a tremendous poultry population in the country, some of the mills that now manufacture mixed feeds are selling more tonnage to poultry feeders than to producers of cattle, or horses and mules, or hogs.

The biggest part of the mixed feed business is in mash feeds. Many poultry keepers feed home-grown grains and do not buy what the trade calls scratch feed. This scratch feed is composed of cracked corn, whole wheat, oats, and perhaps a little barley, sunflower seed, milo maize, and so on. The scratch grain is fed in the litter, on the floor, where the chickens scratch and work for their feed. The mash is usually fed dry in feed hoppers, where the chickens have access to it at all times. Some poultrymen prefer a wet mash, mixing the mash with water or sour milk, and some ferment it by adding yeast. Every feeder, however, is familiar with the dry-mash method for it is simply a case of pouring the feed out of the bag into the mash hopper, keeping the hoppers filled and open, and letting the birds have free access to it. The general practice is to let the birds eat about one-half mash and one-half scratch grain, and this result is secured by feeding about one-half of the ration in the form of grain or scratch feed, and allowing the birds to supplement the balance of their feed requirements by going to the mash hoppers and eating the finely ground meal.

It is a common saying that "the grain holds body weight and the mash makes eggs".

In the grain are found the carbohydrates, the sugars and starches, which serve as fuel for the liberation of energy and as a source of body fat. It may be said that the ground grain in the mash carries the same carbohydrates and fats, but there is this difference: To the mash has been added approximately twenty per cent of meat scrap. The more mash the layer or growing chicken eats, the more animal protein in the form of meat scrap it consumes. When no grain is fed, and the chickens are put on an all-mash ration, the amount of meat scrap in the mash is reduced by half, so that they will not get more animal protein than they can utilize advantageously.*

Protein is highly important in the ration. It is the chief element in the lean meat of the bird's body. It is the chief element in all living tissues. The white of the egg is almost pure protein. It is the protein matter in the feed, therefore, that is so important in the business of feeding hens so that they can make eggs. To give layers merely a corn diet would be equivalent to giving them a superabundance of material with which to make yolks, which contain the fat part of eggs. But to be a good layer, the hen must receive a ration so well balanced that it makes complete eggs; and the proteins in adequate quantity are essential.

It is true that the corn and the wheat in the ration make eggs in the sense that a hen could live on these grains and do some laying; but when meat scrap, dry milk, semi-solid buttermilk, or other rich protein feeds are added to the ration, the whole feeding program is put in better balance, and much higher egg production results.

There is another important part of the egg besides the white and the yolk—the shell, composed of calcium carbonate, a form of lime. Hens should be given a supply of crushed oyster shell or limestone, from which they can draw the necessary lime. Since oyster shell is a product that has been built up by a living organism, the oyster, it is especially relished by layers and is highly assimilable. With hens in confinement that are laying a big egg nearly every day, the body requirements for lime material are so excesisve that it is highly important for them to have daily access to a supply of crushed oyster shell, or lime rock with a high calcium content.

---

* Proteins break up into amino acids, a variety of which are needed. Too much of all or of any one kind may over-tax the organism. The sources and amount of protein are, therefore, questions requiring careful study.

Water is another important part of the egg, comprising about two-thirds of its content. It is also an important part of a fowl's body, permeating the entire organism. Thus both growing chickens and laying hens should have ready access to clear fresh fountains or troughs of nature's pure drink. If ice of winter prevents the hen from getting the necessary water, egg production will diminish within 48 hours. The hen must have all the materials with which to make her egg.

The New Idea in Feeding

"The century will cover it", remarked Dr. G. F. Heuser of Cornell University, in referring to progress in feeding—meaning that all our progress in feeding has been made during the past century. "Under primitive conditions the hens ran out on range and foraged for a large part of their living, eating worms, bugs, seeds, and the tender, succulent shoots of grass. They thus got a complete and complex food. Bugs and insects are whole animals, and the greens are whole plants. Under confinement, with artificial feeds, there was always the danger of omitting some important nutritive factor".

In the beginning, production of eggs was in the spring of the year. The hens did not lay a large number of eggs. Even poultry breeders and fanciers were hesitant about trying to get egg production in the off seasons lest they exhaust the breeding powers of their birds. The thought was that energy should be conserved for spring propagation. The idea of a balanced ration, so complete in all particulars that it supplies the ingredients for making eggs without unduly taxing the vital resources of the bird, is a much more recent conception of the problem.

Indeed, when this theory was first advanced, it had to be backed with the fertility and hatching records of the birds themselves to prove that heavy layers could reproduce; and even then the laying records of the pullets were awaited to see if they could possibly equal the production records of their

Range conditions give vitamin D, guaranteeing good eggs and strong bodies.

dams that had laid and laid, and still had given birth to daughters of good stamina.

Under range conditions, the number of hens on a farm was not greater than the food supply. The hens ran out-of-doors, in the sunshine, ate plenty of green food, worms and bugs, and there was no contamination in the virgin land about the homestead. As the number of hens on the farm increased, or as farm planning necessitated their confinement, it became necessary to supplement the natural food supply. As an increase in egg production developed, and there was a distribution of egg production throughout the year, with a winter egg yield, the question of feeding came to the fore as a vital issue.

Today the test of successful feeding has come to be the old fundamental issue of hatchability.

It is not merely a question of how many eggs a feed will produce; it has come to be generally realized that a ration that produces eggs and keeps the birds in breeding trim is the most successful feed. Feeding dairy cows is somewhat different. A cow gives milk as sustenance for its young. But in the egg is the germ of life that the hen produces to give birth to its young. Feeding cows for milk yield is a matter of increasing the flow of liquid food. Feeding hens for eggs is a matter of increasing the vital processes of reproduction.

The hatching power of those eggs, therefore, is now accepted as the standard by which the efficiency of the feeding methods is judged. Just as in breeding, the poultryman has a different problem than the citrus fruit grower who clips cuttings from a single seedless orange tree and grafts them over a whole orchard, without the need of any complicated study of heredity and transmission of characters, so again, the poultryman differs from the dairyman who feeds for more milk, whereas in the case of eggs each one represents potential offspring.

For good hatchability one of the most important factors is sunshine. A hen that does not receive vitamin D in foodstuffs can get it directly through the action of certain light rays upon the ergosterol-like substance in her skin. One of the effects of sunshine, the incidental effect that shows in the yolk as a result of hens eating green food out on range, is not liked by some city dwellers. Sunshine does not directly color the yolk but it colors the plants, and it is the plant pigments that determine yolk-color. The principal pigments to be found in egg yolk are those called xanthophylls. They occur in green plant tissue, such as the clovers and alfalfa, and in yellow corn. Chickens out on range lay eggs with rich-colored yolks. Many consumers, however, prefer light-colored yolks in their table eggs. This is contrary to their own health interests. Pullets fed on white corn and kept inside, off the range, will produce extremely light-colored yolks. Cows kept in stanchions, and off the clover field pastures, will likewise produce lemon-colored butter, or even white butter. The lemon-colored fats can hardly be expected to be as rich in vitamin A as the golden-yellow fats. Many hatcherymen do not want eggs with lemon-colored yolks for hatching purposes.

Before the fad for light yolks captivated some of the Eastern consuming markets, clover hay was used by poultrymen in winter. It was ground, and sometimes steamed, or softened with boiling water. C. H. Wyckoff, when he was on the original Wyckoff farm at Groton, New York, was one of the first American poultrymen to give special thought to feeding.

Chicks and laying hens need plenty pure water for body growth and egg production.

He carried 600 laying hens, and as early as 1900 was supplementing their grain rations with bran, milk and clover hay. His was a big flock for the year 1900, and he was rated as one of the progressive feeders and leading up-to-date poultrymen in America.

W. H. Wheeler, of the New York State Experiment Station, Geneva, had stated as early as 1895 that if some of the feed of the hens were ground, it would give better results. In the case of a pen of Leghorns that had about one-third of their feed ground and moistened, he found that they produced eggs at a greater profit than did a pen fed on whole grain. The Maine Station at Orono was the first of the agricultural stations to recommend the feeding of dry mash as we now know it.

The Dynamic Power of Vitamins

One of the big stepping stones in the newer knowledge of nutrition was the discovery of vitamins. Dr. E. V. McCullom reported his discovery of vitamin A in 1914, and later of vitamin D. The effects of these hitherto unknown factors stimulated great interest in experimentation. It was found

Broilers can be grown to 2½ pounds in ten weeks in feeding batteries. Thousands are thus produced for market out-of-season.

that the presence of vitamin A in the ration of chickens prevents a form of cold, known as nutritional roup. Vitamin D has its importance in the development of poultry, for the growing of broilers, and for the production of eggs with sound shells.

The study of vitamins has resulted in revolutionizing the whole subject of nutrition, and in accomplishing this, has made possible revolutionary changes in housing of poultry.

The hen factory, and the broiler factory, which once existed only as figments of the imagination, and still seem unbelievable to many people, are nevertheless accomplished facts. It is not impossible today to grow thousands of lively, plump broilers in batteries, or keep laying hens in individual cages, removed from the outdoors and the sunshine.

THE REVO-
LUTION IN
POULTRY
FEEDING

This marvelous change in method has followed the discovery of the vitamins, particularly those designated A and D. All of the vitamins, in adequate amounts, with the possible exception of vitamin C, are necessary in the poultry ration. Vitamin B, for instance, has a particular relation to the control of the nervous system of the body. It is found in abundance in the bran of wheat and the outer part of the kernel of corn.

156   Vitamin G, which is found in abundance in green food, is

Well grown fowls are the result of proper feeding and proper housing. Codliver oil supplies vitamin D to housed fowls.

reported by Dr. Heuser of Cornell to be important in securing normal growth. Vitamin A is found abundantly in yellow corn and green feed, and a deficiency of this vitamin is seldom encountered. Vitamin E, discovered by Dr. Herbert Evans, of California, is found in the germ of cereal grains, especially in wheat germ; it promotes the reproductive processes and increases the fertility of eggs.

Vitamin D is of profound importance in poultry rations. It is the anti-rachitic factor, and is related to the building of strong bones and a sound skeleton framework in the growing chickens. It has a definite bearing on hatchability and on the texture of egg shells. It aids in the proper assimilation and utilization of the mineral matter in the feed. It serves practically the same purpose as the ultra-violet rays of outdoor sunshine, and has sometimes been called "bottled sunshine". It is not widely diffused in feedstuffs, most of them being devoid of it. Codliver oil is one of the richest sources of vitamin D.

For many years breeders of fancy fowl had been aware of the special feeding value of codliver oil. In growing fine chickens, they had given sparingly of it to broods of exceptional breeding and promise. A Red Sussex cockerel that was shown at the New York State Fair years ago, and that weighed nine pounds at 5½ months of age, had received some codliver oil on bread three times a week, from the start. This bird won first prize, and was presented to the Poultry Department at Cornell University. The value of codliver oil at that time, from the standpoint of the new vitamin theory, was unknown.

We know now, however, that codliver oil is a substitute for sunlight, and this discovery has brought with it sweeping changes, just one of which was to put the method of growing chickens in batteries into every-day use. Previously, it was orthodox practice to get chicks on the ground, and in the sun.

In telling how vitamin D is tied up with the promotion of normal growth, F. D. Baird states: "Chicks fed an otherwise balanced ration, but deficient in vitamin D, do not grow normally and develop rachitic leg weakness within four to six weeks of age. The bones of rachitic chicks are very soft and weak. If chicks are permitted to become rachitic, their entire skeletal development will be jeopardized and they may be crippled or deformed throughout life even though corrective measures are taken later to supply their requirements for vitamin D. Vitamin D deficiency in laying hens is evidenced by lowered egg production, low hatchability and poorly textured eggshells. In fact, some hens suffering from a lack of vitamin D will consistently lay eggs with no shells at all".

The fact that vitamin D cannot be supplied by the common ingredients used in poultry rations led to supplementing these rations with codliver oil. A great deal of this oil is used in the tanning industry, and there are other commercial uses for it. Dr. Theodore F. Zucker, of Columbia University, found that one-half of one per cent of codliver oil contains the vitamin D, and the remainder of the oil can be used in industry. He thereupon developed a machine, which looks somewhat like a cream separator, that extracts that part of the oil which carries the active D factor. It is quite a simple operation to take this extracted anti-rachitic element, and fortify ordinary codliver oil with the D factor, raising it to any desired potency. The result is "fortified codliver oil", a very little of which can be mixed by the mill in feed without any oily effect that might lead to rancidity, a point that was a chief difficulty when feed mixed with straight codliver oil was first placed on the market.

In human nutrition, the vitamins are as important as in the feeding of growing chickens and laying hens. Recent research has shown that the egg, from a food or nutritional standpoint, can be influenced by feeding, and that it is possible to increase the vitamin content of eggs. This is also being done in the case of milk, and vitamin-rich milk is being produced. In the case of eggs, the vitamin D content has been increased as much as ten times, and the vitamin A content as much as five times. Not only is poultry being better fed, but mankind stands on the threshold to receive the benefits.

Another field for exploration is the mineral world. The egg contains a large variety of mineral matter, such as iron and sulphur, each in a minute quantity. Chickens apparently have a very high mineral requirement. Excellent results are reported from feeding hard granite grit of small size to chicks, and a grade of larger size to grown fowls. In New England, where some of America's finest poultry is produced, the chickens have had access to the granite rock of the hills for three centuries.

It is not only the nutrients in the poultry ration that every poultryman wants to know, but also the question of relative costs. This is one of the first considerations of good management.

Dr. G. F. Warren, Professor of Agricultural Economics, and Dr. F. A. Pearson, Professor of Prices and Statistics, Cornell University, issue a bulletin entitled "Farm Economics" for distribution to farmers, bankers, feed manufacturers and businessmen in New York state, in which prices are given as an index of trends. The figures in the tables on the next two pages are arranged and reproduced from that bulletin.

Prices, New York State

THE prices for corn, wheat and oats are those paid to producers, as reported by the United States Department of Agriculture. The prices for mill feed, meat scrap and standard poultry ration are wholesale prices on feed in straight cars at Utica, New York.

	Corn	Oats	Wheat	Corn meal	Ground oats	Wheat bran	Standard middlings	Meat scrap 50-55%	Poultry ration*	Chickens	Eggs	Eggs N.Y.C.
	bu. c	bu. c	bu. c	$	$	$	$	$	$	lb. c	doz. c	doz. c
Five-year average												
1910 to 1914_	75	48	99	29.18	32.09	24.83	25.94	52.67	31.90	14.8	28	34.4
1914_____	82	49	99	31.98	32.53	25.84	26.38	57.00	33.35	15.7	30	36.3
1915_____	85	56	119	32.66	36.28	24.58	25.99	57.09	35.49	15.6	29	36.0
1916_____	91	53	124	34.82	36.49	25.14	26.53	56.68	36.72	16.6	33	39.7
1917_____	168	75	211	69.39	52.36	38.44	41.54	76.73	62.70	20.8	43	51.0
1918_____	195	91	209	67.93	62.61	36.32	38.31	104.88	65.12	27.2	51	62.7
1919_____	177	83	219	69.51	57.52	45.72	51.47	102.50	67.85	31.7	56	68.9
1920_____	174	101	236	67.13	67.88	50.27	53.76	114.34	71.31	33.3	61	73.9
1921_____	84	54	133	33.26	36.52	25.70	25.65	90.37	40.25	29.4	47	59.4
1922_____	76	51	113	31.17	34.00	29.17	30.22	90.56	38.39	27.6	40	55.6
1923_____	96	57	119	40.24	38.84	33.74	34.75	89.47	43.29	25.7	41	53.6
1924_____	111	58	124	45.16	43.09	31.61	32.38	69.13	42.99	23.7	39	52.3
1925_____	123	57	164	47.89	40.91	33.30	35.05	70.55	47.95	25.1	43	54.1
1926_____	90	50	149	37.40	38.45	31.20	31.72	70.84	41.99	26.6	40	50.7
1927_____	99	53	131	42.18	42.44	34.73	37.02	79.13	44.09	25.6	38	46.0
1928_____	110	62	145	45.54	45.38	37.99	39.39	75.68	47.12	26.3	40	46.9
1929_____	108	58	127	43.93	41.08	34.14	35.39	71.72	43.54	27.6	42	49.1
1930_____	98	52	99	39.80	35.77	29.72	29.79	64.63	37.68	23.5	35	39.3
1931_____	71	36	67	29.20	28.38	20.43	20.41	43.18	26.33	20.2	27	31.5
1932_____	48	30	55	21.14	23.09	17.01	17.15	36.05	20.80	16.9	23	26.5
1932												
July_____	50	32	52	21.90	22.90	15.38	16.63	30.80	20.18	17.0	20.0	21.7
August____	50	29	52	21.65	21.64	15.75	16.60	37.80	20.64	16.1	22.9	25.4
September_	48	29	53	20.38	21.40	15.50	15.50	46.80	21.03	15.6	25.7	32.0
October___	46	27	52	19.30	20.73	15.13	15.13	45.80	20.33	15.6	31.1	37.1
November_	39	26	47	18.82	19.96	14.90	15.30	39.80	19.07	14.8	34.9	40.8
December	40	26	48	18.50	19.85	15.00	15.00	37.80	18.82	14.4	33.2	34.6
1933												
January___	40	25	49	18.45	20.25	15.88	15.88	32.30	18.44	14.3	28.5	26.9
February__	41	26	50	18.43	19.90	16.81	16.38	33.80	18.88	13.6	15.0	17.3
March____	41	26	52	19.36	20.56	18.75	18.10	34.13	19.79	13.7	15.4	18.4
April_____	46	29	61	21.88	23.58	19.38	19.00	39.80	22.30	13.7	14.7	18.4

INDEX NUMBERS

(The average of corresponding months, 1910–14 = 100)

The yearly prices in the table on the foregoing page compare with the five years averages for 1910–14 as follows:

	Corn	Oats	Wheat	Corn meal	Gr'd oats	Wheat bran	Standard middlings	Meat scrap	Poultry ration	Chickens	Eggs	Eggs[1]
1914_____	109	102	100	110	101	104	102	108	105	106	107	106
1915_____	113	117	120	112	113	99	100	108	111	105	104	105
1916_____	121	110	125	119	114	101	102	108	115	112	118	115
1917_____	224	156	213	238	163	155	160	146	197	141	154	148
1918_____	260	190	211	233	195	146	148	199	204	184	182	182
1919_____	236	173	221	238	179	184	198	195	213	214	200	200
1920_____	232	210	238	230	212	202	207	217	224	225	218	215
1921_____	112	113	134	114	114	104	99	217	126	199	168	173
1922_____	101	106	114	107	106	117	116	172	120	186	143	162
1923_____	128	119	120	138	121	136	134	172	136	174	146	156
1924_____	148	121	125	155	134	127	125	170	135	160	139	152
1925_____	164	119	166	164	127	134	135	131	150	170	154	157
1926_____	120	104	151	128	120	126	122	134	132	180	143	147
1927_____	132	110	132	145	132	140	143	150	138	173	136	134
1928_____	147	129	146	156	141	153	152	144	148	178	143	136
1929_____	144	121	128	151	128	137	136	136	136	186	150	143
1930_____	131	108	100	137	112	120	115	123	118	159	125	114
1931_____	95	75	68	100	88	82	79	82	83	136	96	92
1932_____	64	63	56	72	72	69	66	68	65	114	83	77
1932												
July_____	66	63	51	74	68	66	64	59	63	112	91	80
August____	65	57	54	69	65	64	61	72	63	102	92	82
September_	59	59	55	62	67	63	57	89	64	100	95	87
October___	58	57	54	63	67	64	59	86	63	101	104	82
November_	51	57	48	63	64	62	61	74	60	102	100	74
December	53	55	49	64	64	61	59	71	59	104	81	70
1933												
January___	56	56	49	67	65	61	61	62	59	105	75	68
February__	58	55	50	67	63	64	62	65	60	97	47	51
March____	58	55	52	72	65	72	69	65	63	96	55	71
April_____	65	59	61	79	73	75	74	76	71	93	70	82

[1]Monthly average price of the highest grade of nearby hennery white eggs in New York City, Present Classification is "nearby and mid-western hennery specials."

*The poultry ration was weighted in the following manner: Corn meal, 35 per cent; wheat bran, 10; standard middlings, 10; 50 @ 55 per cent meat scrap, 10; oats, 5; wheat, 25; and barley, 5.

A knowledge of the feed-egg and the feed-meat ratio, as indicated in these tables, is important to the grower of all types of fowl, but it is especially valuable to the producer of seasonable birds as the following chapter will show.*

* See pages 166–8.

FESTIVE BIRDS —
AND SOME HARD
COMMON SENSE

T HE poultry industry is concerned chiefly with four different species—chickens, ducks, geese and turkeys. Light is thrown upon the economic position that each of these groups occupies as much by historical development as by their relation to the price structure. Let us consider these two points, history and prices.

A Character Study of Three Birds

Chickens were kept for eggs even before their flesh was used for food. They are of great antiquity. Geese were one of the first fowls to be domesticated. They were bred in the valley of the Nile four thousand years ago. Ducks also were domesticated early in the history of man. Asia, Europe and America have each contributed varieties to the list of members in the duck family, but the Pekin ducks of Asia have exerted the greatest influence on the present day duck industry.

Ducks are bred and raised commercially, in large numbers, for market. The duck, as a species, is adaptable to large operations, intensively carried on, and a number of duck growers in America produce from 30,000 to 75,000 or more ducks on their farms each year.

The ducks are grown to an age of about ten weeks, when they average about five pounds each. They are called "green ducks." The south shore of Long Island has long been famous

Muscovy ducks differ from all other breeds. Females are silent and males have no tail curls.

as a duck-growing area, but large plants have also been operated in the vicinity of Raynham and Wrentham, Massachusetts, for many years, and more recently large operations in duck growing have been carried on successfully in Illinois and Indiana.

The duck eggs are hatched in incubators, requiring a period of twenty-eight days to hatch. The egg production of a Pekin ranges from 80 to 120 eggs during the breeding season. Ducks of one variety, the Indian Runner, have been known to lay more than 300 eggs in a year, and in England some effort has been made to keep this variety of ducks for eggs, as Leghorn chickens are kept for eggs in America. On the whole, duck farming in the United States is largely a matter of growing green ducks for market.

Geese do not lend themselves to the machine methods employed in duck farming. The females lay fewer eggs, the Toulouse and Embden geese laying not more than three dozen in a season. Canadian and Egyptian geese lay barely a dozen. The Chinese variety is the most prolific, with an egg production of three to five dozen in a season.

Geese are more vicious in disposition than other domesticated fowls. They are not polygamous, as are chickens, and once a mating is made it is not successfully broken up the following

163

The Toulouse goose is largest of the standard breeds. A sympathetic monogamous fowl, cherished in legend, and the feast bird of Europe for many centuries.

year. Geese occasionally attain great age, fifteen years being common, with occasional reports of geese living to twenty-five or thirty years of age.

The chief obstacle in raising geese is the poor hatchability of the eggs. The period of incubation varies from twenty-nine to thirty-three days, or may run to thirty-five days. When goslings are hatched, however, they are hardy and grow with astonishing speed, requiring little feed if given a good pasture field in which to forage, preferably one with a stream running through it. When snow flies and cold weather comes on, they fatten readily on whole corn. Geese are profitable on the average farm, although many farmers do not like them because they spoil too much pasture land for other stock, and then there is the difficulty of hatchability.

"As stupid as a goose" is a common expression, but actually a goose is a clever, intelligent creature. A trainer can teach a goose to follow him through a massed crowd of people and never lose its way. Apparently a puppy dog could not be more loyally attached by friendship to its master. Ancient

Egypt honored the goose as the symbol of filial piety and parental devotion. It was the noise of a flock of these faithful, vigilant fowls that awakened the soldiers of Rome and saved the Imperial City from destruction by the enemy. When Caesar landed upon Britain's shores, he found the goose so venerated by the natives that he forbade his men to harm any one of these fowls.

The goose has played a romantic rôle in the traditions of Yuletide. For centuries in Merrie England and in Europe, the goose has been the feast bird. It was the goose that laid the golden egg.

The goose business has become highly commercialized in Germany where it stands next to chickens today in point of numbers marketed. It is concentrated in the northern part of the country where many thousands of goslings are imported from Poland and Russia for fattening. The German breeds mature too rapidly to gain weight easily during the fattening season, October to December. A fattening farm consists of many small adjoining pens with cement floors and slatted fences to confine 50 to 100 goslings in separate close quarters. Here each bird consumes from 28 to 40 pounds of mixed grains including carrots and lime, in 4 to 7 weeks, and it gains from 4 to 5 pounds weight. A so-called "quick-fattening" process, for Spring markets, brings one-half pound goslings to 9 pounds in 8 weeks by using a mash mixture about 75% grain and bran, 14% fish and meat scrap, 6% yeast, and 2% each codliver oil and lime supplemented by much green feed.

The Germans claim keeping of geese has many advantages for them. The weight of goslings increases faster than that of ducks, and they do not require as careful attention and as expensive feed as other classes of poultry, and their feathers bring an additional 15% in the market. The goose business in the United States is not highly specialized. A farmer at Mansfield, Illinois came nearest to commercializing the goose when he bought droves of the fowls in Tennessee and turned them out in his corn fields in November to "hog down" the corn.

The turkey, native of America, was the last addition to civilized fowls. It was the only domesticated live stock of aboriginal America. The Aztecs raised them by the thousands for religious feasting and as meat for the sacred vultures. The explorer, Pedro Nino, discovered the turkey here in 1499 and took specimens back to Spain. It was introduced into England about 1524. Thus it was domesticated 100 years in the old world before the Pilgrims came to the new. Black, white, and slate varieties were developed in Europe by selective breeding. In addition to these America standardizes the Bourbon Red, the Narragansett and the Bronze—the latter supposedly closest to the original wild form.

All groups of Indians hunted the wild turkey, both for meat and for ceremonial purposes. It has a lasting place in native American lore. In one legend it appears as a great medicine man spirit; it is revered as an attribute of the God of Earth. Among the Puebloans it is known as Spirit Trapper, this interpretation arising from the fact that turkeys are not migratory like geese or ducks and that they cannot fly far above the ground.

The natural habits of turkeys mark them apart from other festive fowls. The males and females segregate when about 6 months old, and roost and range separately. Old gobblers, too, range in bands alone. A gobbler eats sparingly during the mating season so becomes quite thin; he is strongly attached to his group of females, for which he will fight most courageously. He is often defeated by a younger male, then he must join the ranks of the old gobblers or steal another male's harem.

Turkeys are favored as feast birds because of the flavor of their meat, and also because of their size. The average for bronze females is 20 pounds, for males 35 pounds; but occasionally a male has tipped the scales at 55. The turkey business is highly commercialized. In Massachusetts turkeys are grown on wire floors. In North Dakota they forage through the wheat stubble after the grain has been cut. In Texas they are herded like cattle from pasture to pasture. They use to be driven to market like cattle. Droves were gathered by farm to farm by buyers. The long drives caused too much loss of weight so this method of marketing has been discontinued. Now they are taken by truck or rail. Texas alone ships annually 1200 cars of 2000 birds each, totalling 2,400,000.

Until quite recently the United States imported dressed turkeys from Hungary, Russia, Austria, Ireland, and Argentina. When American poultrymen realized the opportunities in this direction, turkey growing became a good business, and the industry has made rapid strides.

Other classes of poultry, such as guineas, pheasants and squabs, occupy a definite place in the industry, but the great volume of production is in chickens and their eggs, and in ducks, geese and turkeys. The chicken stands first because it yields both poultry meat and eggs in quantity. The duck is a very fast grower, and lends itself to mass production. The goose has great advantages and poor possibilities; in America it has been supplanted to a considerable extent as a feast bird by the native turkey. The tonnage of turkeys now produced is much greater than that of geese.

The Most Vital Factor of All

Inasmuch as ducks are largely grown on commercial duck farms, principally in the East, the cost of feed in relation to the selling price of green ducks determines the profit of this industry for any one year.

Geese are largely a farm crop, growing on pasture land, and receiving corn to fatten by Thanksgiving or Christmas. This crop of poultry is not dependent upon the feed-price ratio.

Turkey growing in the East is highly specialized, much of the turkey feed being purchased; and the size of the crop as well as the profit to growers depends upon the price of feed in relation to the selling prices of live and dressed turkeys. In the West, turkey growing is more of a by-product enterprise, the turkeys foraging on immense fields, picking up kernels of grain in the wheat stubble that would otherwise be lost. These Western growers can produce turkey meat at low cost. As far as the wheat they feed is concerned, it is worth about seventeen cents a bushel less than the price quoted at Chicago, this figure representing the differential between the wheat fields and the market.

Relation of Poultry to Prices

This brings up the question of the price structure as it relates to poultry in general. The first point to remember is that when grain and live-stock prices are good, less thought and attention is given to the poultry on the farm. It is the same in the cities and towns—when wages are good and there is full employment, less thought is given to backyard gardens and back-lot poultry keeping. This supplementary production, therefore, shrinks.

When grain prices fall and a crate of eggs is worth more than a wagonload of corn, poultry production on the farm increases, and the situation shows profit to the farmer and leads to "swollen farm flocks."

In commercial poultry farming, the cost of feed is approximately fifty per cent of the cost of producing eggs. Labor, taxes, depreciation, transportation, et cetera, make up the other half of the cost. It isn't merely the price at which eggs sell that makes the poultry business profitable for egg farmers; rather it is the price at which eggs sell in relation to the cost of feed.

To gauge the poultry business from the standpoint of the Eastern egg farmer or grower of broilers, to know whether it will be a good and profitable year, whether conditions are going to stimulate growth or cause a shrinkage in production of poultry and eggs, it is necessary to consider this egg-feed ratio.

The majestic turkey. A native of the New World, and the celebrated feast bird of America. Famous in American Indian symbolism as the Spirit Trapper.

In New York State, according to studies made by the New York State College of Agriculture, it required a little over fifty-eight eggs in 1910 to pay for the feed a hen ate. If the feed is fifty per cent of the cost of production, then it took 117 eggs to pay for the feed, plus the equipment, labor, distribution, et cetera. If a man had a flock that averaged 150 eggs per bird during the year 1910, he had thirty-three eggs per bird as profit.

By 1917, the war had progressed to where commodity prices had risen, including egg prices. Poultrymen were getting big prices for eggs in relation to former years, yet it was a very bad time for Eastern egg farmers. Hen houses were being closed, for grain had also jumped in price. (See table, "Prices, New York State", closing the previous chapter.) In 1917, it took approximately 150 eggs to pay the cost of keeping a hen a year.

Then came some good years for Eastern egg farmers. (See table, "Prices, New York State.") In 1921, feed had gone down so fast that it required only ninety-eight eggs to pay a hen's expenses for one year. That was a great stimulus to poultry prosperity. And because of low grain prices, the poultry business, including the production of eggs, has remained in a favorable position in the price structure. In 1932, it took 102 eggs to pay the cost of keeping a hen a year, according to the New York State figures. That is a low figure for commercial flocks, lower than before the war.

In 1933, the price of feed has been advancing faster than the price of eggs. And this tendency has been accelerated for the moment by the Government's "new deal" policy, which seeks to limit production of basic farm products including corn and wheat. Many of the ingredients useful in the manufacture of poultry feed are thus effected. To limit the production of corn especially influences the price of live stock, and this in turn is reflected in by-products such as meat scrap which goes into the poultry ration. The ultimate effect of this is to raise the cost of poultry feed faster than the price of eggs.

It should be remembered, therefore, that a successful poultryman has many things to consider besides the type of stock he has chosen to perpetuate for his own livelihood. A knowledge of the history and constitutional vigor of his chosen strain, of the methods and principles of breeding, of improved types of equipment, of the nutritional requirements of his flocks—all these are important, but more than these in value is the ability to determine the relationship of costs to the selling price of the final product.

Pearl Guineas. Domesticated descendants of an East African fowl.

170

MYSTERY OF THE EGG AND CHICK

EDWARD N. WENTWORTH, JR.

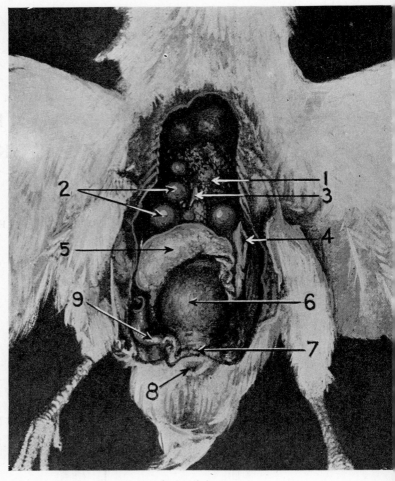

Relative location of oviduct in body of fowl:

1—Ovary tissue
2—Undeveloped yolks
3—Empty yolk sac
4—Funnel opening into oviduct
5—Albumen-secreting region of oviduct
    with yolk inside
6—Uterus with completed egg inside
7—Vagina
8—Cloaca
9—End of large intestine

MYSTERY OF
THE EGG AND CHICK

MAN has created more breeds of chickens than he has the breeds of any other member of the animal kingdom. The foregoing chapters reveal how the lover of sport, the artist and the production scientist have each played a part, and how the maintenance of good quality stock has been influenced by housing, feeding and technical research.

Many beautiful varieties that have been created in the past have disappeared as the demand for food birds grew. They have become extinct because man has chosen that they should not survive. The real purpose behind egg-laying is the continuance of the species, but man has altered the natural intention to suit his own needs, and so the egg is now laid primarily for food purposes. If the hen had her way about it, the egg should bring forth a fluffy yellow chick, and not a fluffy yellow omelet.

Biology has many relationships to the poultry industry, especially to poultry breeding as already indicated in previous chapters, but since the busy world to-day has prime interest in poultry from a food and commercial standpoint, it is á própos to interpolate here a discussion of those phases of biology practical to the producer of eggs and chicks.

Science has been able to solve many things, but all the sages and scientists of history have not been able to answer the riddle as to how the egg can evolve into a chick by the mere protective application of warmth and motion, and as to how the developing chick knows just when to stretch and break its prison shell. Primitive peoples were awed by these things. They danced for the egg and divined by the egg and made it a part of their religions as it became a symbol for the abundance they desired. The modern scientist applies himself just as religiously to the task of studying these secrets that nature guards so well. His object is also abundance.

The Coming of the Egg

Miss Pennington has defined the egg and described its characteristics in the introductory section of this book. A few more words concerning the shape of the egg are appropriate here. Previous to the addition of the shell the egg is a fluid substance contained within flexible membranes, hence its normal shape should be spherical. However, the muscles of the oviduct (the tube through which the egg descends during its formation) produce wave-like contractions, which increase the pressure on the rear part of the egg and push the main mass of the egg to the front so that as the egg hardens the larger blunt end comes first, and the rear end is smaller and somewhat pointed. From the standpoint of survival of the species there is considerable value to the oval shape, for it prevents the egg from rolling out of the nest, its conical form causing it to roll in a small circle.

The Significance of the Ovary

The ovary is the organ within the fowl which produces the ovum, the reproductive female element which is the foundation of the egg. The females of most domestic animals possess a pair of ovaries located symmetrically on either side of the backbone within the body cavity. Chickens, like other birds, possess only one ovary, normally the left. This appears as a mass of tissue lying close to the body wall and is almost centered beneath the backbone.

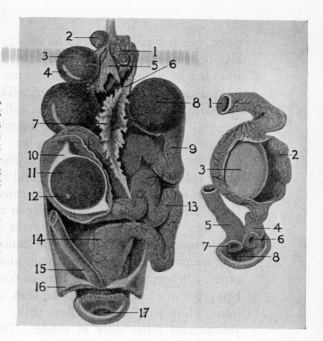

Oviduct of a laying hen: 1, ovary, with minute ovules; 2–3, yolk sacs; 4, suture line; 5, empty yolk sac; 7, funnel opening into oviduct; 8, yolk in oviduct; 9, albumen-secreting region; 10, albumen being secreted; 11, yolk passing through oviduct; 12, germinal disk; 13, isthmus; 14, uterus; 15, large intestine; 17, cloaca. On the right-hand side (1) isthmus, (2) glands of uterus, (3) complete egg, (4) vagina, (5) large intestine, (8) cloaca.

There is an advantage from the standpoint of race survival in this arrangement, for if there were two ovaries, one on each side, the growing eggs would probably never develop simultaneously, hence there would be more weight on one side and flight would become difficult. The greatest advantage lies in the center position, as is also evidenced by the location of the gizzard along the mid-line of the body to allow for its changing volume of food.*

The Formation of the Yolk

The beginning of the egg is found in the development of the ovum. This is a single cell near the surface of the ovary which enlarges through nourishment brought by the blood stream. In the hen the development of the ovum is somewhat compli-

* Figures on Pages 172 and 175 show the reproduction system of the hen, including the ovary, the oviduct, and eggs in various stages of development.

cated, but it finally comes to lie in a cavity, just under the surface layer of the ovary, which is known as a follicle. It is surrounded by a fine-textured membrane formed from the cells immediately adjacent to the ovum. This membrane is in contact with the interior lining of the follicle and finally becomes the yolk membrane or vitelline membrane. This ultimately encloses both the ovum and the yolk.

When the breeding season starts, the young egg cells in the ovary collect supplies of yolk around them from the dissolved proteins and fats brought to them through the circulatory system. Hence, when the body cavity of the laying hen is opened one may see eggs in many different stages of development. These nutrients are laid down in concentric layers within the yolk membrane, in the form of yolk plates, one surrounding the other. When the yolk of a hard-cooked egg is cross-sectioned, two types of these layers may be seen, commonly differentiated into "white yolk" and "yellow yolk," though both are really yellow and differ only in shade. The yellow yolk layer is much thicker than the white layer, the former being laid down during periods of activity and the latter, possessing more water, being laid down during the "rest periods." During the active period of yolk addition, the rate at which the immature egg grows may increase twentyfold. As the concentric layers of yolk are deposited around the ovum, the volume of yolk becomes thousands of times larger than the ovum itself.

The next step in development is the migration of the ovum from the center of the yolk to the surface, the path through which it moves being filled thereafter with white yolk, known as the "white yolk stalk." The ovum then remains directly in place above this stalk. Two facts of practical significance result from this. First, the substitution of white yolk in the path through which the ovum migrated lightens that side of the yolk and tends to keep it, with the ovum on top, where it will be closest to the hen's body. Secondly, it brings the ovum from the center of the egg to a point nearer the surface of the shell.   If the ovum remained in the center of the yolk not only would it be insulated to a greater degree from the heat of the hen's body, but as the chick developed the yolk would be scattered at various points outside of the chick's body rather than being located below the body in the "yolk sac," where its nutrients are conveniently available for absorption by the digestive tract.

In almost all species of animals the ova are microscopic in size, but the yolk of the bird's egg, when added to the ovum, distinguishes it as the largest living cell of the organic world; notably so in the ostrich.   In the case of the hen, the diameter of the ovum, with the attached yolk, is normally about 25 million times the diameter of the ovum of the cat.

The Formation of the Albumen

When the ovum has collected its full quota of yolk, the wall of the follicle ruptures and the yolk is taken up by the funnel-shaped mouth of the oviduct (P. 172), which is pressed against the ovary.   On rare occasions the yolk escapes from the oviduct and drops into the body cavity, where it usually disintegrates and is reabsorbed into the circulatory system.   The lining of the oviduct is ridged, or corrugated, and its walls are muscular in nature.   The upper part of the oviduct is lined with cilia, or moving hair-like processes, which aid the muscles in moving the yolk down the tract.

The region of the oviduct nearest the ovary is called the funnel, and in addition to capturing the ovum and yolk it has the function of secreting the first albumen layer around the yolk.   This layer of albumen is very viscous and sticks together closely in a thin layer surrounding the vitelline membrane. Projections of this dense albumen toward the two ends of the egg, as shown (P. 47), are known as the chalazae.   The purpose of these twisted strands of albumen is not completely clear, but they apparently have a drag effect in preventing the sudden shifting of the yolk in any direction.   This dense layer of albumen also normally prevents the yolk from sticking to the shell.

The second region of the duct is known as the coiled region, and it is here that the so-called mid-albumen of the egg is added. This albumen is less viscous and jelly-like, though still too thick to circulate. It is secreted by glands located in the troughs between the folds of the inner lining of the oviduct—one type of gland being disc-shaped and the other tubular. The disc-shaped gland discharges albumen directly into the oviduct, while the tubular gland has a small storage capacity in its central cavity.

The function of the third region of the oviduct is the production of the membrane which lines the shell. This membrane is made up of two layers, the outer being about twice as thick as the finer, inner layer. In a hard-cooked egg, these two membranes can easily be separated in the region of the air space. Watery solutions and air pass quite readily through these membranes.

The fourth region of the oviduct, or the uterus, deposits the shell over these membranes by means of a special gland, which lies on the oviduct wall in circular ridges and is pitted by many small tubes which carry the lime secretion in liquid condition from its point of formation. While the egg is in the uterus, there is also an addition of the freely circulating watery type of albumen which lies directly under the shell membrane in the finished egg. This layer of thin albumen is taken into the egg by osmotic pressure, passing through the membranes until they are completely distended. Before the completion of this latter process, a considerable amount of shell substance is deposited on the shell membrane.

The time required for completing the shell and laying the egg varies from twelve to sixteen hours, although an even longer time is occasionally required. If the time is short, the shell may be slightly flexible when the egg is laid; but the longer it is carried in the oviduct the harder the shell. A soft shell may be due also to a diet deficient in lime, or to an impairment in the activity of the shell gland.

The fifth and last region of the oviduct is the vagina, which possesses small glands that secrete the pigments and gelatines responsible for the color and gloss of the egg. The gelatine helps to lubricate the vagina and the cloaca during the laying of the egg and dries to form a covering that hinders the passage of putrefactive bacteria through the shell and shell membranes, as well as delaying evaporation of water from the albumen after the egg is laid.

When the egg leaves the last region of the oviduct it passes into the cloaca and thence moves out of the body. If the egg is formed after four o'clock in the afternoon, ordinarily it will not be laid until the next morning. This subjects it to continuous body heat, and starts the fertile egg developing. This "body heating" is a common cause of rejections in candling. Unfertilized eggs are not subject to this difficulty, which explains why they are preferred in the commercial trade.

The Fertilization of the Egg

Fertilization takes place in the oviduct. This process consists of the union of the sperm cell from the male with the ovum. Before fertilization takes place a rather remarkable process of maturing the sex cells occurs. Normally when cells grow and divide, each part of the nucleus in the cell doubles, the nucleus separates into two nuclei and the remainder of the cell divides, each part containing one of the new nuclei. When sex cells mature, however, the first division is of this type, but the second division differs in that the parts of the nucleus are not doubled and the new nuclei contain only half of the structures that were present in the preceding nucleus. Thus each sperm and ovum contains only half of the nuclear material normal to the cell, and when the sperm and ovum unite in fertilization, the normal complement of nuclear material is once more restored. The importance of this last procedure lies in

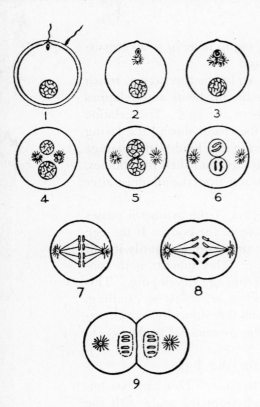

The process of fertilization

No. 1   Entry of sperm.
No. 2   Loss of sperm tail.
No. 3   Division of centrosome.
No. 4   Approach of sperm nucleus.
No. 5   Increase of sperm nucleus.
No. 6   Formation of chromosomes.
No. 7   Splitting of chromosomes.
No. 8   Anaphase.
No. 9   Two-cell stage.

the fact that the agents within the cell which control the hereditary characteristics of the fowl, as well as many of the physiological processes, apparently are located in the nucleus. Hence each parent contributes half of the heritage of the chick.

The sperm cells are produced in the testes of the cock, where they undergo the maturing processes previously mentioned. They then pass through a duct, the vas deferens, to a small sac near the cloaca where they are stored until finally transferred to the cloaca of the female during copulation or "treading."

In the female, the ovum matures by a similar process and enters the oviduct, as already described, where the upward moving sperm cells meet it. Except in rare instances, only one sperm cell passes through the covering of the ovum, the sur-

Method of maturing the egg cell

No. 1 — Typical cell from which egg develops showing nucleus and chromosomes.

No. 2 — Nucleus with four chromosomes.

No. 3 — First division of nucleus, chromosomes duplicated.

No. 4 — Nuclei separated.

No. 5 — A—First polar body.

No. 6 — Each nucleus with two chromosomes. Reduction by dividing.

No. 7 — First polar body divides. B—Second polar body.

No. 2 to 7 show only four chromosomes in order to make method of reproduction and maturity of egg more easily understood although method is the same as no. 1 showing 36 chromosomes.

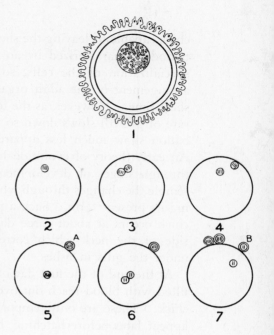

face of the ovum changing thereafter so that the entrance of additional sperm cells is prevented.

Following fertilization, development of the young chick begins immediately. The fertilized ovum divides and the cells formed from it also divide quite rapidly. The length of time from fertilization until the egg is laid varies from 18 to 36 hours, a period long enough for the potential chick to develop to the point where its primitive organs are already formed and the blood circulating. However, under normal conditions, development does not pass the four or eight cell stage, and eggs in this condition may retain their power to incubate for as long as a month under cool temperatures and proper care.

The Development of the Chick

The hen's egg requires twenty-one days of incubation to carry the development from the original fertilized germ cell to a chick capable of leaving the shell. The first part of the growth period is characterized by an exceedingly rapid division and specialization of the cells, so that the general outlines and arrangement of the adult organs become apparent in a rather short time. However, as the form becomes more apparent, the rate of growth slows down so that the last two weeks of incubation show much less apparent change than the first week. An early theory of evolution held that the young animal goes through stages of development to adulthood that closely resemble the changes through which the race has passed in attaining its present form. Such a phase in the development of the chick occurs at about three days, when openings occur in the side of the neck which correspond closely to the openings under the gills in fishes.

At the end of the first day of incubation, small blood vessels filled with blood reach out over the yolk from the developing chick. These are only temporary veins and arteries which disappear later before hatching, but they help to give rise to the adult circulatory system. Their purpose at the time of development is to carry food from the yolk into the body of the chick. Another clearly visible structure at this time is the primitive nervous system, which extends as a streak from a fold at the head end of the embryo.

During the second day the head develops and parts of the brain can be distinguished. Below it the mouth appears and the fore end of the alimentary tract with the newly formed heart pumping blood beneath it. During this day and the two or three immediately following, the development of the pits that form the eyes, ears and nostrils may be observed. Soon after this the embryo is covered by a double protecting sheath, the outer being known as the amnion and the inner as the corion. About this time a projection develops from the body which is later reabsorbed and which has the function of waste disposal and blood aeration. This last organ is known as the allantois. All of these three membranes are character-

MYSTERY
OF THE
EGG AND
CHICK

182

istic, with slight variations, of all of the farm animals. A membrane grows down from the body on this day that covers the yolk, and is later known as the yolk sac. This becomes smaller as the yolk is consumed, and the sac gradually shrinks and becomes part of the digestive organs.

On the third day the rudiments of the digestive organs begin to appear, the liver, stomach, the glands that secrete the digestive juices, and other such organs all being formed then. The lungs begin to develop and the nervous system and sense organs are more sharply defined. On the third day, also, the sex organs begin to appear as tissues, although the cells from which they develop were set aside on the second day.

The fourth day completes the formation of the hinder parts of the body and the rudimentary limbs appear. The fifth day exhibits the origin of the skeletal development, a process that continues until the fowl is well over a year old.

The foregoing outline recites the beginning of development of these various parts of the body at points where they can be distinguished and recognized. It should not be assumed that they are fully formed, for their filling out and development is the labor of the remaining days before hatching. Two interesting facts stand out in the foregoing—first, that the important heart, brain, reproductive system and digestive tract form first; and secondly, that development starts definitely at the head end of the chick and progresses rearward toward the tail.

At the end of three weeks the developing chick has the full set of organs essential to him in adult life and has progressed to the hatching stage. At this time he is lying with his bill pushed into the air sac, for during the last few hours in the egg the lungs are functioning and air is obtained through the pores in the shell. Instinctively his muscles start contracting and he starts turning around in such a manner that a temporary horny outgrowth on the tip of the beak, known as the egg tooth, pushes against the shell with sufficient strength to crack it. Although stopping occasionally for rest periods, the muscular contractions continue until they result in chipping away enough shell to allow the chick to escape. For a brief time it lies beside the shell, resting and drying.

Egg Variations

Heavy, sluggish breeds of fowl, as a rule, have larger, richer eggs than the slight, active breeds of sparser diet, but all types of fowl have certain kinds of unusual eggs that may even appear as temporary or permanent peculiarities in the best stock. Unusual shell or yolk forms are frequently observed, due to some derangement in the production of the egg. In the yolk the most frequent malformation is the dumb-bell shape, due to a constriction of the middle of the yolk by albumen that has pulled together or shrunk. A breaking of the yolk membrane also occurs, allowing it to flow into the albumen. Shells show a great range of variation in form, for during the period when the lime is hardening, the egg can take on almost any contour given by the muscles of the oviduct. Thus, there are eggs that are perfectly spherical and others which are conical, cylindrical or even cigar shaped, with all possible variations toward the dumb-bell included.

Another common variation in egg size and shape is the appearance of the dwarf egg. Many dwarf eggs are incomplete, thirty-five out of every hundred being without yolks. Such eggs are usually filled only with albumen, enclosed in the shell. The stimulus which the shell glands need for their activity is the mere presence of some object. Another ten out of a hundred variations are without a full complement of membranes, while a pathological condition that allows a premature release of the ova before the yolk is fully formed, or that fails to provide sufficient albumen, accounts for almost all of the remaining eggs of this type that are produced. Such abnormal eggs should not worry a poultryman as they are usually isolated cases that appear during the height of the breeding season, although occasionally a diet deficiency may have to be corrected in order to overcome the condition.

When an egg with two yolks is produced, it is an indication that the hen is laying under extreme pressure, the release of the two yolks from the ovary being so nearly simultaneous that they become invested with the same membranes and shell. Apparently there is an instinctive reaction in the muscles of the oviduct to force a second yolk forward more rapidly than the first, if the two are in close proximity, thereafter moving them along as a single body. If the second yolk joins the first in the funnel, they will share all coverings together. If the juncture is near the middle of the oviduct, the yolks will have separate chalazae but joint middle and outer albuminous coats; while union just before the shell gland is reached will result in two eggs with separate shell membranes but united under the same shell. The most extreme case of this last type is that in which a small egg, usually consisting only of albumen but surrounded by shell, has been thrown back into the region of shell formation against the normal egg, with the result that a new shell is formed about both, and a small egg within a larger egg results. Occasionally another odd result occurs when an egg already formed in the shell has been forced backwards, so that new albumen, shell membranes and shell have formed outside of the original egg.

Twinning occurs in the egg of a bird just as it does in man but with far less frequency. Its causes are about the same. Occasionally two ova fertilized by separate sperms may be included together in one egg, while identical twins may be formed as a result of a separation early in the development of the chick, before any of the cells have become specialized into tissues. This results in the embryo being divided into two complete halves, each of which develops independently to maturity. When the two halves are not completely separated but are joined by a single cell, such an oddity as Siamese twins or two-headed, double-bodied, or four-legged chicks may result.

Such cases scarcely ever develop to the adult stage and occur most frequently in eggs of large yolk.

Why eggs "go bad" is a question for both the biologist and the chemist to answer. Some phenomena such as blood streaks and meat spots, which occur in the egg and are uncontrollable in production, are flaws in the eyes of the trade. Nor are fertile eggs the most desirable for the food packers. The ensuing chapters disclose many interesting facts concerning the quality of eggs and the reasons for careful handling; they tell the story of the work of the egg grader and various other processes involved in keeping eggs good from the moment they are laid by the hen until the time they are placed in the hands of the purchaser of food for the breakfast table.

THE NEW ERA OF COLD AND CLEANLINESS

MARY ENGLE PENNINGTON

How Eggs Are Tested.
How Jack Frost Keeps Good Eggs Good.
How the Egg Goes Traveling.
Freezing the Freshness of Eggs.
How Cold Storage Came to the Rescue.
How Chickens are Different and Why.
How Poultry Is Made Ready for Market.
How to Purchase Table Poultry of
Finest Quality.

Candling eggs in Denmark. Flock owners are required to stamp their number on every egg and to guarantee its quality to the final consumer. Complaints are severely dealt with. At the collecting depot the eggs are candled superficially en masse as a check against accidental errors. The association selling the eggs does not take responsibility for the quality as in this country, hence careful candling of each egg is not regarded as necessary.

HOW EGGS ARE TESTED

"YES, Madam", says the grocery clerk, "they are good eggs—just candled," and the customer accepts the statement and buys the eggs, though she has not the slightest idea what *candling* an egg means. Yet every egg on the market which been priced in accordance with quality has had that quality determined by candling. Surely consumers of eggs—and the proportion of people who do not eat eggs in some form is extremely small—should know what candling is, whether white magic, hocus-pocus, or a reliable test method based on facts.

I think we can safely say that candling eggs to be sold in the shell is a reliable commercial method of examining the contents of the shell without breaking or otherwise injuring it, in order to determine its fitness for food.

Indeed, candling is the only method we have ever had by which to see what is inside the shell without breakng it. Our pioneer egg merchants placed the egg to be examined against a small hole in the window shutter on the sunny side of the building so that, with the room somewhat darkened, they could distinguish the yolk within the shell and determine some of its characteristics. By such "lighting" they could find most of the really bad eggs and could see when the air cell had greatly increased in size, a condition that denotes staleness.

189

After that came the use of a candle to replace the sun, which could not be depended upon to shine whenever the buyer wanted to test eggs. A black shield with a hole in it, behind which was the candle, and a darkened room, made a sun which had no whimsies about it; and so egg grading could go on every day. Many an egg in those days had a smudge of black soot on its shell, proof that it had been candled. The kerosene lamp replaced the candle as a source of light in the egg-buyer's store just as it replaced the tallow dip in the home and counting house. Before its brighter rays the interior of the egg could be seen more plainly, and the differentiation of degrees of quality progressed rapidly. Then came the electric bulb, revealing much that had before been obscure, and spelling a new era in the egg trade of the world.

No longer need anyone—buyer or consumer—turn the egg over and over and, in contemplative vein, say, "I wonder if that is a *good* egg." All he has to do is to hold it against a proper hole enclosing a proper light bulb in a properly darkened room and, if he knows those characteristics which indicate a fresh egg, he may determine its condition and fix its grade.

But, you say, "what is a proper light and what are the characteristics that will tell me the egg is fresh or otherwise?" And that is the catch for us ordinary folk not in the business of grading eggs. For in our progress from a ray of sunlight to an electric "candle" constructed with some attention to the laws of optics, we have learned to see so many things within that velvet shell and to correlate them with so many characteristics of the very good or less good egg that candling is now a profession not to be viewed lightly. It calls for skill that can be attained only after study and much practice.

These pages will not make you an egg candler, but they can tell you about some of the more important things the trained eye sees when the egg is "lighted" (I rather like to use that term of the pioneer merchants because it is truly descriptive), and their significance in relation to egg quality. Then we can discuss how these factors denoting quality are related to the grades of eggs sold in our grocery stores and markets, and why there are different prices for the different grades.

In the first part of this book we discussed the egg itself—its shell and yolk and white, their relation to one another, and something of their significance when viewed as the source of another chick or as food for man. We broke the shell, took out the contents and studied its various structural components. In this chapter we must gain the knowledge we need without breaking the eggshell, and we must not in any way injure the egg or its keeping qualities—which, among other things, means that we cannot put it into water to see whether it sinks or floats, as housewives have done for generations, with results that might be, but frequently were not, satisfactory. So in a darkened chamber we send a ray of light through the egg and this is what we see in an egg of high quality.

What We See in an Egg of High Quality

At the blunt end, which we hold uppermost, is a dim and rather irregular line enclosing an area that varies in size from a small dime to a rather large five-cent piece (if there were such things as a small dime and a large five-cent piece). This is the air cell. As the water contained in the white evaporates, the air cell grows larger. When it has become too large, we consider that the other changes which accompany the evaporation of the water have resulted in a certain amount of deterioration, and the egg is no longer rated as of first quality.

Leaving the air cell, we fix our attention on the equator or middle of the egg. There we see a yellow or pinkish area, without a distinct outline, which moves—as we turn the egg—in slow and dignified fashion, never forsaking the equatorial region to any distance, and never coming close to the shell so that we can more plainly see its dimensions and shape. That is the way an egg of high quality behaves. When the yolk (which is the pinkish area that we see) moves quickly, when it rises to the top or falls to the bottom, or comes so close to the shell that we can plainly see how round it is and how large it is, we know that first quality is lacking. Perhaps the hen was not well fed or was not bred to lay high-quality eggs. Or, perhaps the egg has not been kept cool enough, and so it has deteriorated. Whatever the cause, when a yolk moves around rapidly within the shell we believe the egg lacks quality.

Sometimes—especially if the egg has traveled a long distance over rough roads—we see a shadowy, dark little mass between the upper edge of the yolk and the air cell. The small object dashes madly about as we turn the egg before the light, but it stays in the same general locality. This is the upper chalaza (turn back to page 47 to find out what it is) which has had its upper end pulled loose but is still attached to the thick white around the yolk. This does not affect the eating quality of the egg. Possibly we will also see a little dark object floating around which we recognize as a "meat spot", that is, a fragment of the inner wall of the oviduct which the egg has scraped off as it turns around and around, screw fashion, from the beginning to the end of the oviduct. Such fragments are really without effect on the quality of the egg, but, not knowing that, consumers are prejudiced and so such eggs are commonly put into very low grades or even classed as inedible. If we should see a red fleck, it is a blood clot, and such eggs all candlers discard.

As we depart from the interior characters above described, the egg loses quality and falls into lower and lower grades. The size of the egg is also a factor in grading, so that often we have just as good interior quality within a smaller shell, even though the small egg is lower in price.

What the Consumer Wants to Know

Of course, what the consumer wants to know is whether she is getting her money's worth when she buys one or another of the three or four grades of eggs commonly carried in grocery

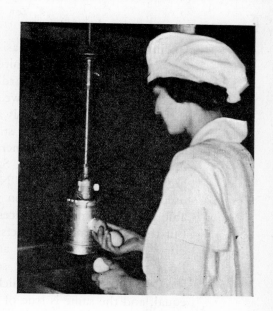

One can see right through the shell of the egg when it is held before an electrically lighted candle.

stores, and between which there may be a difference in price of more than five cents a dozen. Unfortunately there is not a uniform system of grading in use throughout the country. Different stores and different cities have different terms by which they designate the various grades. To a limited extent most states and cities, through boards of health and marketing commissions, keep a corner of an eye out for square dealing in advertising eggs; and some states, among which New York stands out as an example, are really enforcing egg grades and doing a constructive piece of work that benefits both consumer and producer.

Throughout New York State, retail merchants, no matter how fancy a name they may attach to the eggs they sell, must also show the designation A or B or C, and these letters are intended to tell the true story of quality.

Some states, too—New York among them—have made their grades the same as those of the federal government, which makes for additional reliability and also permits interstate trading on a more definite basis. This means that the A-grade egg complies with the requirements of a "U. S. Extra", the B-grade is a "U. S. Standard" and the C-grade is a "U. S. Trade." One other grade we find occasionally, but not often, the "U. S. Special"—which is a true "Hennery"—a term given wide latitude by retailers in states or cities which do not regulate egg advertising. "Hennery eggs" very frequently are Extra in quality rather than U. S. Special. Often, too, we find the highest-priced eggs called "Nearby Henneries"—a term still used to appeal to the person who thinks that the most desirable perishables must, of necessity, be those produced near-by. But those who know the facts about modern methods of handling perishables pay scant attention to the matter of miles. Eggs reaching the Atlantic seaboard from the Pacific Coast show the goal of quality which the near-by producer strives to equal, and the same is true of the finest packs of the Midwest.

In general, however, in stores carrying high-class foods, the highest quality egg corresponds to a U. S. Extra, whether the shell be white, brown or cream-colored. Such eggs, before the candle, correspond to the description on page 191 and they weigh at least twenty-four ounces to the dozen.

The eggs next lower in price are commonly much like New York B's, that is, U. S. Standards. In them the air cell is larger, the yolk moves faster, there is not quite as much thick white, and the weight is about twenty-two ounces to the dozen. For poaching, soft-boiling and coddling, the B egg is not always as satisfactory as the A, but for all other purposes it is eminently suitable. Indeed, one's pennies often bring back more, both in quality and in quantity, when invested in B eggs than in any other grade.

The C grade eggs, which are U. S. trades have pretty big air cells, the yolks move very quickly and may come so close to the shell that they look dark and dense, the thick white is less in quantity, so that they do not fry very well, and they may be expected to weigh about twenty ounces per dozen. But C grade

A flashlight photograph of a group of girls candling eggs. The room must be kept dark while they are working.

eggs are acceptable for general cookery, including cakes, and many a wise housewife buys them for such purposes, supplementing them with A's for table use, and thereby saving a tidy sum, because there is nearly always a wide spread in price between an A and a C grade. To these canny housewives, here is a word of advice. Do not try to keep C-grade eggs for more than a few days and be doubly sure to keep them in a refrigerator. Of course, all eggs should be kept in a refrigerator, and should not be purchased by consumers long in advance of need.

I wonder whether you have noticed that not once, in all that I have said about high-quality eggs and egg grades, have I used the term "fresh." This is because "fresh" as ordinarily used by the consumer involves very largely the factor of *time*. So that to be fresh an egg must not only show all the required characters of an egg of high quality before the candle and out of the shell, but it must be not more than a certain number of days old. And that is where the rub comes in. How many days old may it be and still be fresh?

An egg left in the warm nest all day, then held in a warm place all night, though only twenty-four hours old, will not grade as a U. S. Extra. High temperature has hastened deterioration. Had that same egg been promptly transferred from the nest to a cool place where the conditions would minimize the downward changes, it would still grade as a U. S. Extra after many days. Indeed, modern methods of handling perishables have almost eliminated the factor of time as affecting quality, just as they have almost eliminated the factor of distance.

And now good advertisers and merchandisers are insisting upon selling commodities on the basis of grades which are definite and uniform, for only by this method can the consumer select and buy intelligently and economically. More and more will the housewife stress the *grade* of the egg she wishes, and less and less will she care about calling it fresh, or consider when it was laid or how many miles it has traveled to reach the grocery store.

Retailers of eggs are only just beginning to contemplate seriously refrigerating eggs while awaiting sale in their stores. For all the years that the many conservation agencies throughout the land have worked and preached continuous refrigeration to keep the egg good, a large majority of retailers have contentedly allowed cartons of eggs to stand on the counter and cases of eggs to stand in the back room of the store or in the cellar which is almost never cool enough to be a suitable holding place for eggs. In the two to four—or frequently more—days which elapse between receipt by the retailers and sale, much of the quality (which every one, from farmer to wholesaler may have worked so hard to conserve) is lost—and so, since poor food is a *national* loss, we are all of us the poorer because of the backwardness of this group of merchants.

The time is ripe for the intelligent housewife to remind the retail shop-keeper that, to serve her satisfactorily, he must keep his eggs under refrigeration, and she can hold her ground when he pooh-poohs such an idea, or tries to establish the old alibi of speed ("we get them in fresh every day, Madam.")

which, long ago, for conservation of quality, has been relegated to the past as truly as has the dodo.

Two great reformations are needed to further improve the quality of the market egg—one the handling by the country merchant of which we will speak later, and the other the handling by the retail shop keeper—Will you do your bit, Madam Housewife, to help improve the latter?

HOW JACK FROST KEEPS
GOOD EGGS GOOD

ENOUGH has been said in the section describing the egg itself to show that a rather high temperature is absolutely necessary to produce those changes which result in the development of a chick. We know also that the required temperature must be maintained continuously if the progressive changes are to result in a chick. If there is less heat than is needed for hatching, or if it is applied irregularly, we find a series of changes which, while they do not result in a chick, do none the less finally ruin the egg for use as food. It is these changes—we have grouped them under the term spoilage—which have, in past years, taken a heavy toll of eggs between the hen and the consumer. Many eggs have become absolutely unfit for food and many more have so lost quality that we designate them as stale. This is still a cause of great economic loss to the whole country, each link in the chain suffering but most of all the producer and the consumer.

Of all the various factors that play a part in keeping the good egg good from the moment it leaves the producer until the moment it reaches the consumer—which may in terms of distance mean three thousand miles and in terms of time, six to nine months—none is so important as keeping the egg continuously cool. Foods are kept cool by refrigeration, and in the case of perishable foods refrigeration covers a range of temperature from about 50° F., maintained in some of our refrigerator cars, to many degrees below freezing, as in our refrigerated warehouses. Fortunately, between the farm and the consumer, eggs do not require intensive refrigeration, but they do need it continuously. One hot day in the hen house puts a handicap on an egg that no amount of subsequent care can remove.

Agricultural colleges, state experiment stations, county agents, 4–H Clubs, and many other agencies have been busily teaching and preaching better poultry and better eggs and better care of both on the farm. Such teaching, especially in connection with a country market where both eggs and poultry are paid for according to their quality, or "bought on grade" as the phrase goes, has gone far in helping to reduce losses from deterioration in the country. But there is still a world of work to be done to keep every good egg good.

Contrary to popular opinion, it is not necessarily the egg produced close to the consumer which reaches him in the finest condition. Indeed, the egg produced on the Pacific Coast and shipped to the Atlantic seaboard has made a unique place for itself because it is excellently handled. Its eating quality even though it has traveled three thousand miles and is three weeks or more old, challenges that of the egg laid a wagon-haul away—especially when that egg has not received unremitting care and attention.

It is fortunate for us that the various links in the chain of distribution, all the way from the hen to the consumer, can be so perfectly operated that eggs from any producing section can be shipped to any market the length and breadth of the land and arrive truly "fresh". What I want to make clear here is that this modern achievement in distribution is absolutely dependent for success upon keeping the egg cool, whether the distance be great or small, or the time long or short.

HOW JACK
FROST
KEEPS
GOOD
EGGS
GOOD

Cooling Begins on the Farm

As I have said before—and I am quite likely to say it again, since I cannot overemphasize its importance—the egg should

199

be quickly cooled as soon as it is laid. Assuming that eggs will be removed from the farm or hennery at least twice a week, my experience indicates that temperatures for this period should not exceed 60° F. and for best results should be between 50° and 55° F. Remember, also, that I have said "quickly cooled." Gathering eggs once a day is not enough. Twice or thrice is better, and in very hot weather five or six clearings of the nests a day will mean dollars in the farmer's pocket if he is selling on a graded basis.

A basement, cool cellar, cave or spring house, properly utilized, in most sections will provide temperatures below 60° F. for eight months in the year. The newer knowledge of the economy and increased palatability of foods properly refrigerated in the home is carrying thousands of refrigerators into farm homes each year. Many a housewife has learned that by purchasing a refrigerator large enough to accommodate the eggs for at least the first twenty-four hours after laying (not in cases but in flat wire baskets such as are used in offices to hold letters), then, if necessary, transferring them to *cooled* cases in cool cellars, she will more quickly, if she is selling graded eggs, earn not only the extra cost of the larger refrigerator, but make inroads on its total cost as well.

We have seen that the size of the air cell of the egg is a measure of quality. The aim all through marketing is to keep the air cell whole and at a constant size—the little button-size that is in the brand-new egg. If there is too much moving air around the eggs—especially if the air be very dry—there will be so distinct an increase in the size of the cell during even the few days the farmer holds it that a lower price will be the penalty. A refrigerator minimizes this shrinkage of the contents of the eggshell. If the climate is dry and the temperature high, a clean wet canvas thrown over the egg container will be

HOW JACK
FROST
KEEPS
GOOD
EGGS
GOOD

This cooler, which any farmer can build, was designed by Prof. Berley Winton of the University of Missouri Agricultural Experiment Station.

a wonderful help in holding back shrinkage and in keeping the eggs cool.

Generally, the haul from the farm to the buyer is so short that conserving the temperature to which the eggs and package have been reduced is a relatively simple matter during the trip. Of course, the case of eggs is placed inside the car. A thick layer of cooled newspaper under the lid protects the eggs from heat and prevents sweating on a warm damp day. A damp canvas over the entire case is a great protection against both heat and shrinkage. If the eggs must ride in an open wagon or truck, then cover them well with wet canvas or burlap and deliver them as promptly as possible. See also that they ride smoothly. Rough riding makes broken air cells, even if it does not make broken shells.

In the winter the farmer must protect eggs from freezing. But too often he goes so far in this respect that he delivers heated or shrunken eggs. Eggs in sound shells do not freeze until they reach a temperature below 32° F. Get them out of the hen house in cold weather, and then hold them at temperatures between 32° and 50° F., in a clean, odorless place.

HOW JACK
FROST
KEEPS
GOOD
EGGS
GOOD

Cooling Continues in the Store and Station

Millions of dollars have been lost, largely to the farmer, because the country merchant does not refrigerate, while they are in his possession, the eggs for which he pays cash or—more frequently—takes in trade for goods. Ordinarily the eggs stand in the store, sometimes for several days, even in the hottest weather, until he sends them to the country shipper or to the final market. By that time the finest of eggs are poor and those not so good are often very bad indeed. The fact that the merchant receives a lower price than would have been paid for fresh eggs does not bother him a great deal, especially if he has made his profit from the goods he has sold the farmer or traded to him for the eggs. Another fundamental error in the ways of the country merchant is that he seldom buys on a graded basis. Therefore the farmer with fine hens, who feeds and handles them carefully, is likely to be paid no more than the careless farmer with a flock of scrub hens.

But boys and girls are bringing this information back to the farms from agricultural schools and colleges; and 4–H Clubs and county agents and poultry extension workers are spreading information about marketing all over the farming country, so that each year more and more general farmers and farmers specializing in poultry are selling direct to the man who buys according to grade and who pops the eggs as soon as he receives them into a room which is refrigerated and which is not too dry.

The companies that make a business of buying eggs and poultry and preparing them for market—generally known as "egg and poultry shippers"—have been spreading refrigerators especially made for eggs over a wider and wider territory. This they have had to do wherever they bought eggs on a graded basis; otherwise the egg paid for today as a "first" had to be sold tomorrow or the day after as a "second"—a losing procedure, as anyone can see with half an eye. Also, farmers are rapidly learning that they have more actual money at the

HOW JACK
FROST
KEEPS
GOOD
EGGS
GOOD

202

end of the year if they sell eggs "on grade" rather than "straight" or "case count", as the terms go to designate buying which takes no account of size or quality. So they are hauling eggs and poultry to the fellow who buys on grade, even though the distance may be considerably greater.

What a fascinating game of cause and effect is this marketing of perishable foods! And how the circles of good—or evil—widen and widen when even a small stone is dropped anywhere into the stream between producer and consumer! When a real foundation-stone goes in, like buying eggs on grade, for example, we may trace its effect all along the stream, from finer strains of hens in the country to eggs of a more uniformly high quality on the tables of consumers all the year around. By the same token, should a mistake be made, the detrimental effect causes losses the whole length of the stream.

A good many years ago some thinking person, we do not know who he was nor where, undoubtedly said to himself, "I can sell eggs that are large, clean, fresh for more money. If I pay the farmer more for such eggs, he will make an extra effort to produce them. So we shall both make more money, and the consumer will be better served into the bargain". Having thought that long enough and hard enough, he tried it. Perhaps he succeeded. Perhaps he was so ahead of his time that conditions beyond his control made him fail. But he had thrown in the stone from which is rapidly growing a new conception of the production, conservation and distribution of our egg yield; and that brings us back to refrigeration, because, if that man did fail, it's dollars to doughnuts that a big part if not all of the reason for his failure lay in the fact that in those days we did not have an unbroken chain of refrigeration from hen house to breakfast table.

Throughout the country that produces eggs for market, we more and more frequently find that the small buying station is commonly just a room or two where the agent of a country shipper receives the eggs direct from the farm, and pays for them on a quality basis. There must be enough of these stations to ensure a short haul from the farm. Receipts may be small. The expense of maintenance must be cut to the bone—but refrigeration is essential if the quality bought is to be maintained. Necessity being the mother of invention, a whole family of inventive suggestions for small refrigerators for egg-buying stations in the country is rapidly coming into being. The impractical suggestions will die. The better ones will live, to be improved upon as time goes on, and made as regular a part of egg handling as the refrigerated car is today—though once it was looked upon as a luxury not to be thought of by the ordinary shipper of eggs.

We know now that these small refrigerators should maintain temperatures between 45°–55° F.; that they must have good air circulation to carry the heat from the eggs to the refrigerant, but not enough air movement to cause the water in the egg to evaporate unduly; that the initial cost and the upkeep must be low enough to justify their use during the late summer when such protection is most urgently needed even though receipts at buying stations may not average more than four to six cases a day. They must be small enough to go into a small room, and they must be durable. Last, but not least, they must be so easily operated as to be almost fool-proof.

At the time this book is written these little refrigerators are among the very new topics of conversation in egg-marketing circles. Ten years from now we will smile over how backward the industry used to be.

HOW JACK
FROST
KEEPS
GOOD
EGGS
GOOD

Next, Refrigeration on the Road

I am trying to tell you the story of the egg going to market in a sort of movie fashion, that is, to follow it each step of the way from the hen to the consumer. It is a surprise to almost everyone to learn how many steps there are, and how each must be thoughtfully planned to be efficient and to join the following step properly.

From the buying station, eggs must be hauled to the packing house—sometimes a hundred miles away. Trucks today are generally doing this part of the work, though many eggs are still transported for relatively short distances by rail. If there happens to be an l. c. l., (which means less-than-car-lot, refrigerated service), well and good. Produce trucks in the country are almost never refrigerated, but this, like buying-station refrigerators, is a problem now receiving much attention, and it will eventually be solved.

Meanwhile we are covering trucks with wet burlap or canvas and doing as much of the hauling as possible at night, or early in the morning.

Finally, Refrigeration at the Packing House

In 1909 when I began to study the handling of eggs in the producing sections, some packers—not many—had refrigerated rooms to remove the animal heat from newly killed poultry. But almost none of them had coolers for eggs, and as for cooled candling rooms—well, that was just out of the question.

Today, the egg packer who makes and holds a reputation for eggs of high quality the year around must be provided with a refrigerated room to receive the eggs as soon as they come to him—and then it is his responsibility to see that they are kept continuously cold until they are loaded into the precooled refrigerator car and are on the next leg of their journey. Of course he must have a cooled candling room, and more and more shippers are adding such a room to their plant equipment.

Thus, step by step, do we preserve the quality of the egg from the time the hen lays it until it is loaded into a refrigerated car to be rolled to market. There is a mass of finicky detail, each item of such importance that overlooking any one will result in taking toll of quality by the time the egg reaches the consumer. Each item is an old story to those living in farm sections producing more eggs than are needed for local demands, but the city dweller is generally quite ignorant of the

HOW JACK
FROST
KEEPS
GOOD
EGGS
GOOD

Some South Americans carry eggs wrapped in corn husks. They walk days over m o u n t a i n trails to Bogota markets.

procedure. If we view the routine of handling in the country with surprise, we are lost in amazement when we consider the *number* of eggs produced on the farms of the United States—a staggering total of around 2,700,000,000 dozens. But don't forget that there are 125,000,000 of us to eat those eggs. About half of us live in the cities, so let us now turn our attention to the subject of transportation and see how we get this army of cases of eggs—each holding thirty dozen—to its ultimate destination.

HOW THE EGG
GOES TRAVELING

WHEN I was a very little girl in the city of Philadelphia, one of my keen pleasures was going to market with my mother on Saturday mornings. She always took a small, beautifully woven little basket in which she brought back table butter, cottage cheese and breakfast eggs. Her other purchases were delivered by the market boy, but not eggs and butter.

There were real farmers in that market, who brought their own and sometimes their neighbors' products to sell and who unhitched their teams from their big wagons and tied them comfortably in the narrow street behind the market house. There, unless strictly forbidden, I always went to make friends with the big, gentle farm horses. We knew many of the farmers by name, and occasionally, on long summer afternoons, we would drive in my pony cart to one or another near-by farm to order some special thing that mother wanted on the following market day.

In summer the stalls just overflowed with vegetables and fruits and eggs and flowers, but in winter how bare they were with only carrots, turnips, potatoes and similar vegetables, and such a small basket of eggs that often our quota was less than a dozen. At that time Philadelphia was the second largest city in the country, and I still have quite a few years of grace before I reach my allotted three score and ten, so you see it was not so very long ago, at that.

But even then the small stores were increasing in number and were being supplied from the large wholesale markets to

Real farms are getting farther and farther from the cities.

which the railroads were bringing produce, meats and even fish from a constantly broadening territory. And then the cities, with cable cars and railroads and later trolley cars to carry the people to the city to work, pushed long arms of dwellings out among the farms and absorbed them into suburban communities. So the real farms were always getting farther and farther from the city, and even if the farmer hitched up his team and left right after supper on Friday night with his load of produce, the distance to town was too great to cover profitably. Thus, except in rare instances, the "farmers' market" became a name rather than a fact. Today the motor truck has brought the farmer again within striking distance of the city—and again there are some farmers in the "farmers' market." But now the consumers are spread over so great a territory that they must be served by a multitude of local stores, easy of access. So today the farmers' market can be reached by farmers, but not by the mass of consumers. Such has been the cycle.

Chandler's Absurd Experiment and Its Result

More potent than the mere growth of cities in breaking touch between the farmer and his customer has been the refrigerator car. Indeed, without it we never could have maintained an adequate supply of fresh perishables in such great centers as New York and Chicago. The refrigerator car and the cold-storage warehouse divide honors in providing, the year around, an uninterrupted flow of perishables to cities and towns, making our American diet unique in its abundance and its variety.

Not only has the refrigerator car been a potent factor contributing to our ability to provide farm products to vast numbers of city dwellers, but, conversely, it has enabled farmers far from their markets to produce extremely perishable products with the knowledge that they can be transported to consumers thousands of miles away. Foods produced in the South, for example, arrive fresh and fine and bearing imprisoned sunshine literally by the ton to the North, plunged in its winter season; or again, they carry the cool attractiveness of melons and pears and the new-laid egg or the little broiling chicken to entice the summer appetite.

Do you see now how it became possible for the Rio Grande Valley to "blossom like a rose", and how it was possible to alternate the great forest tracts of Oregon and Washington with orchards of apples and pears, and egg and poultry ranches? The farmers of these regions now have means for conveying their products to the consuming centers, great and small. When, two centuries ago, the poet Alexander Pope wrote—

> "To take to the poles the products of the sun
> And knit the unsocial climates into one",

I wonder whether his prophetic soul even dimly glimpsed the fulfillment of his dream that has become so commonplace a reality in this great century.

Indeed, not until 1957 will the refrigerator car be a centenarian. Back in 1857, in the western part of Pennsylvania, a young man was making an experiment. This young man was W. W. Chandler. No one guessed at that time that one day he would become president of the Star Union Line, the first railroad-owned refrigerator car line. His experiment was so *absurd* that we can well imagine the pillars of the then railroad church laughing in their sleeves and biding their time until the young man should come so hard a cropper that his tendencies toward radical experiments would be sufficiently curbed. Because it was radical in those days to build an inside wall in a wooden box car, fill the four-inch space between the two with sawdust, set a big box filled with ice in each end of that car, load between the boxes carcasses of newly killed beef, and then haul that car to the Atlantic seaboard. The wiseacres predicted that the meat would go bad—and, like many other wiseacres they were wrong. The meat arrived in good condition. Chandler put inner walls and sawdust insulation in more box cars, and lo! a tiny dot on the horizon of the future, a prophet might have seen the green fields of the Rio Grande Valley, and the poultry and egg ranches of the Pacific Coast—the Pacific Coast that was then pouring out gold from its mines, but that now pours out gold from its farms; that was then peopled by scattered lonesome groups of homeless men, but that now is a Mecca for those who would make life a happy mixture of work and play in home dooryards—all largely because of Chandler's invention.

Well, after Chandler's crude car was first built in Pennsylvania, the strawberry growers in the Ohio and Indiana fields wanted to ship berries across the Alleghenies. The peach growers in Michigan wanted to do likewise. They tried and failed, but one Cobden Earle would not give up. He put better insulation into the walls and devised more efficient ice bunkers, and at last a carload of peaches went successfully from Michigan to New York and sold at a profit. This was about 1867; and now the great green stretches and farm homes of the western valleys, and the feathered flocks making the Pacific Coast towns resound to the cheerful songs of an army of laying hens were future achievements perceptibly nearer. Between the blue Pacific and the Alleghenies, which fenced off the rapidly increasing population of the East coast, the refrigerator car wended its lengthening way, stimulating to right and left, production of fruits and vegetables, butter, milk and cheese, cattle, sheep and hogs, and millions upon millions of little feathered ladies to chant the song of the new-laid egg all up and down the Mississippi Valley.

A young man named Swift had been watching Chandler's meat cars. Swift was engaged in the business of slaughtering cattle, sheep and swine, and marketing their meat. Chicago and its contiguous territory was too small a sphere for this young man. He wanted to put his dressed meats on the markets of the Eastern seaboard, and he convinced himself, that it could be done. But, in spite of Pennsylvania's Chandler and his success, no railroad would build especially constructed cars for Mr. Swift to use for his shipments. So, in 1875, Mr. Swift built ten refrigerator cars and paid for them himself. Thus originated the first packer's line of "beef cars."

Willy-nilly, after that, as the shippers of perishables in the West multiplied, the railroads, to meet competition, had to build refrigerated cars of their own.

But not always did the perishables shipped in the various refrigerated cars arrive at the market in good condition. When they did not, there were financial losses and the shippers blamed the railways and the railways intimated that the shippers were ignorant of their business, or worse. Southern California was almost ready to cut down its bearing orange groves and put the land into vineyards. Georgia looked ruefully at the trees on its hillsides and said, "What's the use? We can't get our peaches to market."

However, one Ethan Allen Chase, in Riverside, California (if you will just look at his name I need not further describe the man or his forebears), and a man named Hale, who came from the New England hills and owned peach orchards in Georgia, would not give in. They were sure that their oranges and peaches could be carried to market safely if only they knew how to do it. How could they get the knowledge?

Down in Washington, in the chair of the Secretary of Agriculture, sat an old gentleman from Iowa, of Scotch extraction, known to officialdom as Secretary Wilson and to the loyal folks in the Department of Agriculture as Uncle Jimmy. Always this Secretary kept his eye on the ball—that is, on the development of American agriculture.

Therefore, when in 1903, Mr. Hale visited Secretary Wilson in Washington and told him of the losses to the Georgia peach industry due to poor transportation, and asked his help in solving the problem, three young pomologists, country-bred and college-trained, were sent to study the situation. Among the remedies they advised were precooling of the fruit at the orchard before it was loaded in the cars, and the building of refrigerator cars which would *really* refrigerate. And those recommendations at that time got just nowhere with the owners of the refrigerator cars.

Two or three years after Powell, Steubenrauch and Tenney went to Georgia, Mr. Ethan Allen Chase appeared at the office of the Secretary of Agriculture. He felt that the assistance of the Department of Agriculture in solving the problem of the decay of citrus fruits in transit was so vital—he had heard, vaguely, of the studies made in Georgia—that a journey to Washington to get that help was justified. Soon after that, Powell, Steubenrauch and Eustace were sent to southern California. They revolutionized the methods of handling citrus fruits—on which much of the trouble rested—and they obtained scores of records of temperatures in refrigerator cars in transit from California to the Atlantic Coast. Some far-seeing railroad men, such as Edward Chambers, Vice-President in charge of traffic of the Santa Fe, began to study these records, to ponder upon their relation to damage claims for goods spoiled in transit, and to vision more traffic if the perishables always arrived in sound condition. By 1909, when I appeared on the scene to lead my group of research workers into the transportation field, (we had been studying the handling, in the country and on the market, of dressed poultry and eggs) Mr. Chambers, and many another progressive railroad man, was ready to build more efficient refrigerator cars if someone would tell them how to do it.

Commissioners Prouty, Clark and Daniels of the Interstate Commerce Commission, judicially working for a better, squarer deal between railways and shippers, made us see the importance of the results in terms of human welfare which would follow on the heels of better handling of perishables in transit. The shippers of fruits, meats, eggs, dressed poutry and fresh fish said, "We will cooperate. We will handle and pack in accord with your program, and you may make observations on our actual carload lots, that your results may not be criticized as impractical." The railways said, "We will build trial cars for you to test, and turn them over to you to travel over any rails and be subject to your orders only, within the law and the rulings of the Interstate Commerce Commission."

The Secretary of Agriculture and the Chiefs of the three Bureaus involved said, "We will do our best to get the facts." And then we young people went forth to win our spurs somewhere between the Atlantic and Pacific and the Canadian and Mexican borders. We loaded refrigerator cars with all sorts of perishables—each pedigreed and analyzed—in about every state in the Union; then rode with them to markets "within and throughout the continental United States", as our traveling authorizations said, keeping records of temperatures, car icings, the amount of ice used; and at last—when the market was reached—inspecting, analyzing in the laboratory, holding in the cold-storage warehouse, and even cooking and tasting, the commodities we had hauled.

Icing 1,000 refrigerator cars is an easy day's work for this giant icing station near Chicago. In it can be stored 15,000 tons of ice.

The instrument-makers developed very delicate electric thermometers which we could bury in the egg case or the dressed chicken or the box of apples and, by plugging in suitable wires in our "laboratory car" (which might be a caboose or a metamorphosed passenger coach or even an official's private car—as it generally was when I "rode the freights") we could tell at any time, throughout the entire trip, the exact temperature of the commodity itself—as well as the temperature of the air of the refrigerator car.

Two, four, six experimental cars might be in a train, each differing from its comparison car by only one variable, that there might be no confusion in correlating cause and effect. Occasionally as many as fourteen cars all in one train might be under such observation.

And the work went on and on—almost five hundred experimental shipments, the useful results going at once to shippers, railroads, warehousemen, growers—that no time might be lost in translating the facts into routine practice. Then the United States entered the Great War and part of our job was to provide food for our allies. The conservation of perishables became a world problem of immense proportions and importance. A practical, efficient refrigerator car suited for any commodity was an imperative necessity in the United States.

Then was evidenced the value of just such cooperation as the various and varied elements entering into the study of refrigeration in transit had been developing. Around the conference table the *facts* were set forth—facts about insulation, air circulation, the temperatures required and how to get them; about the basket bunkers for ice, the insulated bulkhead, the floor rack, the dimensions of cars, the construction, especially of roofs and floors. These facts translated the theoretical ideal into the practical real—and as a result there emerged in 1917 a refrigerator car known as "the United States Standard type." This, in its essentials, is today on practically all of our railways, taking "to the poles the products of the sun" be they frozen or chilled or fresh from orchard, field or stream.

Four hundred cases of eggs—thirty dozen to the case—is the regular carload. From 40° to 55° F. is the customary temperature. In winter when the weather is very cold and the haul long, the ice bunkers at each end of the car are sealed off by heavy paper curtains, and straw on sides and floor supplements the insulation to prevent freezing in transit, for too much cold is just as bad for eggs as too much heat.

In warm weather a total of ten thousand pounds of ice may be put into the two ice bunkers at the point of origin, and every twenty-four to forty-eight hours during transit the ice which has melted is replaced at great "icing stations" maintained by the railways for their refrigerator traffic. Here the "reefers", (as railroad men call the refrigerator cars) with hatches open like mouths of hungry birds, are fed with ice, the hatches closed, and on they go, cold and clean—an achievement of this century to be proud of.

Considering how dependent we are upon the foods transported in refrigerator cars, relatively few people have ever seen

the inside of one or know what goes on therein. I am hoping
that the story I have told will help you as you see the long lines
of refrigerator cars, generally painted yellow, to see also the
romance that has been a part of their making.

Enter the Motor Truck

Now comes the motor truck, more and more frequently
refrigerated and growing in favor, especially for the shorter
hauls. Because of its freedom of movement, its ability to carry
goods from door to door, and its speed, the motor truck—rightly
built and operated—holds great possibilities for the transportation of perishables. It is now in very much the same situation
as were the refrigerator cars thirty years ago when the United
States Department of Agriculture began to study them.

The insulation in truck walls may be excellent, or there may
be none at all. The refrigerating devices may or may not maintain sufficiently low temperatures to protect the load, or there
may be an entire lack of refrigeration. Each truckman is a
law unto himself in such matters. The shipper is using the
"cut and try" method with a load or two, just to see what the
results will be. But he does not have, as yet, any nation-wide
study of the requirements of a great variety of perishable products hauled in trucks to fall back upon, nor any standardization
of construction or operation such as has been so painstakingly
worked out for the refrigerator car.

This is a job for the coming years and a very important one.
One thing we must not forget, namely, that mere speed will
not take the place of good handling, in which efficient refrigeration in transit plays so large a part. That is the fallacy
which is so frequently responsible for many failures of near-by
produce to make top grades on the market. The man near his
market depends upon speed to keep his products in good condition. The man a thousand miles or three thousand miles
away from the consumer handles and packs to be as independent
of the time factor as the practical application of the scientific

Loading eggs into refrigerated hold of a Great Lakes steamer. They are shipped to the East, to England, Cuba, and Canal Zone.

principles underlying the prevention of deterioration and decay will permit.

Increasing Use of the Waterways

The export trade of perishables from the United States has required our ocean-going boats to provide refrigerated holds to carry the various products safely. In them we have, in years past, regularly shipped eggs to England and to Cuba, and we now supply our Canal Zone with eggs.

But more important, and constantly developing, is the shipment of perishables, including eggs, eastbound through the Great Lakes. Once we saw fleets of freighters bringing ore and grain down the lakes, but the refrigerated hold was conspicuous by its absence. Now a fleet plies from Duluth to Buffalo from the break-up of the ice in the spring to the closing of lake traffic in the winter, primarily to handle the fruit, butter, cheese, eggs and dressed poultry produced in territory contiguous to the lakes or fed to them by rail from farther west.

These steamers, ocean-going in size, have refrigerated holds which are maintained at the temperature desired—one, for example, filled with frozen eggs in cans to be kept at 10° F., and another loaded with eggs in the shell to be held at 45° to 50° F.

Great refrigerated warehouses in the lakeside cities receive the refrigerated freight to hold it in safety until the market needs it, or to transfer it immediately so that it may complete its journey by rail or truck.

Only three-quarters of a century ago W. W. Chandler loaded fresh meat into a makeshift cooled box on wheels and sent it east across the Alleghenies. Along with MacAdam, who invented rock-surfaced roads that enabled the pioneers to reach new frontiers, Chandler was responsible for the greatest and most far-flung agricultural development the world has ever seen.

The Story of the Egg Package

Twelve thousand dozen eggs in twelve thousand dozen fragile shells to each refrigerator carload of eggs—and yet again and again those eggs are carried mile upon mile until they cross even the continent without breaking—or "damage" as the industrial phrase goes. This is an accomplishment to be proud of; it is even better than the feat old Lightnin' told about, when he drove a swarm of bees clear across the Plains and never lost a bee.

How was it brought about?

There is a long technical story of finding out just how a car should be loaded and unloaded, and how it should be switched in transit and a lot of other details, all of which means much in keeping those twelve thousand dozen shells whole, but this is not the place to tell about it. Instead, I do want to tell you about the individual package in which the eggs—360 of them to each package—are placed when they are ready to go to market—first, because the making of such a package is an achievement, and secondly, because it was one of the very first containers to be studied in a scientific manner to determine its fitness for its job. It was one of the first packages to be stand-

The safety egg barrel invented by Lucius S. Ball in 1876, and the first cup flats. So called Gill fillers are in foreground.

ardized, too, sharing honors with the orange box. Indeed, so sure are we that eggs will go safely to and through the wholesale market in this package that we reckon our stock of eggs on the market in "case" units, and statistically we report "cases" of eggs, knowing that there will be no variation from the thirty dozen to a case.

Farm tradition has it that eggs are carried in baskets. But when the farmer and the ultimate consumer got farther and farther apart, the basket no longer served. When the farmer began to transport eggs by rail, the hazards to the eggshell greatly multiplied. So the early shipper packed his eggs in straw. But very often the straw was damp and imparted its characteristic odor and flavor to the egg. Neither was this packing a sufficient safeguard against breakage. Then eggs were packed in grain—oats seem to have been preferred; and when the men who are now old tell you how, when they were young, they made up the hogsheads of eggs, each egg standing on its point and surrounded completely by the tightly packed grain, it is a thrilling story to listen to.

It is more than fifty years since the forerunner of our present egg case appeared, and about fifteen years since egg shippers, railway officials and market distributors agreed upon the details of its construction—even to the number and kind of nails.

The best grade of egg cases are made of cottonwood; some are made of tupelo and some of gumwood—all from the Mississippi Valley and mostly from its southern reaches. Here many an axe is swung to provide the logs for the mills to transform into veneer for the sides, tops and bottoms, and sawn pieces for ends and center boards, and for the two cleats that brace the ends at top and bottom. On the Pacific Coast the cases are made from sawn spruce instead of veneer and the sides and lid are each in two pieces, but the general construction is the same.

The picture of an egg case on page 221 tells more plainly than words just how the various pieces are put together and where the nails must be driven to hold each piece so firmly to its fellows that a model of strength and rigidity will result. This is where the testing laboratory came into the picture. The Food Research Laboratory and the Forest Products Laboratory, both in the United States Department of Agriculture, joined hands to get the facts on which to construct the egg case. They hammered it on the ends and sides to find out what blows it would stand. They crushed it between heavy weights to see what pressure would do to it. They balanced it on edges and corners and pulled and pushed to make sure that no part would fail to do its duty. Of course, in each test the force used was recorded in foot pounds so that accurate comparisons could be made.

Laboratory findings were embodied in factory-built cases, and then came the testing under commercial conditions. Many and many a carload of eggs was watched from origin to destination to make sure that theory and practice were in accord. After that the railways and the shippers hunted for flaws before they at last accepted the specifications and made them binding upon all who would ship eggs at the established tariffs.

Modern standard egg case. 30 dozen eggs to a case. 400 cases to a car.

Cases which differed from this accepted standard must pay a higher rate.

Inside the case are little cells to hold each egg separately and securely; and each layer of eggs—of which there are five—must be separated from the layer above and below. The honeycomb-like structure seen in the picture on this page we call a "filler," and between the layers of eggs are "flats." A pad of some sort rests on the bottom of the case to receive the points of the first layer of eggs, and over the top layer there is another pad to prevent the lid from crushing the eggs below. This is the principle on which all of the many variations of fillers and flats are based. Some, the oldest kind, are made of strawboard, others of newspaper pulp, and still others of white spruce pulp. But each and all must fit the standard egg case, which is 24½ inches long, 12 inches wide and 13 inches high, and which contains, always, 30 dozen eggs.

The farmer has almost discarded his basket in favor of the standard egg case. No other link in the merchandising chain even considers any other form of container until we come to the retailer, who puts the eggs he sells into cartons, made on the filler principle and holding one dozen each. In them, still with velvet shells unsullied and still with points down, they come to my lady's refrigerator and so to their destiny—the breakfast table.

FREEZING THE
FRESHNESS OF EGGS

THIS poultry packing house, deep in the country, was clean, as packing houses should be—but when the guide opened the door of a room tucked away in a quiet corner, we fairly gasped at the whiteness, the bright light, the utter spick and spanness of walls, floor, windows, apparatus and, last but not least, the tidiness of the girls working there. It was all so brilliantly clean and cool that, the spring day being warm, the visitors stepped inside gratefully as well as interestedly.

Here is the home of the modern frozen egg,—generally further characterized as "prepared especially for bakers and confectioners," but spreading now to hotels and restaurants where well flavored, high quality egg for custards, meringues, pies, ice creams, omelettes and even for the lowly scramble is much in demand. In less than fifty years this frozen product has grown to large proportions (more than 250 million pounds are frozen annually in the United States alone) and has become a very important item in our total supply of egg.

Like many other commercial achievements now accepted without thought or question, frozen egg has a romance behind it.

In the eighties the corn belt was sending eggs to the Atlantic seaboard to reenforce the near-by supply which was rapidly becoming inadequate as the cities grew and surrounded them-

Rooms like these throw light on the subject of egg quality.

selves with suburbs instead of farms. But there were many more eggs, especially between April and June, in the corn belt than were needed either east or west for immediate consumption. Gradually, two methods of preserving the excess production for use during the non-producing season were made practical—one, the storage of eggs in the shell in refrigerated warehouses at 29–31° F., and the other the removal of the egg substance from the shell, freezing it in tight tin containers and holding hard-frozen at 0° F. or thereabouts, until the demand put it into consumption. Eggs stored in the shell were for household use. Egg hard frozen was primarily for bakers, confectioners and users of egg in large amounts.

Experts in Breaking Eggs

Many manufacturers of food products are proud of the surroundings in which the work is done; and with justified satisfaction they show visitors through bacon slicing rooms, chocolate candy rooms, milk bottling rooms, and many others. So it is with the progressive egg breaker, who is second to none in the care which he takes to put a pure product on the market.

The great majority of egg breaking factories are in the small cities and towns of the middle west, where egg production is heavy and where the haul from the farm or country buying station to the wholesale merchant and shipper is short. Such

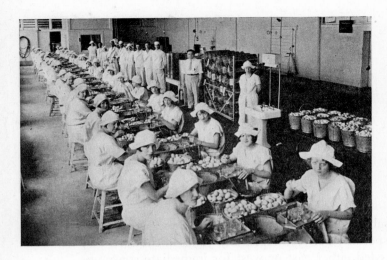

Plants like these prepare thirty-six thousand dozen eggs each day for baker's use.

merchants must, of necessity, accept some eggs which are under-size, dirty or cracked. The capacity of city markets to use such eggs is limited, and when the demand is satisfied, prices go so far down that the farmers suffer. But the egg substance inside the shell that is small or dirty or lightly cracked is not affected by these factors. Therefore, if it is removed and put into a form which is stabilized—such as frozen egg—all the freshness and desirable qualities are held unchanged until the frozen mass is thawed.

So, when an egg merchant in the egg producing section has a breaking room as a part of his business, the incoming eggs are divided into two classes—one to be shipped to market in the shell, the other to go to the frozen egg department. Of course, all the eggs are put into "coolers" just as soon as they are received. An egg cooler is a refrigerated room in which the temperature is held well below 50° F.—generally between 35° and 45° F. The quick reduction in the temperature of the egg prevents deterioration and such pre-cooling as it is called, is an absolute necessity if quality eggs either in or out of the shell are to be maintained.

Neatly holding the shells to drain the contents.

When the eggs are well cooled—that is, the day following their receipt—they are candled and graded. Those to be sent to market are put into new, clean cases and packing and are either set at once into the refrigerated car or returned to the cooler to await shipment.

Those eggs which will not successfully stand transportation to market, such as cracked eggs, very thin and defective shelled eggs, very large eggs, (which are likely to get broken in transit) and eggs that are already at the quality stage in which some country eggs reach the city and so have no reserve to take up the wear and tear of transportation and marketing, are put into other containers and sent immediately to the breaking room. These containers are generally metal buckets or boxes, which are washed after each day's use or even more frequently. In some instances endless moving belts carry the shell eggs, in a continuous procession from the candling room to the breaking room where the girls pick them off the belt to break them. This is, of course, a very clean and time saving device, but it is practical only when a large quantity of egg is packed.

The room devoted to egg breaking is not used for any other

FREEZ-
ING THE
FRESHNESS
OF EGGS

225

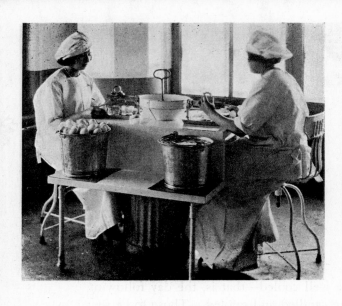

Alert young girls with smooth well-shaped fingers do the actual breaking of the eggs.

purpose. It is brilliantly lighted and floors, walls and ceilings must have a hard smooth finish since they must be frequently washed. Hand basins with running warm water must be plentiful. A refrigerating system should keep the air dry and cooled to between 65°–68° F.

Almost invariably young girls do the actual breaking of the eggs. They must be alert, with smooth, well shaped fingers, quick of eye to catch any undesirable appearance of the egg, and keen of smell to detect any odor. Frequently a girl's sense of smell is tested when she applies for a job, and if it is dull she is rejected. Their odor identifies certain undesirable eggs and it may be so slight that the untrained nose would miss it. Other eggs unfit for food can be identified only by their appearance when out of the shell. This is one reason why so many careful bakers use frozen egg put up by skilled workers, rather than buying eggs in the shell and breaking them on their own premises. This may sound strange, but just wait until you have heard more of the exacting requirements of preparing frozen egg of high quality.

The apparatus on which the shell is cracked and the egg substance collected, varies in the different egg breaking plants but generally combines certain essential features—such as a metal tray on which is mounted a knife edge where the egg is broken, and supports for several cups to catch the white, yolk or whole egg as it is dumped from the shell. This is the egg breaking tray. It must be rustproof and as smooth as possible to eliminate crannies where dirt might lodge, and it must stand sterilization in live steam. The cups should be clear glass, since only in such can the early stages of "green white" eggs be observed, and they should be of a size to accommodate not more than three eggs. The small glass known as a sherbet cup is most generally used by careful packers.

When a breaker gets a bad egg (and remember that she will discard *many an egg* that a housewife would accept), her entire breaking tray goes to the wash room to be cleaned and sterilized and she betakes herself to the sink where she washes her hands and dries them on paper towels. Then, picking up a clean outfit as she goes, she returns to her seat to continue her work. She is dressed in a white suit with short sleeves and a cap confines her hair.

As each egg is broken it is inspected for appearance and odor. When two, or at most three, have been collected in a

227

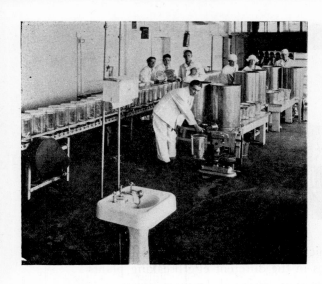

From the mixer into the can and then by a mechanical conveyor immediately into the below zero freezer.

cup, they are emptied into a pail or large can. This in its turn is again tested for odor, then poured into a mixing machine or churn where white and yolk is made into a homogeneous mass ready to be drawn off into the cans in which it is to be frozen and held.

As soon as they are filled, the cans are taken to a low temperature freezer, where at zero and below, the egg soon becomes a solidly frozen mass ready to retain almost indefinitely the properties of fresh, well flavored egg.

To see one of these egg breaking plants in operation gives a feeling of satisfaction with our modern food producing establishments. The room is so speckless and spotless, so brilliantly lighted, so cool, the girls doing the work so fresh in their white uniforms that confidence in the purity of the product is automatic.

After inspecting this room, we don heavy woolen warehouse coats and step into the freezer where neat stacks of shining cans from the floor almost to the ceiling attest to the popularity of the product with the baking fraternity.

Thousands of pounds of eggs in freezer storage ready for the baker.

A Story With a Happy Ending

Frozen eggs, put up in the country, near the farms, made from good eggs, were always justified economically and they were justified commercially. The demand for them, especially, on the part of bakers, grew rapidly. But back in the 90's frozen egg was also being prepared in cities from stock of such low grade that there was no sale for it in the shell and under conditions which were highly unsanitary. Reputable bakers would not use it, but none the less, their business was hurt by the poorer, cheaper cake made from the undesirable frozen product. The food inspectors, local, state and federal, were constantly making seizures and prosecuting the owners of the inferior egg product, who simply moved elsewhere to continue the same old trade under a new name. Finally, the federal food officials and the larger manufacturers of frozen egg in the egg producing sections of the Middle West cooperated to determine what eggs should be used for their product; how the process of removing the egg from the shells, getting it into cans and freezing it should be accomplished; and how the

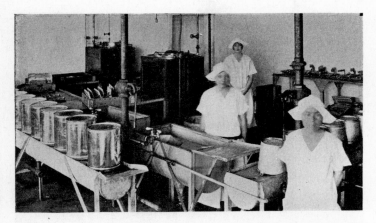

product should be kept in the cold storages and transported to the bakers far from the point of frozen egg manufacture.

Considering the fact that the basis for the existence of the frozen egg industry is economically sound, there could be only one result from such a cooperative plan carried to a successful issue, namely, a much bigger and better industry with a recognized and honorable place in the commercial scheme of things. There was a sufficient number of egg breakers in the original group cooperating with Uncle Sam to furnish a large proportion of the frozen egg going on the market. Adopting the improved factory methods as fast as they were worked out, they soon had so much excellent frozen egg for sale that it made hard sledding for the inferior stuff which tried in vain to hang on to its old time customers. It was not long before frozen egg was as likely to be pure and good as any other food product and more likely than some. Now it is universally recognized as an indispensable part of the supplies for high class bakeries, which consider themselves no more competent to select, break out and prepare the eggs for their dough mixes than they are competent to mill the flour or crystallize the sugar they use. Breaking eggs for bakers is a highly specialized and creditable industry.

The hospitals have nothing on an egg breaking plant when it comes to sterilizing dishes.

I have given you this outline of the rise of the frozen egg industry because there are still some people who may remember only the early days of it, when the industry's very right to live was in serious jeopardy. They have not learned of the exquisite cleanliness required in the egg breaking rooms, nor of the training of girls who do the work in determining the fitness for food of the egg going into the product.

Outside the egg industry and its related trades, the people who know about frozen egg are few indeed. Even teachers and research workers in home economics are surprisingly ignorant of the product after so many years of use by food-manufacturing firms. When the time comes that home demonstrators and teachers of cookery in our schools become sufficiently acquainted with canned egg and its dependable quality (even superior character in some respects) then will the processor be able to put it on the market in containers convenient for family use. And when the retailers are generally equipped to keep frozen products frozen, the house-wife can buy a dozen egg whites to whip into an angel food batter and she need not worry about utilizing the same number of unnecessary yolks.

Economically the frozen egg industry is a boon to the producer and to the baker. In a form which does not deteriorate it conserves the eggs produced in the spring for which there is no immediate market, and thus it tends to equalize prices the year around. It also saves an enormous amount of good food by putting into a stable condition eggs that would not survive the trip to and through the market if shipped in the shell. Combined with the cold storage of spring eggs in the shell, it assures the farmer of a sale for his product at far better prices than he could hope to command if immediate consumption were his only resource. To the consumer this means a fair supply of new-laid eggs in autumn and winter, because the farmer can safely maintain flocks large enough for a production beyond his personal needs during the season of scarcity without the fear of an unmarketable excess in the spring.

HOW COLD STORAGE
CAME TO THE RESCUE

DAME Nature planned to have chicks hatched in the spring when sunshiny days and warm nights would help Mother Hen with her job of raising a family. So Mother Hen laid her clutch of eggs in the spring, raised her family and called her duty done until the next spring came around.

But this did not suit the businessman, who wanted eggs to eat as well as to hatch. Mr. Platt tells in another section of this book, how selective breeding can increase the number of eggs a hen lays; yet, even so, the principle of old Dame Nature's spring eggs for spring chicks still dominates so many hens that between March and June, inclusive, we have more than half of the year's total production of eggs.

You can easily see that, unregulated, such a state of affairs would mean such low prices for eggs in the flush season that it would not pay the farmers to produce them, and such high prices in the season of scarcity that people of moderate means could not afford them.

Into this situation came one of the most extraordinary achievements of all the many achievements, in the handling of perishable food products, that have given the people of the United States the most varied diet in the world and a year-round perfection, so far as the condition of perishables is concerned, that no other nation enjoys. I am referring to a combination of careful selection of high quality foods, accompanied by the best of processing methods, and then the application of exactly the right low temperatures under exactly the 233

Refriger-ated eggs to be used when Biddy is off her job of laying.

right environment to preserve that quality from the season of plenty through the season of scarcity.

The common name for what I have described is "cold storage", but so few people realize what even the essentials of cold storage are that I have emphasized them in the foregoing paragraph. By and large, only perishables of high quality go into cold storage. Low grades almost invariably lose money for their owners. It is difficult, also, to say just where refrigeration, which we have previously discussed, ends and cold storage begins, since we may utilize the same temperatures for the few days or weeks required for what we term "immediate consumption", as are used for "delayed consumption", which means that the products are held to be marketed in the season of scarcity.

Years ago, when the science of preservation by low temperatures was young, a few states passed laws intended to regulate the storage of certain food-stuffs, among them eggs and dressed poultry. In these laws, commodities were termed "cold stored" only after they had been held thirty days. Such a specification, however, is entirely arbitrary and could not now be logically upheld on either economic or scientific grounds. Happily, the old prejudice against what we might more truly call intensive refrigeration of perishables is passing as the younger generation sees the facts, finds high quality foods available the year round at reasonable prices, and grows straight and lusty and strong on the unchanged vitamins, proteins and other constituents so delicate chemically that only by low temperatures can they be maintained in their original condition.

The Problem of Out-of-Season Eggs

Now let us apply these fundamental observations to eggs.

We have seen that an overwhelming number of our total supply of eggs is produced during one-fourth of the year. If we are to have a balanced industry and if the people are to have a uniform supply of eggs during the season of low production, we must hold the spring surplus for the autumn and winter shortage. This we do by the proper application of low temperatures. Before we had suitable refrigerated warehouses, eggs were held in lime water, or lime and salt water. Under skillful management, some eggs were held in fairly good condition, but refrigeration has completely supplanted "pickling" or "liming" as it was called.

Oiling the Egg's Shell

We are told, especially by producers on farms, that oiling the shell of an egg will preserve its content, and such easily obtained fats as lard and butter, are recommended for this purpose. But questioning brings out the fact that such oiling of the shells was practiced long ago and is now almost or quite obsolete. Refrigeration for a commercial long hold and waterglass for the remote family's needs have supplanted all other methods of preservation.

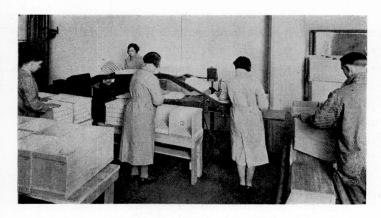

However, the old practice of oiling shells held the germ of an idea which developed into a commercial practice and is today commonly known as the "sterilized egg", or the "sealed shell egg." Neither appellation can be accepted unqualifiedly, because the shells are neither entirely sealed by oiling nor are they completely freed from the presence of mold spores or bacteria. But the pores in the shell are partially closed by means of a coat of mineral oil generally applied hot (which formed the basis for the term "sterilized") and thereby the evaporation of water from the egg (called "shrinkage" in the trade), is much reduced. Twenty or more years ago, when this process was first developed, the oil was heated to more than 200° F. and the eggs quickly dipped into it. Little by little, however, there has grown a preference* for dipping at lower and lower temperatures until now we know that a temperature of 100° F. or slightly higher gives the sealing effect desired.

HOW COLD
STORAGE
CAME
TO THE
RESCUE

Eggs so treated have a characteristic sound when clicked together, the "belling" of the untreated shell having changed to the "tinny" note which egg graders quickly recognize. The shell becomes shiny and smooth and sometimes distinctly oily

---

* Particularly on the Pacific Coast, and when mineral oil is used as the sealing agent. In the Middle West other sealing agents, it is claimed for one process, are held in a light oil solution which is applied at higher temperatures.—The Editor.

to the touch. This oiliness may be removed by sanding the egg, thus restoring the dull appearance of the shell. But generally oil-dipped eggs are marketed without any such treatment.

This method of treating the shell to reduce the evaporation of water is most used when there is a very long railroad haul to market, or when eggs are to be cold stored. If the eggs are very fresh and the shells are clean; and if the oil is not heated above the temperature at which the albumen of the egg coagulates, the effects are decidedly beneficial in reducing shrinkage during the railway haul. Less and less dependence is being placed on oiling shells of eggs going into storage because the newer methods of air conditioning now used in cold storage warehouses have so reduced evaporation that in most cases other treatment is unnecessary.

Let no one think that oiling the shells does away with the need for refrigeration. In refrigerator car, warehouse and retail shop, we must keep the shell treated egg cold if we are to maintain high quality, just as we do the egg with a natural shell.

How Eggs Used to be Preserved

One of the oldest methods of preserving eggs was to bury them in salt. Another method, and one widely used fifty years ago, was to bury them in oat hulls or clean, dry oats. Great hogsheads were used as containers for the oats and eggs and many of these were shipped from Ohio and Indiana in the early days.

Keeping eggs in lime water was also practiced on a commercial scale. Vats, about four feet high, were partly filled with lime water containing a little cream of tartar and enough salt to make the eggs stand on their pointed ends when immersed. Into these vats baskets of eggs were lowered and carefully tipped over so that the eggs rolled gently out. The vats were full when the eggs reached to within about two

HOW COLD
STORAGE
C A M E
T O T H E
R E S C U E

237

inches of the top and then the expert egg "pickler" watched for the formation on the surface of the liquid of the thin film of calcium carbonate, which told him, even if he did not grasp the chemistry of the process, that the solution was properly made. As the weeks went by he watched to see that the film was always there and he added a little more lime water if it disappeared. He also put bins of ice into the rooms when the weather was hot. Little did he think that before many years had gone by his chemical process would be a half forgotten page in history and refrigerated warehouses holding millions of cases of eggs would replace the vat and the pickling room.

In Europe, however, liming eggs still persists, and probably will until refrigerated warehouses become more common. Indeed, during the Great War about twenty carloads of limed eggs were shipped to Europe from Grand Junction, Iowa, the last stronghold here for eggs so preserved. Now the commercial liming of eggs in the United States is as dead as the proverbial door nail.

First cousin to liming, but much more successful on a household scale, is the preservation of eggs in colloidal sodium silicate, popularly known as waterglass. Impractical from the commercial standpoint, it is, nevertheless, much used in homes. Many a farm and small-town woman, remote from the refrigerated warehouse, depends on waterglass eggs for a large part of her supply during the winter months, using them just as she does those newly laid, except that she puts a tiny needle hole through the shell before boiling to prevent the bursting of the shell.

Plainly, if we were to have a continuous supply of good eggs the year around, we had to find some better methods of keeping them than waterglass and pickling.

So, forty or fifty years ago people began to study the conservation of eggs in cold storage. By the trial and error method, the warehousemen overcame one difficulty after

another. Later the United States Department of Agriculture

turned its well trained chemists and bacteriologists onto the problem. The shippers of eggs, learning mostly by costly experience, found that only very good eggs can be satisfactorily cold-stored.

City populations and the demand for eggs in the season of scarcity, grew faster than did our knowledge of just how to cold-store eggs so that the pristine flavor and other attributes of high quality, even the bloom on the shells, would be preserved.

Of course, under these conditions, some eggs not satisfactory for breakfast use found their way to the consumer, who, on learning that they had been cold-stored, promptly condemned all eggs from cold storage. Other persons besides consumers, who were either ill-informed or perhaps had ulterior reasons, also disparaged cold-stored eggs. Retailers, to enhance the value of their better grades of eggs, labeled them "fresh" as distinguished from small, dirty or stale eggs, which they described as storage eggs—though frequently both kinds came out of the same case, and sometimes they had been in storage and sometimes they had not.

In recent years, however, better and better eggs have been put into storage by their owners, and better and better equipment and operation of warehouses have put on the market a supply of eggs which is successfully competing with winter-produced country stock. Indeed, in most cases, high grade U. S. Extras held under the most improved conditions cannot be distinguished by candling, breaking out or tasting, poaching or soft-boiling, from eggs of like grade that have never been near cold storage. Strange as it may seem, cold-stored eggs are frequently to be preferred for baking and general cookery. For example, angel-food cake is more tender and has a better texture when made from refrigerated eggs—but why this is so no one has yet discovered.

The New York State egg-grading law very wisely makes *quality* its only requirement and criterion. Its makers were charged with the responsibility of ensuring, for the people of the state, good eggs so marked that their quality would be apparent to any purchaser. Whims and fancies of consumers and past habits of egg vendors all gave place to the simple A, B and C grades which have been previously described.

The refrigerated warehouses in the New York metropolitan area normally carry two million cases of eggs at the end of the season of production. New York area consumes, per annum, about ten million cases of eggs. Translate this relationship into appropriate figures for every metropolis in the country and then try to imagine what would happen if we should suddenly be deprived of cold-stored eggs!

Storing Frozen Eggs

But cold-stored eggs in the shell are not our only resource. We have, also, "frozen egg", which has been previously described. About 250 million pounds of frozen eggs a year are prepared and used in the United States. This represents approximately three billion eggs—a tidy number, you will admit, and a most important one because, held at zero F. or below, they are almost imperishable, and so can be drawn upon in accordance with market demands. Eggs in the shell will not keep indefinitely. Generally the warehouses are emptied of eggs in the shell by January, but frozen egg can be depended upon to last until the new crop is prepared and the canned egg is again flowing into the warehouse freezers.

HOW CHICKENS ARE
DIFFERENT, AND WHY

W E HAVE looked with interest and some astonishment
at the structure and composition of the egg and have
noted many times that Mother Nature plainly intended
it to become a chick rather than food for man. Now let us
look at the chicken which, marvel of marvels, has used yolk
and white, heat and moisture to enable it finally to step out of
its fragile prison into the big round world.

Our interest in the chicken, as it was in the egg, is from the
food viewpoint. Let us then discuss it from that angle to see,
especially, what its edible constituents are and what are the
differences, if any, in the flesh of birds of different ages, or
between birds fed on range and those fed on fleshing station
rations. We know that the fine flavor which we so enjoy is
lowered by bad handling during preparation for market; perhaps we may find out why this is so. But first of all we must
learn to speak of specimens of *gallus domesticus* by their
market names at different marketable ages, and not call them
all indiscriminately "chickens."

CHICKENS to your market man, are birds which have not
yet reached sexual maturity. They are *broilers* which are little
chickens weighing from one to two and one-half pounds, *fryers*
which weigh about three pounds, and *roasters* which weigh
three and one-half pounds or more. But all of them were

241

hatched in the spring of the year during which they were killed, and therefore we sometimes hear them collectively called *Springs.* Occasionally we are offered *pullets,* which are young hens about ready to lay eggs, just as *roasters* are young cocks almost ready to assume the responsibilities of parenthood. Pullets are deliciously tender and well flavored, but as their eggs are generally far more valuable than their little bodies, they seldom come to market until they have laid eggs for at least one season and more often for two, by which time they are known as FOWL but never as chickens. So if your butcher offers you a "nice young fowl" for fricasee, or a "soft-meated chicken" for roasting, you will know at once why he makes the distinction. And should you, by chance, try to fricasee the roaster or roast the fowl, there will be no doubt in your mind that the differences go much deeper than mere market designations. Let us see what some of them are. To do that satisfactorily we may have to discuss some generalities, such as the question of the skin, which will apply to all poultry.

There is relatively less skin, by weight, on broilers than on roasting chickens, and fowls show the highest percentage in terms of the total edible meat. Also, the relative weight of the skin of chickens increases when they are fleshed for market in coops (feeding stations will be described in later pages), while that of fowls remains about constant. The actual quantities may vary from about seven per cent for broilers to fifteen per cent for fowls. As the young bird fattens, the amount of water in the skin decreases and the fat increases—a very important observation because upon this fat depends much of the delicious flavor of the broiler and also of the roaster. Cooking, as Mrs. Snyder will tell you, brings out this flavor in a well fatted, well handled bird. If, however, refrigeration has not been adequate and continuous, long before decomposition has reached the point of producing undesirable tastes or odors in the flesh, the fat will have lost its essential blandness and acquired a harsh or somewhat rancid character.

H O W
CHICKENS
ARE DIF-
FERENT,
AND WHY

242

So delicate is the fat of the chicken or fowl that it is used by the chemist as an index of good condition. He measures in the laboratory the amount of acid the fat contains. In the perfectly fresh bird the acidity is very low, but as deterioration progresses the acid value rises. We know, also that scalding a bird to remove the feathers causes a rise in the acidity of the fat in the skin; and the flavor of scalded birds, as well as their keeping quality, is generally accepted as inferior to that of dry-picked birds.

Of course the skin contains proteins, that most valuable class of nitrogen-containing substances whose role in nutrition Mrs. Snyder will tell you about. The largest amount of protein is found in the skin of young birds—about eighteen per cent in the case of range broilers; and the smallest amount—about ten per cent—in the skin of hens.

Proteins we think of as the primary constituents of flesh, by which we mean muscle and we are not apt to stress the fat content of what we call lean meat. In poultry we have both. Usually we find about twenty per cent of protein in the flesh itself, though in hens it may be a little higher and in broilers a little lower than this figure. Fat ranges from about three per cent in range broilers to seven per cent in hens. When young birds are fatted for market, part of the water in the flesh, just as in the skin, is replaced by fat, and to this fact is due much of the tenderness of the fatted bird. In the flesh of a fatted chicken we may expect the fat content to rise to about six per cent.

In birds of different ages there are interesting differences in the amounts of the various proteins that normally occur in flesh. We find more of the proteins that are not soluble in water in the flesh of mature birds; while the soluble sorts, such as albumoses and peptones, are found in greater quantity in the flesh of broilers and roasters. This is as one would expect because of the greater tenderness of the young bird.

As is the case with the dark-colored meat of certain fishes, so with poultry we find more fat in the dark than in the light meat. Ordinarily, there is four to five times as much fat in the dark as in the light meat. There is a little more protein in the light meat than in the dark and a good deal more of it is of the water-soluble sort. This again corresponds with the tenderness of light meat.

When poultry is prevented from taking exercise and fed an abundant and fat-forming ration, as is the case during coop-fleshing for market, the birds not only gain in weight and in quality of flesh but they actually produce a greater proportion of edible meat. For example, broilers coming off the range have about fifty-six per cent of edible parts, while after *flesh-ing* they have about sixty per cent. Roasters show an increase from sixty-two to sixty-four per cent, and hens, which gain the least, increase from seventy to seventy-one per cent. The ration and the inactivity tend toward the production of flesh and fat and do not stimulate the formation of heavy bone. This is a point of practical interest to the consumer, since it means that, quite aside from increased tenderness and flavor in *milk-fed* birds, one has less actual waste.

HOW POULTRY IS MADE
READY FOR MARKET

EAST of the Alleghenies and west of the Rockies, one occasionally sees specially built railway cars full of live poultry bound for the poultry abattoir. Now and then one also sees coops of live poultry on trucks bound cityward. But throughout the Mississippi Valley the motorist is constantly meeting coops of live poultry being hauled in almost every sort of conveyance and, seemingly, in every direction. In almost every little town one finds buyers of eggs and poultry who deal directly with the farmer or country merchant. Many of them pass on their purchases to poultry and egg packers who have headquarters in the towns and who prepare the products for market. We have discussed the role they play in marketing eggs. Now let us see their function in regard to poultry, both alive and dressed.

Shipping Poultry Alive

The big wire cages on wheels, filled with live birds, which we see now and then on railways are called "live poultry cars." They serve in new farming country to get poultry to distant markets until the volume in a given locality is sufficient to induce the investment of capital in a packing house. They also serve to perpetuate an old country custom of some of our foreign born population which prefers to buy poultry alive or to see it fresh-killed. Most of the birds transported alive go to the Jewish slaughter houses and thence to the Kosher shops, which guarantee to their patrons that the ancient rabbinical requirements for orthodox Jews have been complied with.' The

All the way from
Texas to New
England live
poultry may
travel in cars like
this.

fact that the trade still exists because of rules made thousands
of years ago to protect a primitive people living in a warm
climate, rules which are scarcely compatible with our time and
its sanitary requirements—this has made the proper regulation
of the live poultry traffic in some localities almost an impos-
sibility.   It is one of the food problems to be faced by both
Jew and Gentile.

About 400 million pounds of poultry annually is shipped
alive to our cities for local consumption, a quantity large
enough to hold our attention until we learn that our dressed
poultry traffic amounts to approximately 800 million pounds, a
figure so startling to most of us that we may well turn our
attention to some of the many activities which govern it.

Where the Poultry Starts

Let us imagine ourselves on almost any farm in the Mississippi Valley (you know we depend on the Valley for the bulk
of our egg supply, so of course we depend upon it for poultry,
too) between the months of June and August.   Mother hen or
her substitute, the brooder, has brought the little chicks to the
broiler stage.   The little pullets are rounding out and the
young cockerels are beginning to put on airs of masculine superiority and trying their best to crow in grown-up style.

The thrifty farmer selects a certain number of these cockerels and sells them to his country buyer or to the poultry packing house. Long ago he learned that the final preparation of poultry for market could not be done as well on the farm as in the packing house where there are skilled killers, pickers and packers, refrigeration to remove the animal heat and a "feeding station."

"What", you ask, "is a feeding station?" and I hasten to tell you since it is, to me, one of the most interesting developments of the poultry industry. But before telling you of our American ways, I must go back and tell you a little of feeding chickens in the old world. Let us take England, for example.

Forced Feeding in England

In certain sections of England, notably in Sussex, the preparation of poultry for market is an old, old industry. It is a specialty which is handed down from father to son so that for generations the same family on the same farm makes a livelihood from it.

When the birds are adjudged ready to be fatted for market, they are placed in small coops made of wood slats mounted on legs to raise them several feet off the ground. Sometimes they have a hip roof with wide eaves to shed water and afford protection from rain. Here the birds are kept for from two to three weeks and fed grain and milk (a ration rich in fat and carbohydrate) to make their flesh soft and tender as well as to increase their weight. But the birds do not, of their own volition, eat as much as their digestive and metabolizing machinery can turn into flesh, so the feeder resorts to "cramming".

That is, once each day he introduces through a tube directly into the bird's crop just as much as it will hold of a specially prepared mixture of finely ground grain and certain fats, with milk enough to give the mixture the consistency of thick cream. His skill consists in knowing to a nicety just how far he can stretch the crop and just how much food the bird can success-

Following the American tradition for mass production, our feeders serve many birds with grain and buttermilk. The station may house fifty thousand birds.

fully manage to digest to reach its maximum weight and tenderness. He must know, also, when the height of quality has been attained. Then the bird is killed, picked and sent to market as "milk-fed" or "milk-fatted." All such crammed poultry is generally known as *Surrey fowl*.

So tender and so deliciously flavored are these birds that it is no wonder our Americans wanted to duplicate the English industry.

America Develops the Poultry Hotel

Being Americans, we began the job on a truly American scale. Instead of a few hundred birds in little coops set in a sheltered field or dooryard, we put thousands and thousands of birds into one big building, confining them in wire cages built like four-storied tenements, six to ten birds to each compartment, and in the hot and dry climate of some parts of the Middle West, and the hot and moist climate of other parts, we proceeded to cram in true English fashion.

While the weather was fairly cool, disaster just threatened, but when a hot wave came, the birds died by the hundreds. The English plan would not do in America. Then we went back to scratch and began to learn how to milk-feed American

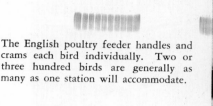

The English poultry feeder handles and crams each bird individually. Two or three hundred birds are generally as many as one station will accommodate.

birds for an American market. We learned so successfully that now putting the poultry through the feeding station as it comes from the farm is a routine matter.

So universal has the poultry feeding station become—it might almost be called a poultry hotel where the birds are favored guests—that even the smallest poultry packing house now puts practically all the birds it receives "on feed" for from three days to two weeks before preparing it for market. The original wire and wood coops, or *batteries* as they are called, have been modified to make them more sanitary and more comfortable. Rations have been adapted to American birds and the American climate, and cramming has been absolutely discarded. The batteries are set in rows wide apart, in airy, shaded buildings. In a day or two the birds are accustomed to the new surroundings, they eat heartily of the finely ground grain and buttermilk mixture, the "chickens" gain weight and the "fowls" acquire a smoother, softer flesh.

A visit to a poultry feeding station is a fascinating experience to one who has never seen it. In this large, airy, well lighted room, there are rows and rows of wire cages in tiers, each cage containing about ten birds. A long, clean wooden trough runs the length of the cages, just close enough so that the birds can reach it easily by thrusting their heads between the vertical wires.

Birds are sorted into cages for size and age. When small and large birds are together, the big ones get all the titbits.

Just before feeding time there is a lively din of crowing and cackling. Suddenly down the wide center aisle comes the rumble of the feed tank, followed by the clank of the feed dipper in the spouted bucket. Instantaneously, as if some invisible leader had barked the order "Eyes right!" every chicken's head turns toward the one interesting point in the room—the feeding truck. As the man with the bucket goes down each aisle, partly filling the troughs, heads follow him, just as the gallery at a tennis match follows the ball. The moment the feed touches the trough the birds begin eating, pecking away as if they were in a contest. At first the individual pecking of beaks on wooden troughs is distinguishable, then more and more join the banquet, until the pecking is a sort of rhythmical tattoo. The tattoo diminishes in volume as the birds that were fed first empty their troughs. Then the feeder starts all over again, and the soft pecking, growing to a crescendo, repeats itself.

The feeder uses the same psychology in feeding his birds that a mother uses in feeding small children; she gives only a small serving at a time and waits until every bit is eaten. Then she gives another small serving, and waits until it is eaten, and so eventually the child, especially the finicky one, gets all the food

Birds in feeding batteries are comfortable and happy and always full of food to their liking.

he needs. Poultry, too, cleans up each small serving, and many small servings may make more than one large serving which might if all of it were placed before the birds at one time not be eaten. After the troughs have been emptied the last time, the birds are ready to rest and transform the feed into juicy chicken meat for our dinners.

Such is the milk-fed poultry advertised on American markets, and it is to such a diet of clean grain and buttermilk that the farmer of whom we were speaking will take those young cockerels to be suitably fed for broilers and then killed, picked, thoroughly refrigerated, packed in boxes holding twelve each and dispatched in a refrigerator car to the chosen market.

Later on in the summer and, indeed, all through the autumn, the farmer will select his larger cockerels and take them to the poultry buyer to be milk-fed and marketed as soft-meated roasters. By the time the next breeding season comes around, he will have sold all the male birds except the few he may keep for breeding purposes. When, finally, their turn comes to go to the market, they will be known as "old cocks" and will probably end their careers as the foundation for chicken soup.

All through the year most farmers, now and then, have a few hens to sell. Of course, in the spring when the hens are laying, very few are sold. Then as the lay falls off the farmer may sell some of his two-year-old birds or those which are not well shaped or those which are lazy about their egg-producing job. In the autumn he goes carefully over his flock and sells all the hens except those which will be good layers and will pay for their board and keep through the winter.

This is the time when we get the finest hens—or fowl, as the market term goes. They have had many a good meal as they followed the harvesters, and the green grass had provided a plentiful supply of vitamin A to ensure strength and vitality. Since, nowadays, all poultry is sold by the pound and not by the piece as it used to be, the farmer sees to it that the birds on his place are well fed and that they go to the packing house in prime condition to be "finished" in the feeding station.

The New Way of Dressing Poultry

No normal person likes to kill any living thing. Unfortunately, someone must kill our food animals. Therefore, methods of slaughter have been devised which are as painless as possible and which makes death instantaneous. The old

Removing feathers in a modern clean fashion.

method of chopping the head off a chicken is far too crude for the modern poultry packing house where thousands of birds are killed each day. Instead of the proverbial block and ax, the poultry killer has a small sharp knife with which, in one deft motion, he pierces the brain, thus paralyzing the bird and destroying sensation. Then he cuts two big veins in the throat so that the blood may escape from the carcass; otherwise it would be unsightly in appearance and its resistance to decay would be lowered.

Destroying the brain relaxes the tiny muscles which hold the feathers and so makes their removal an easy matter if they are pulled out before rigor mortis sets in. Immediately after "bleeding", the "rougher" pulls the big feathers of wings and tail, then dips the bird into a bath of water having a temperature between 120° and 130° F., which still further loosens the soft body feathers. "Tippers" or "pinners", who are usually girls, take these out, being careful not to tear or scar the skin. Then the bird is ready for singeing, after which its head is neatly covered in a cleverly twisted and shaped paper bonnet—the "headwrap." The bird is hung by the feet on a metal rack holding a hundred or more, and this is immediately wheeled into a "chill room," where the temperature is between 30° and 35° F. The cold, circulating air speedily removes the animal heat. For high quality the bird should be cooled through and through in less than twenty-four hours.

Now the rack is taken to the packing room, also refrigerated and maintained at 30° to 33° F. Here graders sort the birds for size and quality and collect them into groups of twelve, each bird being as nearly as possible the exact counterpart of its fellows. Each dozen then goes into a paper-lined box, which they exactly fit—and so to the refrigerator car or to the freezer to be available when we want them.

The century has seen a vast change in the dressing of poultry for market. So long as the city and the farm were close neighbors, the farmer not only raised but frequently killed the birds and even delivered them himself to his customers. His facilities for handling did not often include refrigeration, although he might have a supply of ice stored on the farm if the climate produced ice in winter time. When he raised more birds than he could market dress, as he soon did in the Middle West, he sold to the poultry packer, who was a smaller and less well educated edition of our present incumbent. This man had ice—and depended upon large tanks of iced water to remove the animal heat. It was a difficult matter to keep these iced tanks cold enough. The water got dirty, too. If the packer could not get enough birds for a shipment in one day, he had to hold the dressed birds in chopped ice until the necessary quantity was obtained. When he packed the birds for the journey to the consumer, he generally put them into barrels, placing layers of ice and layers of birds, alternately.

The ice melted and the water ran out of the barrel, carrying with it much of the fine flavor which, as we have learned, resides in those compounds that are soluble in water. Also, the flesh of the birds absorbed water, so that the consumer paid for some water at chicken prices. Broilers would sometimes absorb as much as ten per cent of their weight by the time they reached the consumer. Worst of all was the actual spoilage

in transit or while waiting on the market so that the birds

After cooling the birds are taken from the racks and sorted for size and color. On the other side of the bins the birds are packed in boxes —twelve to a box.

were unfit for food. Thousands of pounds annually were condemned by food inspectors and destroyed.

The autumn was then the great poultry-selling season because the packer depended upon the cool nights to remove the animal heat. The farmers from far and wide brought the great bulk of their salable poultry to the packer between October and Christmas. Gluts on the market made ruinous prices. Neither did the weather always cooperate, which meant tons of "green struck" poultry on the market. A warm autumn was truly a calamity to the poultry industry.

Then, slowly but surely, came the spread of mechanical refrigeration throughout the poultry country of the Mississippi Valley, the abandoning of the iced tank and the leaky barrel, the development of the better and better refrigerator car, all making possible our standard package with twelve birds to the box, and last, but by no means least, our ability to freeze dressed poultry and hold it hard frozen until the market demands it. But that plays so important a part in our every-day-in-the-year supply of high-quality poultry in fine condition that I must give the story a chapter to itself. I warn you, too, that I am likely to ruthlessly upset some popular opinions regarding frozen poultry. But I shall set forth the facts, and then you may decide for yourself.

HOW TO PURCHASE SPRING

CHICKEN THE YEAR AROUND

WHILE the incubator and the brooder have helped to overcome the seasonal limitation set by Dame Nature on the hatching and rearing season, the great majority of the birds sent to market to provide broilers and soft-meated roasters for the general consuming public must be dressed between June and December. If the consumer is to be supplied the year around with so seasonable a product, obviously some method of conservation must be available. Drying and smoking are not satisfactory. Canning is of limited service only. There remains the use of temperatures so low that bacteria cannot grow and enzyme action is so retarded that its effect is negligible.

Very crudely, conservation by low temperatures was tried in the 1880's and 1890's, mixtures of ice and salt being used as the refrigerant. Then came a wider application of the refrigerating machine, and the gradual building of warehouses with insulated walls in which, by mechanical means, the temperatures were reduced far below 32° F. and constantly maintained. Butter, dressed poultry and meat products in increasing tonnage were stored in these low-temperature rooms, and, if they were fine products when they were frozen and if the freezing and the holding was properly done, they emerged fine products at any time during the period of scarcity.

It was one of the great achievements of this great century. Not only could gluts on the market be lessened, with their consequent losses from producer through to consumer, but production and distribution could be placed on a more stable

The first experiments on refrigerated poultry were made by Sir Francis Bacon, March 1626, when he stuffed a hen with snow. The flesh of the hen did not spoil. Sir Francis caught a cold and died of it on Easter day.

basis. Even more spectacular, if not more fundamentally important, low-temperature refrigeration combined with the refrigerator car is partly responsible for the rapid increase in the population of our great cities. Should some great cataclysm cut off the food supply of a city, the warehouses could, for a week or two at least, take care of the vital demands for butter, poultry, some meat products, frozen cream and eggs. Of more importance, economically, is the fact that a reserve store of essential food is always at hand to be drawn upon as the fresh market receipts indicate and to act as an equalizer between the very high prices of the commodity which is out of season and the very low prices of the commodity which is in the flush of production. No wonder great quantities of broilers and roasters and even hens, since they are of decidedly finer quality in the autumn, should be put each season into the freezer. The strange thing is that so few consumers, relatively, understand the matter and so few demand, in the off season, hard-frozen birds of the kind they desire. Certainly the widespread prejudice against frozen foods is not only unfounded but works out to the detriment of food quality and the consumer's pocketbook.

It is hard to tell how such prejudices arise, but generally they can be traced to the ignorance and the cupidity of tradesmen who fear the effect of innovation on their business. At the first International Congress of Refrigerating Industries, held in Paris in 1908, the French butchers created a great disturbance outside the Sorbonne where the Congress was in session, fearing that frozen meats would take away their livelihood, and most unappetizing were their descriptions of what such meat would be. In the early days of hard-frozen foods in this country, when the near-by farmer was still a factor in the food supply of the city, he might easily, though in less dramatic fashion, have spread misleading information about *cold storage.*

We consumers, being in general lamentably ignorant of the history of our foodstuffs and of the laws of chemistry and bacteriology which govern the deterioration of organic tissues, are an easy prey to such propaganda. Many of us are still gauging *freshness* by the period of the time between the source of production and our kitchens, quite ignorant of the fact that a single hour of bad handling will work greater destruction to quality than many weeks of sojourn in a clean warehouse at temperatures which have been proven by elaborate scientific study and practical observation to retard deterioration almost to the vanishing point. Therefore, we demand of the retail merchant "fresh" roasting chickens, perhaps in February or March—a season when an immature cockerel is almost a museum specimen; or reasonably priced "fresh" frying chickens at the same period, likewise a seasonal curiosity. When the merchant tries to be honest and tells us he can give us the finest of such birds hard-frozen, we scornfully seek another shop where the conscience of the proprietor is more subservient to his pocketbook. The birds we get *were* frozen, but they have been thawed. We are apt to pay a higher price to correspond with the out-of-season status of the roaster, broiler or fryer as the case may

HOW TO
PURCHASE
SPRING
CHICK-
ENS THE
YEAR
AROUND

be. Worse still is the merchant who sells first-grade chickens as "fresh" and second-grade as "cold storage" regardless of the facts, and thus contributes to the prejudice and misinformation of the consumer. You may be very sure that the fine hotel or high-class restaurant which you frequent because they serve such "marvelously delicious chicken" uses only very excellent packs of frozen poultry most of the year. They allow it to thaw slowly in cold air, and carefully keep it away from water or chopped ice until cooking time arrives.

Two factors are working toward the practical education of the public regarding frozen foods—one, certain retail shops most of which belong to chain stores, and the other, the distribution of "quick-frozen" products. The retail shops are displaying frozen poultry and selling it frozen; the quick-frozen commodities are in small packages and every effort is made to deliver them to the purchaser as near zero Fahrenheit as possible. Here the frozen condition is, rightly, made an asset and not a liability. The quality speaks for itself—and the users of quick-frozen foods pay a slightly higher price for that quality in spite of the freezing.

I trust that by this time you are sufficiently interested to want to know how I am so sure that good frozen poultry is comparable with good fresh-killed poultry, and what, in general, is the routine for the freezing and holding of dressed poultry.

Finding the Facts

About 1905 there began some agitation in the daily press concerning cold-storage foods. Some overenthusiastic warehousemen had made foolish statements, probably as a joke, concerning banquets serving turkeys ten years in storage. Dr. Wiley, who was then battling to put through Congress the Food and Drugs Act, wanted an investigation made of these

HOW TO
PURCHASE
SPRING
CHICK-
ENS THE
YEAR
AROUND

259

cold-stored goods to determine their actual condition. Because I had training in biochemistry, bacteriology and histology, all of which would be needed in such a study, I was invited to make the study under the auspices of the Bureau of Chemistry. Some warehousemen, being convinced that this was no political move but a truly scientific study of their new industry which could not fail to be of service, opened wide their doors and gave every sort of assistance in untangling the problems. For problems there were, of course. Some poultry out of storage was ideal, some was not so good, and some left much to be desired. Chemical and bacteriological studies in the laboratory, and "organoleptic tests", as our eating quality studies were called (Scientists do seem partial to queer names)—all these revealed much of scientific interest, and one outstanding practical fact—*if poultry went into a freezer which was 0° F. or below in good condition, it came out at any time during the season of scarcity in good condition.* Beaker, test tube and microscope in the laboratory, through hundreds and hundreds of analyses, testified to the truth of this generalization, which may sound simple enough, but oh! into what far fields it led the staff of the Food Research Laboratory, as our unit in the Bureau of Chemistry was called.

What did the poultry packer do, or not do, that led to fine birds or poor birds when they came out of storage? Was the ration in the feeding station responsible? Or refrigeration in transit? Or a host of other items which might or might not affect quality after storage?

Back to the laboratory from feeding station, killing room, chilling room, refrigerator car, cold storage warehouse, and every other link in the chain to the consumer's kitchen, went sample after sample of dressed poultry with every item of its history recorded and evaluated. Each step in the preparation of the bird for market was finally translated into terms indicating quality to the consumer. The laboratory was used not only to identify links where improvement was desirable, but to help forge new and better links.

Out, at once, to feeder, packer, railway and storage man went the helpful information just as soon as the laboratory staff was sure of its authenticity. Better practices were substituted for those less desirable by the progressives first, and more gradually by practically all of the industry. Cooling in iced water instead of cold air, which was found detrimental to the good keeping of birds hard-frozen, has almost disappeared; likewise, shipping birds to the freezer packed in chopped ice—bad for reasons already discussed. Quick and adequate removal of the animal heat is now universally practiced; emptying the crop and intestines by not giving food for some hours before killing, which leaves the body cavity of the bird much cleaner than does eviscerating; and many another important item in maintaining quality, whether the bird is or is not destined for a sojourn in the storage warehouse. Indeed, greater care is used in selecting and preparing birds for the freezer than for immediate marketing, because to all the other charges against them will be added that of storage, and only stock of fine quality, well handled, will be likely to sell at a profit.

There are in this country over 600 poultry packing houses which ship several carloads a week of dressed poultry and eggs, and innumerable smaller killing stations which dress birds for local consumption. It is these 600 or more that send poultry to the refrigerated warehouses. The condition of this poultry is almost invariably above reproach. A condemnation of frozen poultry by pure food officials on account of spoilage is almost unheard of. Probably no other food commodity, except milk and butter, has been so thoroughly studied from the viewpoint of consumer protection as has dressed, frozen poultry. If the consumer will insist upon buying it hard-frozen and then thaw and clean it in her own kitchen, or, if she will insist upon the presence of some ice in the body cavity when the retail dealer draws the bird, she will be likely to receive uniformly fine. palatable poultry the year around especially if she has chosen a good, trademarked brand.

If the consumer, for reasons of convenience, wants poultry which is drawn at the packing house and shipped eviscerated, then she must receive it hard-frozen, because only by freezing immediately after drawing, and maintaining the carcass in a frozen condition, can decomposition be avoided. The well starved, well chilled bird "in the round" or undrawn, is a sealed package well protected by the bird's skin. But when that skin is broken, as it must be when eviscerating, bacteria are sure to be given access to the soft tissues beneath where they thrive luxuriantly unless hard freezing stops their activities.

The number of bacteria in the lining of the abdominal cavity of the undrawn bird shipped to market under good refrigeration, but not hard frozen, is relatively small, while in the full-drawn bird shipped under the same conditions, the number of bacteria in one gram of flesh is generally found to be in the millions and may be in the billions. This being fact and not sentiment, it is easy to see that dressed poultry must continue to be put on the market, in the round, until such time as the consumer shall be educated to accept drawn poultry hard-frozen throughout the year.

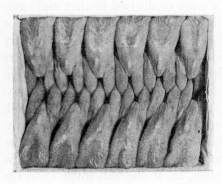

A prize pack of poultry. Uniform color and size make an attractive display.

CONSUMER, FLOCK OWNER AND MARKET MAN

PAUL MANDEVILLE

Some Price Curves and
Consumption Facts.

An Industry Emerges.

The Road To Progress.

An instructive and decorative exhibit in a modern scientific poultry show.

SOME PRICE CURVES AND CONSUMPTION FACTS

THE hows and whys of fresh eggs have been told in considerable detail. But some people will be asking, no doubt, for confidential information as to when and where they can be assured of obtaining eggs fresh. It is a fair question; in general terms it can be answered in complete fairness to both the commercial poultrymen who specialize in supplying new-laid eggs in season and to those poultry dealers who supply the general market with fine, fresh eggs irrespective of season.

Most of us in the great cities north and east of Memphis depend upon some retail dealer for good table eggs. Those who get eggs "fresh from the country" often are only patronizing another dealer who finds it to his advantage to represent himself as a producer, or at least that he is closer to producers than the city dealer. The diagram on the following page will assist all dealers to understand the seasonal changes in the quality of the eggs they handle.

The consumers also, if informed, will be reasonable as to the kind of eggs and the prices they may expect. The market and the preconceived ideas of consumers do not always permit a retail dealer to charge what the best obtainable eggs are worth, and sometimes they seem to justify him in charging more than the eggs are worth. This last statement may appear to be wrong, but suppose we consider all the facts and see to what conclusions they lead.

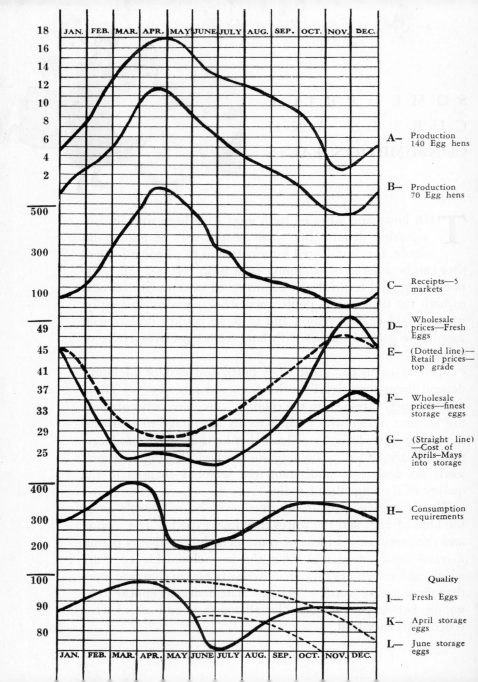

	JAN.	FEB.	MAR.	APR.	MAY	JUNE	JULY	AUG.	SEP.	OCT.	NOV.	DEC.

A— Production 140 Egg hens

B— Production 70 Egg hens

C— Receipts—5 markets

D— Wholesale prices—Fresh Eggs

E— (Dotted line)—Retail prices—top grade

F— Wholesale prices—finest storage eggs

G— (Straight line)—Cost of Aprils-Mays into storage

H— Consumption requirements

Quality

I— Fresh Eggs

K— April storage eggs

L— June storage eggs

EXPLANATION OF CHART

The diagram at the left shows the seasonal changes in egg production, egg prices, egg consumption and egg quality, expressed in lines. Ascending lines indicate increases or improvement; descending lines indicate decreases or deterioration.

Curve A indicates the monthly rate of egg production of flocks which average 140 eggs per hen per year. The figures at the left of Curves A & B indicate the number of eggs laid per hen per month.

Curve B indicates monthly rate of egg production of flocks which average 70 eggs per year per hen.

Curve C indicates the combined weekly receipts of eggs in five principal markets, showing the average variation for five years—1924–28, inclusive. The figures at the left indicate the approximate number of thousands of cases of 30 dozen each.

Curve D (solid line) indicates the average monthly variation in prices for fresh eggs during ten years, 1919–28 inclusive.

Curve E (dotted line) indicates average monthly variation in retail prices of top grade fresh eggs for five years 1924–1928, inclusive. Obtained by the U. S. Department of Labor in 51 cities.

Curve F indicates the average monthly variation in wholesale prices for finest storage eggs, suitable for top grades when sold at retail—for ten years 1919–1928, inclusive.

G (straight line) indicates the average wholesale cost of finest April and May eggs stored for ten years 1919–1928, inclusive. All the other price curves are adjusted to this cost line. Figures at the left are comparable prices per dozen for all the price curves.

Curve H indicates monthly variation in requirements (consumption) in five principal markets for five years 1924–1928, inclusive. The figures at the left of this curve indicate the weekly requirements in thousands of cases of 30 dozen each.

Curve I (solid line) indicates the normal monthly variation in quality of the main supply of new laid eggs obtainable.

The decline of quality in new laid eggs during the summer months is partly due to a lack of cooling facilities on farms and the resulting loss of quality during the first 24 to 72 hours after eggs have been laid; partly also to the physical condition of the hens and their varying ability to produce fine quality eggs during summer weather and with the usual care (or neglect) of flocks, their housing, feeding, etc.

The three quality curves, I, K and L are approximations; the figures on the left indicate variations from commercial perfection—100 equals commercial perfection—90 and 80 equal the degree (%) of perfection as judged by differences in prices paid on the market for eggs of the qualities indicated.

SOME
PRICE
CURVES
AND CON-
SUMPTION
FACTS

Good eggs are always obtainable in the large consuming centers, and yet the diagram shows that about the month of May each year the consumption of eggs falls off sharply and is usually at the lowest ebb soon afterward. According to the price curve, it is not caused by high prices, nor, according to the production curve, by any scarcity of eggs in the country, and, according to the quality curve, eggs are of better quality than they are later on in June and July. But many of the finest eggs produced are withdrawn for incubation purposes and many more for storage. Both operations begin earlier than the month of May, but with the advancing season more care must be exercised in selecting eggs and more price cutting is done to sell for consumption those eggs which are sound but which do not show the fine edge of quality desired by the hatchery and storage men. Retail markets are burdened with too many of these somewhat inferior eggs, and consumers turn away from them. During the months of May and June dealers who supply really fine eggs to consumers are entitled to more money for them and so are farmers who produce them. At this season of the year consumers should not have to pay extreme prices in order to obtain the best eggs which are being produced, but they must expect to pay a fairly good price.

And here is something new to many dealers and to most consumers—with the coming of real warm weather the quality of eggs declines, and especially their keeping quality declines, as the diagram shows. Many claims are made by city retailers about the freshness of their eggs at this season but the very finest eggs of all are sleeping in one or another of the great warehouses. Many a shrewd dealer with fine trade to protect, and knowing this fact will, during and after a hot spell, resort to the warehouse, often paying a smart premium for the sleeping beauties—the earlier laid and really better eggs.

About the middle of summer in most of the important egg producing states crops are being harvested and loose grain is

SOME
PRICE
CURVES
AND CON-
SUMPTION
FACTS

268

lying about where chickens range; what is more important, the nights are cool and the chickens can get their rest. The eggs improve in quality, becoming quite fine, but the number laid declines because chickens are molting and resting from egg production while renewing their feathers. The production curve is going down on the diagram. At this season the market usually advances to a point where dealers can, if they wish, always obtain from storage a dependable supply of eggs for fine trade at prices in line with the prevailing demand. It will be seen by the diagram that soon after hens begin to molt and to lay fewer eggs the consumption expands (September–October). This may seem strange in view of advancing prices and fewer eggs laid. It may be due to a greater relish for warm breakfasts in the cool autumn mornings after the long series of cold, fresh fruit breakfasts which the summer demanded. There is, we know, an ample supply of good storage eggs with which to supplement the shortage of eggs from the hen house. It is obvious that the available eggs give satisfaction else consumption would not increase at this season.

Consumers often run the market up on themselves by too insistent inquiry for "strictly fresh" eggs and thereby they bring pressure upon retail dealers to place eggs which are of finest quality, but out of storage, into grades carrying prices which correspond to the shortage in new-laid eggs. They are often marked fresh and seldom marked storage. On the other hand, the same consumers when buying storage eggs erroneously expect an inferior quality and object to paying a price which is even fair when they prove to be fine eggs. Many retail dealers, and some jobbers no doubt, cut the Gordian knot by frankly selling all their undergrades from candling in one lot at a right price and all their top grades in another lot, at a price about in line with the market for new-laid eggs. This may satisfy most of their customers but it often results in an overcharge for eggs of the top grade.

Speaking broadly, and excepting those communities that have

revised their laws to admit selling eggs on their just merits, more than half of all eggs offered in the top grades at retail during October and November, and called fresh, are spring storage eggs. There are, of course, poor quality storage eggs but many eggs of poor quality that have never been in storage are labelled "storage." The larger proportion of all eggs stored are of fine quality.

It is only in December that the supply of new-laid eggs expands sufficiently to approach filling the normal demand for fine eggs, and from December on the quality of new-laid eggs is consistently superior to eggs held from the previous spring. Now this is the low-down on eggs as every well informed egg man knows. It applies to eggs obtainable in our cities whether from retail stores or by carriers of one kind or another "direct from the country." Why not be sensible about it and reasonable with your dealer, frankly paying him a good price but not an excessive price, and then expect him to supply you with good eggs the year around? A good product is deserving a good price and generally brings it.

How Markets Are Made

Changes in the prices of eggs are due, of course, to changes in the supply or the demand. But, in the language of the street, markets are "made" by the device of an accepted quotation. Depending on the accuracy with which quotations reflect values, the markets, so determined, will govern operations and therefore it is important that markets be made openly and upon actual transactions. In recent years, egg quotations have been determined chiefly by open trading on exchanges or at egg auctions. The daily papers report the market in most cities, including the market for storage or refrigerator eggs.

An intelligent city consumer can judge fairly well what the retail prices should be at any given season of the year from the wholesale market as published in the newspapers. Generally speaking, retail prices rule about ten cents higher excepting in

SOME
PRICE
CURVES
AND CON-
SUMPTION
FACTS

Chicago Mercantile Exchange. A silver cock stands at one end of the trading floor. Blackboards are seen in the rear. Lower right: The Chicago Mercantile Exchange Building.

late winter and early spring when eggs do not require as much grading and there is more dumping owing to large supplies. It will be noticed in the chart on page 266 that the dotted line which represents retail prices follows a course about ten cents above the wholesale market for fresh eggs until September, when its course is deflected downward during the fall months under the influence of good quality storage eggs, but it continues to follow a course about ten cents above the price line of the latter.

The spot market prices of storage eggs in Chicago, New York and other large cities are quoted during the storage season, along with fresh egg prices. Quotations are made on refrigerator extras, refrigerator standards and refrigerator firsts.

S O M E
P R I C E
C U R V E S
AND CON-
SUMPTION
F A C T S

These are technical terms which have little meaning for consumers, but they distinguish for the trade slight differences in the average value of carlots. These differences usually do not exceed one cent a dozen.

To these wholesale prices, must be added the cost of candling the eggs out of storage, grading them for specific trade, packaging (if in cartons) and of jobbing to the retailers in case lots. The retailer's cost of handling and often of delivery, together with his profit, must again be added. All in all, these operations account for the ten cent "spread" between the newspaper quotations and retail prices.

The Chicago Mercantile Exchange is the largest trading center in the world for egg futures. The Exchange handles from 50,000 to 70,000 carlot transactions a year. In 1928, total sales of butter and egg futures combined exceeded 98,000 cars. Trading in eggs is in carlots of 12,000 dozen each. You will notice that the term "carlot transactions" is used. The actual eggs are not delivered until settlement day, but promises to deliver are dealt in, sometimes called "paper eggs." The cost per car of such transactions is relatively small and there are good arguments in support of the economy of this manner of making a market.

The greatest use of the futures market is for "hedging", as it is called. In the spring of the year, when eggs are going into storage, the price of the October delivery follows closely the cost into storage plus cost of carrying, affording buyers of actual eggs an immediate place to hedge. This enables them to continue buying eggs although they may not like the price prevailing.

Transactions on the Chicago Mercantile Exchange are wired by press associations, radio and ticker service throughout the country. Spot sales are wired to hundreds of dealers in every state and they are the basis of paying prices to farmers. The publicity of this method of making a market is one of its good features.

AN INDUSTRY EMERGES

FOLLOWING the Civil War, economic conditions were similar to those of today. It was a period of readjustment. New land was offered to settlers. A huge territory in the upper Mississippi Valley, then known as the West, was suited to general farming. There was a demand for poultry with which to stock the homesteads.

Cincinnati was the gateway for distributing these birds and many of them started from New England as told by Mr. Platt. During the eighties and nineties it was common for dealers in Iowa or Missouri to foster production on a larger scale by procuring a supply of birds from the East and distributing them in the territory where they operated. The demand for breeding stock thus created was a mainstay of the poultry business on the Atlantic Coast.

About the same time insulated ice-cooled storage houses were developing, and these, in the early nineties, became quite a factor in the spring egg market, affording an outlet the year around. The marketing of eggs and poultry centered in receivers or commission merchants in the large cities and in country packing establishments large enough to ship carlots. Neither dealt to any extent directly with farmers but with general store keepers and peddlers who bought eggs and dairy butter from farmers. Many of the general stores in the country handled enough eggs to ship carlots in the spring of the year; some of them had small cold storages and were in fact packers.

These larger merchants and the regular carlot packers were guests of the receivers when they visited the big cities and the usual visiting place was the exchange or board which met for a short half hour or hour to trade in eggs and butter for imme-

Market day at a country packing plant for eggs and poultry.

diate delivery. Trading in futures was a much later development in these commodities. The receivers also had traveling representatives and the principals themselves often attended meetings out in the buying territory. Country packing houses were beginning to develop technique and there were state meetings of dealers to discuss their common problems.

Thus a loosely expressed national consciousness of a vast industry began to be felt. Fred L. Kimball, a Waterloo, Iowa, printer, in 1895, founded the Egg Reporter which immediately became the popular organ of the newly developing western egg industry. F. G. Urner, editor of the New York Produce Review and American Creamery, contributed the leading market analysis for the younger publication in the West. It thrived and in a very short time had a circulation of 20,000 monthly. It is difficult for those now in the business to visualize so many dealers in eggs. The circulation was chiefly in the country, centering in the State of Iowa and reaching out into the whole corn belt area and to the far western Pacific states. The days of consolidation and large packing plants were yet to come.

The American Poultry Association, established in 1873, com-

Car being loaded with live poultry in a Kentucky market. Many reach New York.

posed of breeders, exhibitors and publishers, was for nearly a third of a century the only national body representing the industry before the public. Its members were far removed, by the nature of their problems, from the trade in eggs and poultry. It was not until 1906 that a group of New York poultry and game dealers, who made annual pilgrimages into the West, led a movement to organize the National Poultry, Butter and Egg Association. The success and influence of the Egg Reporter suggested that a new egg world was forming. Business no longer hung entirely or chiefly on New York and other eastern markets. The future of the organized industry lay in the Middle West and the eastern leaders were quick to sense the change. They sought to bring both city dealers and country packers into one national association. Railway and supply men, cold storage warehousemen and state associations were soon included in the scheme. The activities were chiefly protective and defensive, as they are today.

Meanwhile there was accumulating pressure on the breeders and exhibitors to produce birds to answer the growing demand

Grand Prize awarded American-packed poultry at Paris Exposition of 1900. Packed by Boardman Brothers, Priebe & Simater, and Swartzchild–Sulzberger.

of the cities for food. The back-yard poultry flock was giving way to a garage. Town people were more interested in "gasoline alley" than they were in gardening or poultry raising. Poultry was drifting to the farms; and farmers, working for profit, were not interested in exhibition birds. A new industry was developing—the sale and shipment of baby chicks.

The old American Poultry Association seemed unable to accommodate its policy to the changing times. Many of its members held to the opinion that the breeding of good foundation stock and exhibitions of fancy birds were more important than commercial hatching and resisted the efforts of incubator manufacturers and of dealers in supplies for the hatcheries who were intent on developing the baby chick industry. In 1916, the International Baby Chick Association was born, a husky youngster which soon claimed the leading annual convention and manufacturers' exhibition of technical improvements, centering around the hatchery business. Today it is estimated that not less than a billion eggs a year are needed for hatching in incubators, large and small. The American Poultry Association meanwhile continued to center its activities on breeding

AN IN-
DUSTRY
EMERGES

Testing flavor of eggs of known history. Three U. S. bureaus and Beltsville government farm cooperating.

and on exhibitions of fancy stock. The consideration of utility classes of poultry came later when there developed so called R. O. P. (record-of-performance) associations of breeders. These are now to be found in half or more of the states.

What were the Land Grant Colleges and Experiment Stations doing? In 1907, a small handful of instructors and investigators in poultry husbandry organized what is now the Poultry Science Association. Its annual meetings of about three hundred scientifically trained members have become one of the three annual fact-finding conferences of importance, conducted respectively by the Poultry Science Association for the scientists, by the International Baby Chick Association for the hatcherymen, and by the Institute of American Poultry Industries for the industry as a whole. The institute is supported chiefly by packer-distributors and reflects consumer demand as expressed in the markets.

This most recent national movement was educational in purpose—the United States Egg Society, beginning in 1925, now the Institute of American Poultry Industries. It left to others already in the field all defensive measures and controversial subjects and centered attention on the product itself. Its annual

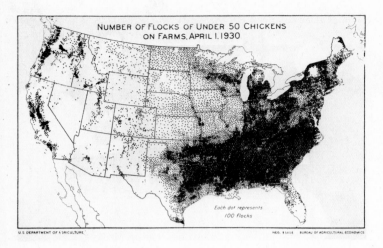

NUMBER OF FLOCKS OF UNDER 50 CHICKENS
ON FARMS, APRIL 1, 1930

Each dot represents 100 flocks

U.S. DEPARTMENT OF AGRICULTURE   NEG. 15012   BUREAU OF AGRICULTURAL ECONOMICS

Small flocks for
family u s e a r e
found chiefly in
the old South.

Fact Finding Conferences have no political or exhibition objectives but only the encouragement of fact-finding, chiefly related to the products themselves, the wants of consumers, and how those wants are to be satisfied.

There are in all twenty or more national associations which deal in matters relating to eggs and poultry, including the manufacturers of feed and packages and farm or incubator equipment, cold storage warehousemen, officials of colleges and state marketing, commercial poultrymen and specialty breeders of all the important breeds. In addition there are hundreds of state and local organizations amongst both shippers and producers. It is a much organized industry.

It may be of interest to note that the circulation of publications devoted entirely to poultry (chiefly monthly journals) aggregates about two million. The Institute of American Poultry Industries publishes the United States Egg and Poultry Magazine, which circulates only within the organized industry. However, by supplying key literature to about fifty leading agricultural publications, two to three hundred leading food columnists in the daily press, and to others including many editors of technical publications, college classes and public

AN IN-
DUSTRY
EMERGES

278

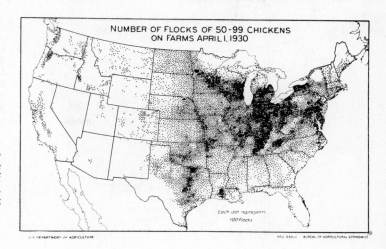

NUMBER OF FLOCKS OF 50-99 CHICKENS ON FARMS APRIL 1, 1930

Flocks of 50 to 400 birds are characteristic of the corn belt. See following three maps.

Each dot represents 100 flocks

U S DEPARTMENT OF AGRICULTURE   NEG 25016   BUREAU OF AGRICULTURAL ECONOMICS

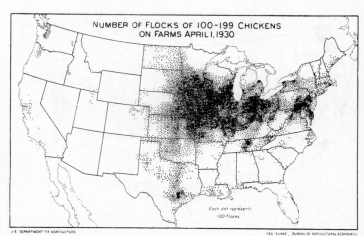

NUMBER OF FLOCKS OF 100-199 CHICKENS ON FARMS APRIL 1, 1930

The most popular size of flock in Illinois, Iowa, Indiana, and Ohio.

Each dot represents 100 flocks

U S DEPARTMENT OF AGRICULTURE   NEG 25086   BUREAU OF AGRICULTURAL ECONOMICS

conventions interested in food problems, the Institute reaches indirectly an audience estimated at ten to fifteen million. Thus the marketing industry has a means of expression that touches both producers and consumers. Scientists and officials everywhere, who are concerned in the production and uses of eggs and poultry read this magazine which circulates in every state and in many foreign countries.

279

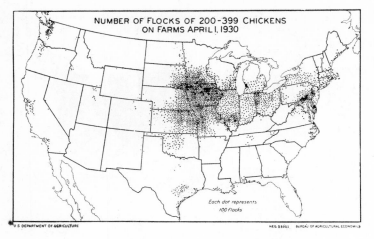

NUMBER OF FLOCKS OF 200-399 CHICKENS ON FARMS APRIL 1, 1930

Each dot represents 100 flocks

U S DEPARTMENT OF AGRICULTURE   NEG 23921   BUREAU OF AGRICULTURAL ECONOMICS

Topography and large farms of the Central West favor dual purpose fowls.

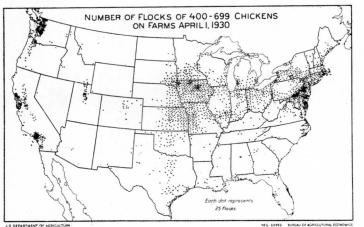

NUMBER OF FLOCKS OF 400-699 CHICKENS ON FARMS APRIL 1, 1930

Each dot represents 25 flocks

U S DEPARTMENT OF AGRICULTURE   NEG 23922   BUREAU OF AGRICULTURAL ECONOMICS

Climate and small farms favor egg-production flocks on the Pacific coast and the North Atlantic seaboard.

It remains to mention and emphasize the importance of the World's Poultry Congresses, held under the auspices of the International Poultry Science Association. In 1930 it was participated in by sixty or more nations through official delegates appointed by their governments. This body has met four times, the last meeting having been held in London in 1930. On one boat out of Montreal 411 American poultry specialists

280

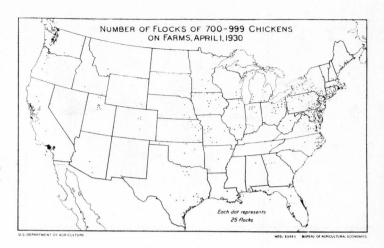

NUMBER OF FLOCKS OF 700-999 CHICKENS
ON FARMS, APRIL 1, 1930

Flocks of this size or more are strictly commercial enterprises.

Each dot represents 25 flocks

U.S. DEPARTMENT OF AGRICULTURE   NEG. 25023 · BUREAU OF AGRICULTURAL ECONOMICS

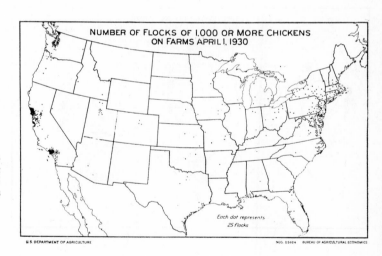

NUMBER OF FLOCKS OF 1,000 OR MORE CHICKENS
ON FARMS APRIL 1, 1930

Note concentration on Pacific coast and in industrial centers of the East.

Each dot represents 25 flocks

U.S. DEPARTMENT OF AGRICULTURE   NEG. 25024 · BUREAU OF AGRICULTURAL ECONOMICS

and their families sailed to attend this Congress, which filled the great Crystal Palace with its exhibits, fact-finding meetings and social affairs. It is sponsored by the International Poultry Science Association of which the Poultry Science Association of America is a division. Both of these associations publish excellent scientific Journals.

281

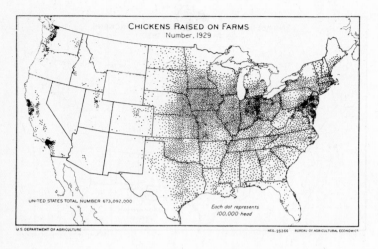

Combined map showing the density of the poultry population of America.

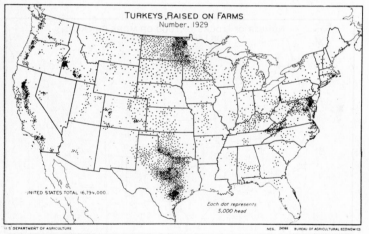

The distribution of the turkey population is somewhat different from that of chickens.

Climate and Geography Determine Many Things

The public wants the best and most economical eggs and poultry, and a hundred things may work for or against the achievement of this goal. Climate and geography are among the most important; they make and unmake would-be poultry 282 men. Favored by climate, an intensive development of poultry

A flock of pure-breds roosting in a peach orchard near Memphis.

raising has grown up around Petaluma, California. The California poultrymen commonly have twenty-five hundred or more birds in one flock. The flocks in the State of Washington, on the other hand, are more often of five hundred to eight hundred birds and they are usually managed as a side line to fruit growing or other farming. By standardizing the feed and servicing the flock owners the Pacific Coast poultrymen attain uniformity in their eggs which is an aid to marketing. Climate gives the State of Washington an annual yield of eggs per hen somewhat higher than in California.

In the Central West climate and the type of farming give a lower yield of eggs per hen, but a lower production cost. A dual purpose bird is commonly preferred, resulting in a better meat bird and, some think, in a hardier egg for keeping, if properly handled from the nest.

In the Northeastern States, industrial centers provide nearby markets and selective trade in sufficient volume to favor the intensive development of commercial poultry raising. The eggs and poultry are often sold by the roadside—a development

AN IN-
DUSTRY
EMERGES

made possible by automobiles, thousands of miles of highway, and the ease of handling eggs in the shell.

In the South the custom of procuring eggs from the home flock survives to an extent not true elsewhere in the United States. The climate of our Southern States is favorable to outdoor life on the part of the birds. There are fewer and simpler poultry houses. The birds commonly roost in orchard trees. A great deal of the old South is mountainous, and in some sections poultry is handled much as it was three hundred years ago.

The 150-egg Six-pound Hen

The 150-egg six-pound hen is, on the whole, a high attainment as a flock average. If this hen should some day be approximated on general farms in the upper Mississippi Valley, as it can be, the commercial poultry farmers, in order to compete with her, will have to utilize all the arts of the breeder, feeder, sanitary engineer and veterinarian. The farther production is stimulated beyond the easy attainment of healthy individual birds, the more dependent are the birds on good management. The general farmer is seldom equal to the task of successfully handling a flock that can maintain a record higher than 150 eggs per bird. He can, however, with adequate servicing by specialists, step up both the rate of production and the quality of eggs and poultry far beyond the average common today. The present average egg yield is about seventy eggs a year per hen.

Here is an important field for engineering or good commonsense planning, which may accomplish the same thing. Such planning is often systematic and includes teaching the farmers how to apply uniform methods. This may be done as a sales or buying service on the part of packer-buyers, hatcherymen,

150-egg six pound hens of general purpose breeds are the ideal for farm flocks in the upper Mississippi valley. From left to right: Buff Orpington, White Wyandotte, Rhode Island Red and Barred Plymouth Rock. Reds have been bred for heavier egg production until most of them are smaller than the bird here shown. See pages 82 and 83.

feed manufacturers, state officers and college men, who may also cooperate in a given shipping area to unify the practices of flock owners so that a more uniform and therefore a more salable product will result.

A forerunner of this movement as applied to general farm flocks in the Middle West has been the merchandising success of far western poultrymen who have practiced farm servicing on a large scale for about two decades. Credit is often given to cooperative marketing for this success, but it has conspicuously followed other methods of marketing as well. In no part of the country, however, have the principles of uniform production and centralized marketing of eggs been applied to the extent, or with the success, that they have to the eggs produced in the far west.

As applied to poultry, the same goal has been reached more

AN IN-DUSTRY EMERGES

285

An egg packing house near Petaluma, California. A favorable Climate and superior organization for dispatching the eggs make handling possible in large open-air pavilions.

conspicuously in the Middle West, where the climate and type of farming favor the production of good meat birds. Here the final finish of the birds is given in enormous feeding stations, part of the central packing plants. These have been delightfully described by Miss Pennington in her chapter on How Poultry Is Made Ready for Market.

In merchandising methods the Pacific Egg Producers, Inc., a sales agency representing certain cooperatives of three states, has developed excellent outlets through balancing the movement of eggs and assuring the buyers of a uniform and uniformly good product. Uniformity has been attained on the Pacific Coast in considerable measure not only by rigid grading but by payment of farmers strictly according to grade. It is true that this creates unrest as often among members of a cooperative association as it does when applied to farmers anywhere, but it is one price of success in the food business. Which is another way of saying that consumers are selective, and poultry farmers and merchants who succeed must be also.

W E ARE said to live faster than we did 100 years ago, and, according to vital statistics, we are living longer. We thus pack more changes into a human life-time; and the human machine, on the whole, seems to have adjusted itself and to thrive.

The stories in this book suggest that there are cycles of change, and that they occur with a degree of periodicity, sometimes with the regularity of seasons. The short time cycles may be anticipated and "discounted" in the market; but the great periods cannot. A major event like the World War introduces a new epoch. Only a very long-lived person or a qualified student of history can span an epoch. Hence books and other means for recording the changes of time are needed if we are to understand what is going on about us.

How Food Research Started

After the Civil War, people felt the pinch of an inadequate food supply. One result of this was that Congress passed an act granting to the states a good deal of land with which to provide for colleges of agriculture, so that food production might be stimulated. All such schools are known as Land Grant Colleges. Many of them have assumed university status. They expanded their activities and received increased support from the states. Here we find some of the ablest research workers in subjects related to agriculture. The aim of the Land Grant Colleges was to encourage farming and to improve the lot of the farmer. But the consumer, too, shared in the benefits. And the processor and distributor not only aided but 287

also were aided by the research in the particular foods that they handled.

A question occurs in this connection as to whether our food supply is a concern of farmers or of consumers. The federal government administers food research chiefly in the Department of Agriculture. In this department, the Bureau of Home Economics, primarily interested in *consumer* study, has had a total appropriation of about $200,000 annually, out of which a portion goes for studies in food and human nutrition. But in other bureaus of the Department of Agriculture, primarily interested in *production* study, a total varying in the past few years from 10 to 20 million dollars annually has been spent for food research. Even larger sums are spent in the aggregate by the different states, the federal government often cooperating with the state experiment stations. A million dollars a year is spent on egg and poultry research alone, and the state experiment stations take a leading part.

Much of this food research work originates in a demand from agricultural industries, and it reflects the interest of farmers and of industry in certain problems. The government is impartial in such work, reflecting the best ideas of scientific

The President and family watching the Easter Egg Rolling festivities. A ceremonial side of the government's interest in egg production.

detachment, which is a condition of successful research. Yet the projects do not originate primarily in demands of consumers but in the needs of particular industries.

The New Trend in Research

Too much emphasis can easily be given to one viewpoint. In poultry raising and egg production, as in all agricultural industries, the weal of the flock owners or other elements, important though it is, may be emphasized until the consumers' viewpoint seems quite subordinate. We are entering a new business era and facing problems of importance to consumers. Flock owners might well keep in mind three facts: (1) that consumers govern the use made of all that is produced; (2) that every flock owner is himself a consumer; and (3) that while there are five million flocks large and small, there are twenty-five consumers to every flock owner in this country. Moreover, the interest of consumers in food is primarily to secure good quality at reasonable prices.

Food research has become a regular business of processors and distributors, who are closer to consumers in the chain of marketing than are farmers. By and large, however, the study and regulation of the nation's food supply rests with departments of the government or with colleges established to promote agriculture. Competition between different products of agriculture has, to be sure, caused each industry to study and improve its own, but this is not always equivalent to consumer research.

A change is impending in which the study of the nation's food supply seems destined to become an increasing concern of the consumer and to make his needs paramount. Whether or not people directing such studies are trained in agricultural schools, they must understand not only the needs of the consumer, but also the possibilities and the limitations of industry, of production and processing as well as of marketing, and they must have a sound knowledge of facts—including the facts about eggs and poultry.

Animal food is perishable until it is processed or cured, and the condition in which such food is delivered to consumers is a matter of vital importance to state and city departments of health where, for the present at least, activities intended for the protection of the consumer are centered. All who are charged with the people's health—including doctors, dietitians, homemakers and teachers of these subjects—should have a good understanding of the means for protecting perishable foods, especially of freezing, or, as with shell eggs, cooling to a temperature just high enough not to freeze.

The demand for capable trained directors of municipal health departments led to the establishment of schools of hygiene and public health. Among them is one in The Johns

Hopkins University at Baltimore. It is directed by Dr. E. V. McCollum who is at once recognized by all readers of food literature. Dr. McCollum began his studies at the Wisconsin State College of Agriculture in the subject of animal feeding. Many if not most of our greatest authorities on human hygiene and nutrition began with the study of animals and animal foods. This has been largely due to the fact that their studies were carried on as part of a curriculum in Land Grant or agricultural colleges.

What it might mean to millions of flock owners and to dealers and distributors of eggs and poultry to emphasize the consumer's viewpoint in food research is worth considering. It would undoubtedly encourage the growing emphasis on quality in production and on merchandising in distribution. It would be reflected back into departments of agriculture and experiment stations in a healthful way and would tend to unify food research and reduce the competitive feature between foods as such, while intensifying the competition to produce and market better food. This viewpoint should therefore be encouraged by consumers and by all who have the general good at heart. The producer is the person most directly interested in his pocket book, and he will not give up his job of doing good research work or of getting it done.

The possibility of more exchange of scientific effort between this country and other countries should be considered. When the rapid expansion of commercial poultry keeping in Great Britain necessitated an extension of the facilities for advanced research and instruction in poultry and rabbit husbandry, Professor Willard C. Thompson of the New Jersey Agricultural Experiment Station went to England from November, 1924 to September, 1926 to assist the National Institute of Poultry Husbandry, to outline courses of study and to initiate poultry research. In October, 1927, Professor Raymond T. Parkhurst of the University of Idaho became Director of this Institute for a five-year period. During that time, the buildings and

Volume of eggs is determined by the amount of water displaced at a given temperature.

poultry plant were completed, advanced courses of poultry instruction put into effect, and the research program greatly expanded. The efforts of the two American investigators have been sincerely appreciated.

What the Chemist and Physicist May Teach Us About Eggs

Miss Pennington has told how, many years ago, the federal government through its food research laboratory began the study of egg chemistry. For about a decade after the laboratory was discontinued, chemistry studies in eggs lagged, but recently they have again been resorted to for solving many of the problems of production, preparation for market and marketing. From small beginnings, notably at Cornell, such studies spread to other colleges and to the commercial laboratories until in a very short time they were looked upon as a field for professional training and vocation.

Chemistry and physics can solve some common problems of egg producers and dealers. Among the important problems that might be tackled by chemists are these:

Disclosing the structure of the egg and how its white becomes watery; what it means if it does become watery.

Unique property values in eggs, such as fats, proteins, pigmentation and effects of diet, are discovered by chemical observations.

Preventing fertility by sterilizing the egg. This may prove to be a problem in electricity.

Why, and under what condition, new-laid eggs sometimes do not "stand up" in commerce or appear "weak" and watery when laid.

The variation in food value of individual eggs, and the reasons for the variation.

The sources of vitamin D in eggs and how it may be increased. The relation between color of yolk and vitamin content.

How to make profitable use, in manufacture or for animal food, of three or four hundred million eggs which fail to hatch in incubators.

How to standardize egg meat quality during production by simple control measures.

How to make the grading of eggs more accurate.

New uses for egg whites which tend to accumulate in the market due to a larger demand for yolks.

The influence of various storage conditions on quality.

Breeding and farm management and how they affect quality.

The utilization of the egg in human nutrition and what happens to its various constituents, especially the proteins.

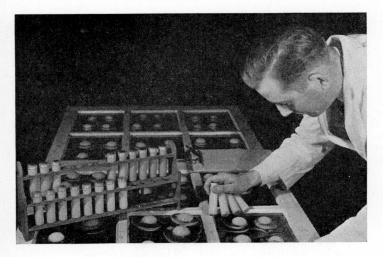

Intensity of yolk color is measured by matching glass vials marked in varying degrees of yellow.

The problem of regulating egg yolk color by flock management and how to obtain yolks of high color for manufacturing bakers and mayonnaise manufacturers while at the same time supplying lighter-colored yolks if wanted for table use.

How to find inexpensive and accurate methods of accomplishing some of the above things by grading, thus relieving producers of the more complicated problem of producing different eggs for different uses.

This is only a partial list of the things that a study of chemistry and physics of eggs might tell us. It will take time just to explain some of the phenomena that have been common knowledge of egg men but have not been understood. We know, for example, that the Chinese make Pidan, a cheese-like food, from eggs and we suspect that the accumulating surplus of whites of eggs might be profitably utilized as skim milk is utilized by studying its chemistry. However, little if anything is accurately known about the changes that might be made in egg white by processing.

The increasing use of bulk eggs, both frozen eggs and dried eggs, makes a problem in balancing the use of the parts of the egg. One concern, for example, last season needed the yolks

Diameter, depth, and stand-up quality (or breaking strength of the yolk) is measured with calipers.

of two hundred carloads of eggs in dried form for ready-prepared pancake flour. Have you ever considered the problems that such demands make on our industry?

The study of egg chemistry has an industrial future that promises a livelihood for quite a few college graduates and rich rewards for the more successful.

Opportunities for Package Research

Stimulated by the enormous quantities handled and by the chance for profit, package manufacturers have contributed in a fascinating way to the development of the egg and poultry industries. The egg case, baby-chick box, poultry shipping coop, frozen-egg can and dressed poultry container, not to mention the several kinds of batteries or cages for housing young and old chickens in mass operations, all have undergone changes which have sometimes been determined by commercial standards for the product and sometimes have determined such standards.

An interesting example of how the package may influence production aims, is the standard 30-dozen egg case with its honeycomb filler which has so established itself that the dimensions of trucks and railway cars, egg rooms and, of course, the dozen-egg carton, have been adapted to it. The package structure, in this instance, has become so rigid that instead of accommodating the egg in its natural range of sizes, hens have been bred to lay two-ounce eggs which are neither too large nor too small to fit the filler cell.

For a long time a given type of package may seem to have come to stay; then something occurs to cause a radical change in the package to adjust it to some better way of handling the product.

Influence of Personality

Changes seem at times to be the direct result of some strong personality entering the industrial picture—someone who is seized, as it were, with a life mission. The story of a century of progress might be written about the lives of such men and women. And there have been many interesting lives lived for the lowly hen and her eggs.

People who have left a marked impress on our industry all deserve to be mentioned in a story of progress but the lives of many are hidden; their influence is scarcely understood or their importance realized in their own day. We are not astute enough to measure their value until long after they have left the stage.

An example of a man who is not well known outside the frozen egg industry but around whose life and ideas that industry built a new method of operating and of merchandising was H. J. Keith. Mr. Keith was a New Englander who early in life migrated to Minnesota. There, with Madison Cooper and a friend of both of them, George A. Dole, who owned one of the early cold storage houses designed by Mr. Cooper, he began experimenting back in the nineties with egg meats and their preservation for convenient marketing in cans, frozen.

Both Mr. Keith and Mr. Cooper were practical men with inquiring minds, and Mr. Dole provided the freezing and storage facilities and loaned them money. Madison Cooper later returned to his native state, New York, where for many years he continued to develop the science of cold storage, while Mr. Keith went to Boston, where he continued his development of the frozen egg business. This was about the turn of the century. The early experiments in Minnesota had been financially disastrous for Mr. Keith.

From the very beginning Mr. Keith broke only eggs of good quality. While most of his competitors regarded the freezing of eggs as a salvaging business to use up eggs too poor or unfit for commerce in the shell, Keith believed that if good eggs could be broken out under sanitary conditions and frozen, they were a superior article to the best shell eggs for bakers. He visualized long in advance of others what the business might become but it was some time before he mastered two problems: to convince the bakers of the superiority of his eggs for baking and to get them to accept the eggs in the spring of the year at manufacturing cost plus a reasonable manufacturer's profit, which eliminated the market risk for him.

He had to convince bakers of his knowledge and accurate judgment of quality, and of his integrity in carrying out an agreement.

His amazing success in later years pointed the way to others. He had not only educated many young men in the new art of freezing eggs and in sound conduct of the business, but he accumulated and held on to the one outstanding fortune made exclusively from eggs.

His early struggles with adversity left him sympathetic with harrassed or thwarted people everywhere. His fear of the consequences of ignorance and superstition had been sharpened by his experience in dealing with ignorance in his business. Having no children, his thinking led him into a broad humanistic outlook, finally expressed in a trust which survives him and to which he bequeathed all of his fortune. He directed that it should be allotted to schools like Antioch College, Yellow Springs, Ohio, whose Morgan held similar ideas about the use of money for deserving and needy students to complete an education, namely, that they should also work for a living. Keith's benefactions under this trust reach into many institutions of learning. Unobtrusively and unknown to many of his intimates, this thought had taken hold on his vision.

I share the view of many that Keith was one of the most princely of the men who have passed through our industry and left their impress upon it. He had what was known in the eighteenth century as *noblesse oblige*—a sense of the responsibility incurred by success or station in life, a sense of the right of the underconditioned to share the rewards of progress. Keith was self-denying and careful of small expenditures long after his fortune was ample for every personal need. He had a deep sense of social integrity.

As Time Moves On

A Century of Progress is a thought worth juggling. It reminds us that changes never cease. We try to appraise a small segment of time in terms of the changes occurring and we call it progress. The effect of forcing change before its time is often to destroy something valuable. On the other hand, beneficial changes may be hastened by cultivating those orderly processes of nature we desire and by weeding out anything that interferes. This is the well known method of the good gardener.

In our book the authors have cited many instances of controlled intelligent progress by the gardener's method of selection and refusal. Looking backward but a short time, the progress appears to have been slow, but after reviewing a more distant past as one may do in this book, we see that great progress has been made. Time alone and the forces of natural selection will do much, but nature apparently desires man to control her. Whether the rate of progress be slow or fast, depends a great deal on our ability to cooperate.

To those who are growing old in this business I would say that only the old, if they will, can bridge the gap between maturity and youth, between the past and the present. General information, so far as it may have been reduced to teaching, is more accessible to youth and far more readily interpreted by youth in terms of the present. But there the advantage ends. Time and tide, it has been said, wait for no man, and when the youth has acquired the training of faculties and of judgment which experience alone can give him, he is no longer young. Only the old in experience can bridge the gap that time is continually making between succeeding generations, and then only if the old continue sensitive to *the value and importance of change.* How few there are who do!

Of this endless rhythm of birth unto birth, the egg is a fitting symbol.

A Dutch painting by H e n d r i k Bloemaert, dated 1632. It hangs in the Rijksmuseum at Amsterdam, Holland.

Leaf comb—Old English
Houdan.

Cushion comb—Chantecler.

Pea comb—Light Brahma.

Buttercup comb—English
Buttercups.

Rose comb—White
Wyandotte.

Natural absence of comb—
Polish.

Petal comb—Breda.

V-comb — Creve-coeur. C f.
Antler comb—LaFleche p. 90.

Single comb—Silver Campine.

300

Strawberry comb—Malay.

Excessive earlobe—White Faced Balck Spanish.

Walnut comb—Malay.

The brilliant eye of a good layer. Note the head poise. Compare pp. 55, 63, 82.

Left: The parts of a feather. Plumage of fowls differs in type, texture, color and size. Color pattern and its inheritance is the chief factor in breed varieties.

Right: A laced feather perfected in the Silver Sebright Bantam and in the Silver laced Wyandotte. The Mossy feather, farthest to the right, is a defective laced. The white edging is called frosting, also a defect.

301

Penciled.

Striped.

Striped with Diamond Center.

Half-laced spangle (defect).

Barred.

Stippled.

Diagonal Spangled.

Irregular penciled (defect).

Spangled.

Mottled.

Spangle tipped.

Splashed (defect).

302

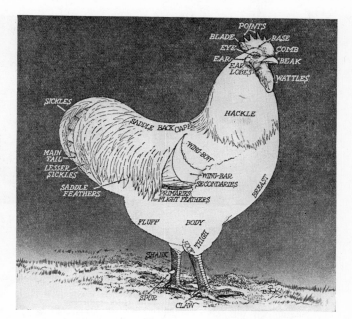

The male has long narrow pointed saddle, covert, sickle and lesser sickle feathers which the female does not have. The female has a cushion instead. Feather markings on male and female differ also. In the penciled varieties females are penciled and males are not. Combs of females are smaller, and wattles are rudimentary.

When the hen is coming into production the pelvic arch widens and abdominal depth increases. When the laying season is over this region shrinks.

300-egg hens maintain four-finger width and four-finger depth most of the year. Culling for high record breeding stock is done as shown in the accompanying figures. Capacity should be coupled with pliability for good layers.

303

Cushion, fluff and toe feathers—
Buff Cochin hen.

Ear muff and beard—
White Faverolles hen.

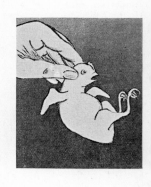

Sex selection of baby chicks. For many centuries the Chinese have sold baby chick pullets and cockerels separately. The profession of sex determination is hereditary.

Two methods have come down to us from antiquity. One is by gently pinching the anus to observe male or female organs.

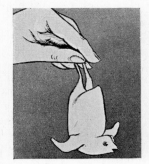

The anus is examined with surprising speed, and this manner of segregation has proved accurate and valuable to the Chinese hatcherymen through many generations.

The other method is by suspension as here shown. Males are inactive as indicated in figures on the left. Females fight and curl their bodies as shown in figures on the right.

304

BOOK II

THE BEST OF FOODS
EGGS AND POULTRY

CLARA GEBHARD SNYDER

Alas! my child, where is the Pen
That can do justice to the Hen?
Like Royalty, she goes her way,
Laying Foundations every day,
Though not for Public Buildings, yet
For Custard, Cake and Omelette.
No wonder, Child, we prize the Hen,
Whose Egg is mightier than the Pen.

Oliver Herford—The Hen

My Dear Mrs. Snyder:

I am pleased to see that your artist has pictured two roosters (on the jacket) introducing your excellent book on the cooking of eggs. The rooster, I have always held, is the original advertising man. He is the gentleman who crows when somebody else lays an egg.

It is here my pleasant duty to crow over the recipes that some one else has prepared. And take it from one who has spent a goodly portion of his existence in the pursuit of egg recipes, most of those found here are for dishes fit to snatch away from a king.

Writing this introduction reminds me of the time when I was a scholar (and a gentleman). That time my life was troubled by the mysterious "X" which I industriously pursued through thousands and thousands of algebra problems. Now that I have thrown away all my books (except yours and the ones I write myself), I find the only "x" left in my life is "what shall we have for dinner tonight?" And I have found eggs a frequent answer to that 'x' ".

It has been said that there are 742,367 ways of preparing eggs. I have never checked carefully on the accuracy of this figure, but I can tell you from a lifetime spent in associating with eggs that I believe that each way of preparing eggs is the best.

My advice to those who may possess this book is that they make some pleasant history by trying the recipes that are given here.

with best wishes

George Rector

THE ART OF HAPPY EATING

IN THE turmoil of the past twenty years, during which time changes
in our manner of living have been very marked, we Americans for
the most part lost interest in the old fashioned sumptuous table of
home-cooked delicacies. Tempted by the ubiquitous scales we learned
to drop a penny to the god of health who claimed we were gaining or
losing in physical efficiency according to our daily weight. Doctors
told us we ate too much, and much of what we did eat was not good
for us.

We were taught to consider the chemistry of our bodies and to suspect all food of being deficient in something essential to our physiological needs. We chose our food by calories, then by mineral con
tent, vitamins and what not. We sought to balance each and every
meal.

Instead of relying upon our feelings in the matter, we were told to
use our brains, to eschew the good old guide appetite, and to ask o
our diet books whether we were denying our livers and bones, skin
teeth, and endocrine anatomy something they should very much have
We ate in fear and anxiety.

Now cooking, as an art, is founded upon pleasure in eating; and
when some psychiatrist, and perhaps a food columnist, suggested tha
food which is attractive might have superier physiological value, th
scientific world in general wisely said "yes". Indeed we now appea
to be headed toward a better day when the way we eat, and how ou
food is cooked and served will again become important.

What a difference it makes in the ease with which we begin ou
digestive processes, if the food is attractive! And appetizing thoug
the food may be, how easily is good digestion defeated by hurry, c
by the habit of engaging in conferences on business or other seriou
subjects during the mealtime!

To arouse the sense nature so as to perform the digestive functior
properly, eating should be combined with relaxing subjects—mirtl
beauty, homely satisfactions. Service, decorum, environment, pride i

the way food is prepared or acquired and presented—all these have health as well as pleasure value.

Some of the simplest people with the simplest eating habits live longer and happier than others more highly circumstanced. The meal is their social rendezvous, and they enjoy it. They may live close to the soil, and intimacy with the things they grow is helpful to the appetite. They take keen satisfaction in watching the development of their food crops, and so rejoice in the fatted capon or the plump ear of corn when it is ready for the table. They learn to select good food by watching it reach maturity. We city people seldom have that privilege, but we make eating needlessly complex. Granted that we are far removed from the soil and that much of our food may have lost valuable elements by soil depletion, poor processing and what not, the laboratory is not the only reliable guide to the facts in the matter. And valuable though the science of nutrition appears to be, a sensitive organism, with an appetite tuned and trained by love for good food, is also a reliable guide.

Sensitiveness to food can be cultivated. There is much more to appetizing food than mere flavor. Food has qualities of succulence, temperature and texture. It may be savory and have tang and aroma. It may have a dressed appearance. These are the prompters that make food attractive to the organism in varying degrees.

One of the charms of variety in food is the surprise element—new and enticing ways of preparing things to eat. Along this delightful way the following pages lead us. In this book are recipes, 800 of them, ranging from the modern—true because they have been experimentally tested—to those of our forebears which are true because they have been tested by time. And recipes which are of quaint or historical interest have not been overlooked. They all contain eggs or poultry in some important way, and this will not surprise the reader because Mrs. Snyder tells the reasons why eggs especially are so necessary an ingredient of good cookery.

—THE EDITOR.

C O N T E N T S

INTRODUCTION

THE PLACE OF EGGS IN THE DIET

The symbol of Venus—Why eggs nourish—Eggs are easy to digest—Eggs in the child's diet.

THE PLACE OF EGGS IN COOKERY

The bubble-making egg—The interfering egg—The film-forming egg—The thickening egg—The binding egg—The adhesive egg—The clarifying egg—The decorative egg.

PRACTICAL HINTS ON BUYING EGGS

How many to buy—Community refrigerators—Eggs with protected shells—How to care for eggs at home.

EGG ODDITIES IN FOREIGN LANDS

Eggs of other fowls — European preferences — Oriental preparations.

FROM BROILER TO FRICASSEE

.Chicken Dinner, yesterday and to-day—How to select poultry.

BIRDS OF THE FESTIVE BOARD—with recipes

HOW'S AND WHY'S IN COOKING POULTRY—
with recipes

RECIPES FROM FAR AND NEAR—potpourri

HOW'S AND WHY'S IN COOKING EGGS—
with recipes

APPENDIX—Useful Information

How to carve a bird—Abbreviations used in recipes—Useful facts about eggs—Useful facts about poultry—Amount of poultry to buy.

Recipes—Curious and Historical

INDEX TO RECIPES

LIST OF ILLUSTRATIONS—BOOK II

Decora-
tive and deli-
cious for
b r e akfast,
lunch, dinner
or supper.

THE PLACE OF
EGGS IN THE DIET

THE egg is always cropping up usefully in conversation.
"You can substitute a turnip for an egg only once," says
the Chinaman.

"You can't make an omelet without breaking the eggs," says
the Frenchman.

"Don't put all your eggs in one basket," says the American.

"From eggs to apples," said the ancient Roman, meaning
"from soup to nuts."

"He's a good egg" is high praise in modern slang.

Gastronomically, the egg is even more dominant.

"The chef is the slave of the egg," said a great French chef.

Another remarked, "The egg is the cement that holds the
castles of cookery together."

Nutritionally, the value of the egg is indicated by this statement from a book called "Ultra-violet Light and Vitamin D in
Nutrition," by Blunt and Cowan:

"The richness of eggs in vitamin D is one of the many reasons for their dietary value. Physicians and nutritionists are
realizing that the educational campaign for increasing the use
of milk could well be supplemented by a similar one for eggs,
to the great advantage of babies, children and adults."

331

The Symbol of Venus

As a source of that most precious and mysterious of all things, life, the egg has been the subject of fascinating legend and myth. All peoples in all lands seem to have built up customs and beliefs about eggs.

Centuries ago, so goes one ancient legend, a mysterious great bird appeared and deposited on the waste an immense egg, from which developed the world. In ancient Mongolia a similar legend, perhaps related to it, tells that the great bird laid the mystical egg on the bosom of a god. When it was hatched, the god dropped it into the water, breaking it. The upper part of the egg became the sky, the lower part became the earth, while the white formed the sun and the shattered bits became stars. The existence of many such legends explains why the egg has often been considered the symbol of the universe.

Gigantic eggs are comparatively common in legend. Hyginus, keeper of the Palatine library, wrote about the immense egg of Cyprus which one day fell into the Euphrates River. When fishes had rolled it to the shore a great dove appeared and settled on it. Finally from it emerged Venus, goddess of love and beauty. The egg was her symbol, as it was also the emblem of Castor and Pollux, patrons of Roman horse races. Even the tracks on which the races were run were oval or egg-shaped.

The egg has played an important part in the rites of most religions. Eggs were a favorite peace-offering to offended gods. Ancient Hindus held eggs in great respect as the source of all things. Egyptian hieroglyphics used the oval frequently, and pictures of the Egyptian god of creation, Kneuph, show him with an egg in his mouth.

THE PLACE
OF EGGS IN
THE DIET

Why Eggs Nourish

The modern scientist, like the ancient priest, sees in the egg the source of life, but in quite a different sense. In this small, sealed, two-ounce package the chemist has found all the constituents necessary to build a body.

The package itself, miraculously constructed and delicately lined, makes up about one-tenth of the weight of the egg. When the package, or shell, is broken, the edible part of the egg, the "egg meat," is released—one of the most fascinating foods in the world. Let us see what it contains.

Like many another food that is easily digestible, the egg contains a large proportion of water. In fact, egg meat is about three-fourths (73.7 per cent) water. Dissolved or suspended in this liquid are the various food constituents that make up the egg. Chief of these, so far as quantity is concerned, are the proteins—a rather large variety of the important ones, for there are many kinds of proteins. Proteins are the body builders, the building blocks that in the growing child make new body tissue, and in both children and adults replace the body tissue which suffers in the wear and tear of normal daily activity.

All proteins are made up of substances which the chemist calls amino acids. Altogether there are nineteen or more of these substances, put together in this way and that to make different proteins. Not all of these substances are present in every protein food. But the body needs all of them, and in certain proportions. So the protein foods which contain all of the amino acids in approximately this proportion needed by the body are superior protein foods for human nutrition. To this group belong eggs, milk, cheese, poultry, meat and fish. The proteins in these foods are often said to have high biological value—that is, they are changed most easily and with least loss from their form as food into body tissue.

In spite of their high food value, the fuel value of eggs is low. One egg yields only 70 calories. A pound of whole egg gives 670 calories, a pound of egg white 230 calories, and a pound of yolk 1645 calories. The striking difference in the caloric or fuel value of the yolk and the white is due to the fact that the yolk contains fat, while the white is practically

THE PLACE
OF EGGS IN
THE DIET

333

fat-free. Because eggs are low in calories, and at the same time high in minerals and vitamins, they are an ideal food to include in the reducing diet.

In spite of the fact that both egg white and egg yolk are protein foods, they differ widely in many respects. Even the most casual observer sees the difference in color, thickness and form. The cook knows that they act quite differently in cooking, and everyone knows they taste different. The chemist knows they are different in structure and composition, and that these differences account at least in part for differences in appearance, performance and flavor.

The white, which makes up about 57 per cent of the total weight of the egg, is more than four-fifths water (86.2 per cent). The remaining fifth is almost pure albumen, one of the best-known proteins. Because egg albumen is available in such pure form and is so easily obtained, it was used in most of the

FOOD VALUE OF EGGS

	1 whole egg	1 egg white	1 egg yolk
Weight	48 gm.	30 gm.*	15 gm.*
Calorie yield	71 cal.	15 cal.	54 cal.
Protein content	6.4 gm.	3.7 gm.	2.4 gm.
Fat content	5.0 gm.	——	5.0 gm.
Calcium content	0.032 gm.	0.008 gm.	0.021 gm.
Phosphorus content	0.170 gm.	0.008 gm.	0.079 gm.
Iron content	0.00044 gm.	0.00006 gm.	0.00128 gm.
Vitamin A	+++	——	+++
Vitamin B	+ to ++	——	++
Vitamin C	—?	—?	—?
Vitamin D	++	—	+++
Vitamin E	+		+
Vitamin G	+++	++	+++

THE PLACE OF EGGS IN THE DIET

+ indicates that the egg contains the vitamin.
++ indicates that the egg is a good source of the vitamin.
+++ indicates that the egg is an excellent source of the vitamin.
—— indicates no appreciable amount.
? indicates doubt as to presence or relative amount.

* Approximately. It is difficult to separate the white and the yolks absolutely. These figures are based on the average weights of whites and yolks as separated for cookery purposes.

early studies on proteins. Egg white, as the table shows, contains small amounts of minerals and is practically fat-free.

The yolk, which is the most complex part of the egg chemically, makes up about a third (32 per cent) of its weight. It is complex because in addition to water and proteins it contains fats, fat-like substances, and a variety of minerals and vitamins. Contrasted with egg white, the yolk is a concentrated food, and it is made up like this:

It is only half water (49.5 per cent), compared with the four-fifths of water (86.2) per cent of the white.

Although it weighs only about half as much as the white, it contains two-thirds as much protein.

Even so, it has twice as much fat as protein; it is about one-third fat.

Because of its fat, it yields more than three times as many calories as egg white.

An egg yolk weighing only 15 grams yields 54 calories. An egg white weighing twice as much, or 30 grams, yields only 15 calories.

Because of their rich vitamin content, eggs belong in the class of protective foods—that is, the foods which protect against certain deficiency diseases. Most of the vitamins are in the yolk, though the white is a good source of vitamin G, which protects against pellagra and some types of nervous disorders.

It should be pointed out here that the first thing scientists found out about vitamins was their protective value. Nowadays, however, they have come to consider them more and more not only as protectors, but as positive builders of health and well-being. It is this new viewpoint that gives the egg, rich in vitamins, special significance.

The yolk contains almost the whole vitamin alphabet, except vitamin C, and most of them are present in generous amounts.

To begin with, there is vitamin A, the growth vitamin. This is the one that is associated with orange-colored and green

foods, and egg yolk is no exception. The color of the egg yolk
depends on the feed the hen has had. The more green feeds,
such as grass and alfalfa, and the more yellow feeds, such as
yellow corn, that the hen eats, the richer in color are the yolks
of her eggs. Yolks may thus vary in color from palest yellow
to richest orange. The coloring material, as has been explained in the first part of this book, is a pigment called
xanthophyll, which the hen gets in her food. It may even be
that the hen that eats the largest amount of green and yellow
foods lays eggs whose yolks are unusually rich in the growth
vitamin.

This richness in vitamin A is one of the reasons for the importance of eggs in the diet. For it helps make children grow
and it improves the general health and stamina to such an
extent that the body has increased resistance to various infec-
tions, especially those of the mucous membranes and the respir-
atory tract. The mucous membranes have been called the
body's "first line of defense" against disease, so anything that
helps to keep them healthy is especially important.

Vitamin D, the sunshine vitamin, is not nearly so generally
found in foods as are other vitamins. Fish oils are the richest
source of this vitamin, and egg yolk comes next.

The importance of egg yolk as a source of the sunshine
vitamin was demonstrated by some investigators at Johns Hopkins University. They selected seven Negro children, all of
whom had rickets, some of them severely. To the daily milk
and cereal diet of these children they added one egg a day. In
a few cases they added two eggs. In a surprisingly short time
all of the children were cured of rickets.

Since rickets is more difficult to cure than to prevent, this
experiment was marked proof of the importance of the sunshine
vitamin in egg yolk. And amazing as it may seem, the vitamin D content of eggs can be enormously increased simply by
proper feeding and handling of the laying flock. This little
egg machine we call the hen has the unique ability to absorb

the sun's health-giving rays, imprison them in the yolk of her eggs, and seal them there so securely that neither cooking nor preserving nor storing nor freezing destroys or even appreciably diminishes them.

Vitamins B and E complete the vitamin alphabet in eggs.

Dr. Lafayette B. Mendel of Yale University refers often to the importance of little things in nutrition. Minerals are just such little things, for although the body requires them in only minute amounts, they are tremendously important. Like a pinch of salt in food, they make a lot of difference. Phosphorus and calcium are necessary for building strong bones and teeth and for keeping them so. Iron and copper keep the blood good and red.

Eggs are rich in phosphorus, though somewhat low in calcium. But their iron content is rich. The iron of egg yolk is truly a good blood builder, too, for it is associated with copper, which must be present if the iron is to serve its purpose in the body. Fortunately, the iron and the copper content of egg yolk does not vary. So the person who eats an egg a day in some form may depend on getting from that egg about a tenth of the day's requirement of iron, and an amount of copper necessary for the body to use that iron.

Eggs are a seasonal food. During the egg season, spring, when eggs are plentiful as well as unusually good in quality, some of them are put into refrigerated warehouses to be held until fall and winter when eggs are scarce. Fortunately this storage is such a satisfactory method of holding eggs that not even the vitamin content is diminished. This is particularly important in regard to vitamin D, the sunshine vitamin, which is so necessary in the winter diet. All the other vitamins, as well as the proteins and the minerals, are there in undiminished amount, ready to be used by the body to maintain its health and stamina.

Eggs Are Easy to Digest

The fact that eggs, with milk, have for years served as the basis of successful diets for convalescents and for those with digestive disturbances indicates that they are easily and completely digested. The method of cooking makes some difference in the time required for digestion. Contrary to general belief, hard-cooked eggs, finely mashed, are most quickly digested. Next comes the soft-cooked egg, and last of all the raw egg. In hospitals the tendency is to feed fewer raw eggs than formerly, except in special cases. When raw egg is taken, it seems to be digested most satisfactorily when it is thoroughly beaten. This is especially true of egg white. So in making egg nog and similar dishes, the yolk may be beaten with the milk and then the white beaten stiff before folding it in.

Eggs in the Child's Diet

Diets for children have come in for a fine share of sensible attention in the modern theory of eating for happiness through health. As knowledge of foods and nutrition has increased, emphasis on various foods has shifted.

For a long time the place of eggs in the child's diet was a questionable one. Gradually, however, as the chemist studied the egg and found in it vitamins and those important minerals, iron and copper—both so necessary to make good, healthy blood—eggs took on a new importance in child feeding.

THE PLACE
OF EGGS IN
THE DIET

Especially was this so in the feeding of bottle babies, some of whom showed a distressing tendency to develop some form of anemia. Thoughtful physicians, seeking a preventive for anemia in babies, considered egg yolk. It was not only relatively rich in iron, but the iron seemed to be of a type that babies' digestive systems could use unusually well. When later discoveries showed that the presence of copper was necessary for the utilization of iron by the body, the explanation seemed at hand, for egg yolk contained copper as well as iron.

Moreover, the egg, like milk, was especially designed by nature to be food for the young. Since the egg is the sole food supply of the developing chick, it must contain all of the things necessary for building a body. So it was quite natural that some thinking physician should reach the conclusion that if a child was not doing well enough on milk alone, perhaps the addition of some egg yolk might help. It was tried, and many of the babies gained remarkably.

Today the addition of egg yolk to the diet of bottle-fed babies is an accepted procedure. Physicians do, however, still differ as to the age at which egg yolk should be introduced into the child's diet. That age may vary with individual children. For this reason it is best to follow the doctor's advice in the matter, since he knows the individual child and his needs. Dr. Alfred Hess, one of America's leading pediatricians, begins giving egg yolk to bottle-fed babies when they are five weeks old. He gives only a little of the egg yolk at first, gradually increasing this amount until at about six months the child is getting a whole yolk each day.

At first the reason for giving egg yolk to babies was its rich iron content. Then it was discovered that egg yolk contained a lot of vitamin A, the growth vitamin. A little later it was found that it was also rich in vitamin D, the sunshine vitamin. In fact, so rich was it in this latter vitamin that tests showed that one egg yolk a day in a child's diet would protect that child from rickets, provided the proper amount of the bone-making minerals, calcium and phosphorus, were in the diet.

Regarding this matter of vitamin D, Dr. H. C. Sherman of Columbia University says, "The greater acceptability of egg yolk over fish oil and the richness of the yolk (or even of the egg as a whole) in so many other nutritional factors as well as vitamin D, combine to make eggs an important source of vitamin D in practice." In England egg yolk has for centuries been valued as an antirachitic.

All of the modern discussion of the new emphasis on eggs in the child's diet is of special interest in the light of an old medical record. Simon de Vallembert, writing in 1565, recommended the following "formula" for artificially fed babies, to be given to them when they were three months old: "Bread or flour, which may be first dried in the oven, grated, cooked in broth, with milk of the cow or goat, and finally butter or egg yolk added to make it more nutritious, and honey to guard against constipation." Remarkably like the modern basic formula for bottle-fed babies.

Similar to Simon de Vallembert's formula is that used by Dr. W. Stoeltzner in his children's clinic at the university in Koenigsberg, Germany. Dr. Stoeltzner calls his formula an "egg soup," and he reports that he has not only had great success in feeding normal babies, but that he has been able satisfactorily to nourish premature infants, the feeding of whom is always a serious problem. Dr. Stoeltzner hard-cooks the egg and mashes it very fine before adding it to the infant's food.

For most children, the gradual introduction of egg yolk after the third month, until a whole yolk is fed each day, is the most satisfactory procedure. Until the child is a year old, only the yolk is given. This is due to the fact that some children are sensitive to egg white. This sensitivity is much more marked in young children than in older ones.

There is good reason to believe that hard-cooking the egg white makes it less likely to cause digestive disturbances than serving it raw or soft-cooked. Quite contrary to earlier belief, hard-cooked egg, thoroughly mashed, is most easily digested. For this reason hard-cooked egg mashed and mixed with cereal or spread in sandwiches or mixed with vegetables is excellent for children who are not especially fond of eggs in other forms.

The egg-a-day for the child need not always be given in the form of an egg, poached, scrambled or cooked in the shell. It may be served as custard, in custard ice cream, in egg sauce on vegetables, in sandwiches, in plain sponge cake or in any of the many dishes that are wholesome and suitable for children. Dietitians have recently pointed out that plain cookies made with eggs, milk and butter are entirely satisfactory for children to have at proper times.

T H E   P L A C E   O F
E G G S   I N   C O O K E R Y

U PON the well known fact that heat coagulates or "sets" egg
protein depends the ability of eggs to perform at least eight
distinct cookery functions: leavening, interfering, emulsifying,
thickening, coating, binding, clarifying, garnishing.

The Bubble-Making Egg

Leavening by means of eggs—that is, using them to raise or lighten
mixtures such as dough—is one of the most fascinating of the many
curious things that occur in every-day cookery.

The unique quality of the egg which enables it to entangle air and
then hold it firmly enough so it can actually be stirred into a batter or
dough is one of the reasons eggs are often called the indispensable
cookery ingredient. No other ingredient performs this particular function quite so efficiently as does egg. In fact, some dishes, such as
angel food cakes, soufflés, meringues and similar combinations depend
so entirely on this quality that without eggs there could be no such
dishes.

Let us see how the egg does this leavening job.

When an egg is beaten it is transformed from its liquid state into a
foam. The particular proteins of which the egg is made have the
ability to form a stable foam which will stand up even under a surprising amount of handling. This foam really consists of millions of
tiny air bubbles, each bubble a sort of small balloon made of an
exceedingly thin "bag" inflated with air.

When this mass of tiny balloons is incorporated into a batter which
is then put into a warm oven, the air in the balloons gradually expands
and the little balloon bags stretch. As they do so they actually lift
the load of flour and sugar in the pan, just as a balloon lifts a load off
the ground. Gradually, when the air in the bubbles has expanded to
its limit and the cell walls have stretched as far as they can, the heat
in the oven cooks or coagulates the cell walls so that they will not

342

collapse when the baked product is removed from the oven. If the bubbles in the foam were very small, the finished product is likely to be fine-grained. If the individual bubbles were moderately large, the fininshed product is likely to be somewhat loose in texture, though it may still be pleasantly tender.

Whole egg, egg white and egg yolk all have this ability to form foams. But they have the ability in widely varying degrees. Egg white, because of its composition and structure, is by far the best leavener. Egg white on whipping increases its volume seven to eight times. In other words, one cupful of egg white can enmesh six to seven cupfuls of air. An old baker's rule is that a pound of egg white leavens or aerates a pound of flour. In home cooking, one cupful of egg white, as used in angel food cake, is usually used to leaven one cupful of flour and from one to one and a half cupfuls of sugar.

Egg yolk is quite different in composition from egg white. Its protein constituents are different, and it consists of about one-third fats and fatlike substances. It is very much more concentrated than is egg white. This may be one reason why it forms a much finer, more compact sort of foam than does egg white. Moreover, the increase in volume is much smaller. A cupful of egg yolk will yield two cupfuls of foam. Often when egg yolk is used as a leavening, as in sponge or sunshine cakes, water is gradually added during the beating. The water dilutes the proteins in the yolk and has the effect of actually making them go farther.

As might be expected, whole egg has greater leavening power than the yolk alone, but slightly less than the white alone. A cupful of whole egg when beaten yields six cupfuls of foam. If the yolk is separated from the white and each is beaten separately and then the beaten yolk is folded into the beaten white, the resulting volume will be about the same as when the whole egg is beaten.

The Interfering Egg

When a substance freezes, ice crystals form. A clear liquid allowed to freeze without stirring forms a solid block. If fruits or other substances are added, the crystals that form are more or less coarse. If the mixture is stirred during the freezing period the crystals tend to be smaller, for the stirring beats in air. This is part of the secret of the ice cream freezer with its paddles. But when stirring is stopped the small crystals grow by clustering together unless there is some substance present which keeps them apart.

Differences in the character of egg yolk and egg white make it possible to combine them in various ways in the same food dish.

Beaten egg, especially beaten white, acts as such an interfering substance. When a mixture is frozen without stirring, it is necessary to use some other means to incorporate air. For this reason many recipes for frozen dishes, especially those to be frozen in the mechanical refrigerator without stirring, call for beaten egg white. The tiny bubbles of egg and air prevent the ice crystals from getting together and forming large icy masses which create a texture usually described as grainy.

Egg white, and sometimes egg yolk, performs a similar service in candy making. In order that candy be creamy and smooth, the sugar crystals must first be made small and then kept so. Here again it is simply a matter of putting into the candy some ingredient which will keep the tiny crystals apart. This is exactly what egg white does in such confections as divinity, fondants, filling for chocolate creams, some marshmallow, and frostings for cakes. Pouring hot syrup over the beaten egg cooks the walls of the bubbles and prevents them from bursting and thus losing their air while the candy is stored.

THE PLACE
OF EGGS IN
COOKERY

The Film-Forming Egg

Such a mixture as mayonnaise is an emulsion. An emulsion consists of innumerable tiny globules of fat, each surrounded by a thin film of some substance which keeps it from combining with the remainder of

344

the fat. In other words, fat in an emulsion does not run together but stays in separate particles. In mayonnaise as well as in many other foods, such as cakes which contain fats, egg is the substance that forms the films around the fat globules. It is therefore called an emulsifying agent.

Chemists say that the most efficient emulsifiers are substances which are themselves emulsions or emulsion-like. The fat in egg yolk exists in emulsified form. In fact, egg yolk is the most stable emulsion known. It is also the most efficient emulsifying agent known. Its emulsifying power may be judged from the fact that one egg yolk can emulsify from nineteen to twenty-seven times its own weight in oil. One egg yolk will easily emulsify from a cupful to one and one-half cupfuls of oil.

Just as egg white has greater leavening power than does egg yolk, so in emulsifying power egg yolk is far ahead of egg white. Here again in performance whole egg stands between the yolk and the white.

The Thickening Egg

An egg properly mixed with a cupful of milk can transform that cupful of liquid into a delicate, pleasing, jelly-like mixture. This fact is made use of in preparing such dishes as custards and cream fillings for pies. The proportion of egg to liquid and the method of cooking determine how firm the custard will be. Stirred custards are not nearly so thick as baked (unstirred) custards, even when the same amount of egg is used. A standard rule is that one whole egg or two egg yolks will thicken one cupful of liquid. When egg yolk is used for thickening gravies, soups, sauces and fillings, one egg yolk takes the place of one tablespoon of flour.

The Binding Egg

In some dishes eggs act as a binding agent. Meat loaves or vegetable rings would not hold their shape if they did not contain some ingredient, usually egg, which during cooking becomes firm enough to hold the other ingredients together.

The Adhesive Egg

Uncooked egg is somewhat sticky and may therefore act as a sort of edible adhesive in cookery. In order to make crumbs stick to a croquette or a veal chop, the cook first dips the croquette or chop into slightly beaten egg and then into crumbs. The uncooked egg holds the crumbs tightly, and during the cooking the egg sets so that the crumbs stay on the finished product, thus increasing its attractiveness, food value and flavor.

The Clarifying Egg

When slightly beaten egg is put into a hot semi-clear liquid, the egg cooks. As it does so, it entangles in its meshes the sediment which makes the liquid cloudy, and which is too fine to be strained out. The cooked egg, firmly holding the tiny particles, is then strained out and the remaining liquid is sparkling and clear. This is the reason for using egg in coffee and in clear soups.

The Decorative Egg

From time immemorial clever cooks have used the white and gold of the egg to lend attractiveness to what might otherwise be quite uninteresting dishes. The first cook book, written many years before Christ, records, "There was set before us a platter of marvelous smell of the Seasons, shaped like the hemisphere of Heaven's vault. For all the beauties of the constellations were on it—fish, kids, the scorpion running between them, *while slices of eggs represented the stars.*"

Eggs hard-cooked and sliced, quartered or halved, minced eggs, poached eggs, whipped eggs, eggs in almost every form are used as garnishes on various types of dishes. Their service here is not limited only to beautifying, for they add food value as well as attractiveness, and sometimes they contribute much to the texture of the dish.

Practical Hints on Buying Eggs

Each egg is a complete sealed package of food. Since it cannot be opened before purchasing, a sort of x-ray method has been developed for examining the contents of this small package of food before it is sold. This method is called candling. It gets its name, as Dr. Pennington has pointed out elsewhere, from the fact that candles were formerly used as the source of light. Today electric light bulbs are used.

Candling is the process of twirling each egg before a light to determine its quality. So when a sign is displayed in a retail market saying, "Our eggs are candled," it is an announcement that before the eggs were delivered to the dealer each egg was carefully examined before a light.

On the basis of what he sees in the interior and on the exterior of the egg, the candler puts it into one of the various market grades. Some of them are fancy eggs, some not quite so fancy, some very good, some fair.

The exterior, visible qualities that the candler uses to help determine the grade of an egg the housewife can also see. These qualities are cleanness of shell, size of the egg, regularity of shape (not too round nor too long and narrow). Obviously, the largest eggs of finest interior quality go into the fancy class. They may weigh as much as thirty to thirty-two ounces per dozen, whereas the average market egg weighs twenty-two to twenty-four ounces per dozen.

Not all eggs, even when newly laid, can go into the fancy grade. Pullet eggs, for example, might often qualify for the fancy class except that they are small in size. So they are usually sold at a lower price. Sometimes, if the weather is rainy, the hen gets into the nest with muddy feet and the eggshells become soiled. Although the interior of the egg is of excellent quality, the soiled shell disqualifies it for the fancy class. In some parts of the country eggs with brown shells are considered more desirable than those with white, and in others white shells are more popular, although there may be no difference whatever in interior quality.

In the past the chief requirement that the consumer has made for eggs is that they should be fresh. And freshness has been interpreted in terms of time. That is, if a housewife was told that the eggs delivered to her were only ten or twelve or twenty-four hours old, she thought she was getting the finest eggs available.

It is true, of course, that freshness is a desirable quality in most foods, but newness alone does not insure fresh quality. It is an accepted fact that not every apple on a tree is of fancy quality. There are large ones, small ones, highly colored and less highly colored ones, some of irregular shape and some with spots. Yet all of the apples are equally fresh. But the apple grower sorts the fruit, putting all the big ones together and all of the small ones. The home manager then buys the fancy ones for special service, but she buys the small or irregular ones for pie-making and for apple sauce, since she knows they are of satisfactory quality and probably have excellent flavor, yet they are less expensive.

So with eggs. The fancy ones are especially desirable for poaching, frying and cooking in the shell, when the appearance of the egg as it is brought to the table matters. However, in cake-making, omelet-

THE PLACE
OF EGGS IN
COOKERY

347

making, for scrambling and creaming, the other grades are not only entirely satisfactory, but the use of them is a mark of thrifty home management.

How Many Eggs to Buy

A week's supply of eggs is a good quantity for a homemaker to buy at one time under ordinary conditions. This quantity varies with the size of the family, but it is easily computed if one egg a day is allowed for each member of the family, when egg prices are moderate or low. When prices are higher, an egg a day should be allowed for each child under sixteen years of age, and three or four eggs per week for each adult. Thus, for a family of father, mother, son (ten years old), daughter (seven years), and son (three years), the weekly allowance would be thirty-five eggs, or about three dozen. Nutritionists are repeatedly pointing out that, in view of the high nutritive value of eggs, their cost should be considered in relation to the many valuable elements they furnish in the diet. Dr. H. C. Sherman of Columbia University in the most recent edition of his book, "The Chemistry of Food and Nutrition," says, "The discovery of the marked antirachitic value of egg-yolk, following quickly on the finding that it is a rich source of vitamin A, calls for a new evaluation of the importance and economy of eggs in the food supply."

In other words, an egg is a small thing, so it may sometimes seem high in price, but it is packed tight with food values. A five-dollar gold piece is small, too, compared with a dollar bill.

When buying eggs it is preferable to purchase them at a market where they are kept in a refrigerator, or at least in a cool place. Eggs are a perishable food, and should no more be kept on a counter at room temperatures, sometimes even at summer temperatures, than should milk. No matter how emphatically the sign above the egg basket says, "Fresh country eggs," if the eggs are allowed to stand in a window, perhaps with the sun beating on them, or in some other warm place, they lose their fresh quality.

This brings up again the matter of freshness. Fresh quality, or what is usually meant by freshness, is a matter of handling methods rather than of time. As Dr. Pennington has emphasized, an egg properly handled may be of fresh quality weeks after it was laid, while an egg improperly handled may have lost its fresh quality within a day or two. Proper handling includes refrigeration or keeping the egg cool from the time it is produced until it is used.

Community Refrigerators

Elsewhere Dr. Pennington has described modern egg storage methods. Modern storage houses have aptly been called community refrigerators. Into them a great part of the great spring crop of fine eggs goes to be carefully kept under proper conditions until the fall and winter egg shortage sets in. Then out they come, with their quality intact, to supply eggs at moderate prices. The eggs that were fancy when they went into storage are still of fancy quality, suitable for poaching, frying and cooking in the shell. Other grades are desirable for other cookery purposes. For making cake, meringues, and similar dishes, expert cooks prefer eggs stored in the spring of the year, for they whip up to make large, fine cakes.

Repeated careful tests have shown that modern storage methods, properly applied, not only protect quality and flavor but food value as well. Even the vitamin content is as rich when the eggs come out of storage as when they went in.

The real point about all this is that whether eggs are fresh or whether they are stored, their quality depends on the meticulousness with which they have been handled (see Book I pages 187–240).

Eggs With Protected Shells

In some sections of the country where the air is very dry, or when eggs have to be shipped long distances, precautions are taken to prevent excessive evaporation of moisture from the eggs. These precautions may be the lining of an egg case with a moisture-proof paper of some kind. Or they may be the dipping of fresh, cooled eggs into a clear, colorless, tasteless mineral oil. The oil seals the pores of the shell and very little, if any, of the water evaporates. Moreover, the oil may help to prevent absorption of odors and flavors.

In some sections of the country all of the eggs that go into storage are so oil-dipped. They are frequently sold as "shell-protected" eggs, a name which adequately describes the process and its effect. However, sometimes the oil leaves a slight shininess on the shell. Many homemakers believe that a shiny eggshell indicates that the egg is of poor quality, and so it does sometimes, but just the opposite may be true, too. In some markets the eggs are put through a sanding machine which lightly roughens the shell and removes the surface shine, while the pores remain sealed and the egg contents protected.

How to Care for Eggs at Home

As soon as eggs have been delivered to the home they should be put into the refrigerator. Eggs, like milk, cream and butter, absorb odors and flavors, and should therefore not be placed near highly scented foods if they are to keep their delicacy of flavor. They need not be kept in the coldest part of the refrigerator, however.

If the shells are soiled they may be wiped with a rough dry cloth or with one of the metal sponges used in kitchens or with steel wool. They should not, however, be washed until just before they are used. Washing removes the thin albuminous layer which forms a natural seal for the pores of the shell. When this seal has been washed off, water evaporates more quickly from the egg, and odors and flavors are more easily absorbed than while the egg remains protected by its natural seal.

EGG ODDITIES

IN FOREIGN LANDS

I N THE United States the word egg usually refers to the eggs of
the hen. But people in other countries use eggs from various
other fowl as well as chicken eggs.

In Germany and England, for example, the eggs of the lapwing or
plover are much prized. In England plover eggs have been gathered
with such zeal that a legally closed season has had to be declared lest
the bird, already rare, disappear entirely from English fields.

The story is told that one spring a loyal English subject sent King
George V of England two plover eggs for his birthday. Spring, the
breeding time, is the closed season, and the eggs were promptly returned to the sender, since King George considers himself subject to
the laws of his country. The need of the protective law may be
judged from the fact that several years ago smart London restaurants
were serving plovers' eggs at one guinea (approximately $5.10) per egg.

In some countries eggs of various sea-fowl and water birds are used.
Continental Europeans, especially the Austrians and Germans, are fond
of goose eggs. Most Austrian families living in smaller communities
have at least a few geese, and each day the village green is a meeting
place for the goose-herds. An American once wanted to take a picture
of the geese going to pasture in an Austrian rural community. Her
host saw no reason for her wanting a picture of such an ordinary
sight. When she explained that it was one which we do not see in
America he asked in surprise, "Then where do you *keep* your geese?"
Geese are so much a part of the "household equipment" in this
Austrian village that the inhabitants can hardly imagine a home
without them.

Goose eggs are stronger in flavor than are hen eggs and duck eggs,
though duck eggs in turn are less mild in taste than are hen eggs.

Where guinea eggs are obtainable they are much prized for their
delicacy of flavor. In South Africa, where ostrich raising is a regular
industry, the eggs are considered excellent for cooking purposes and
value is attached to them as a food. Imagine a poached ostrich egg on
toast! There's a man-sized breakfast.

Although the term "egg" as usually understood refers to the eggs of birds, other types of eggs are also eaten. Russians are credited with having invented caviar, one of the delicacies of the world. Caviar is simply the cleaned and salted roe or eggs of a large fish, the sturgeon. In some parts of the world turtle eggs are considered a great luxury.

Nor do all peoples want all of their eggs in the fresh state. In contrast to the American custom which demands that every effort be made to maintain the original quality of the new-laid egg until it reaches the consumer, customs in some other lands call for quite the opposite procedure.

One frequently hears mention of the "ancient eggs" of China. An eminent Chinese student has pointed out that these preserved eggs are not at all synonymous with bad eggs any more than cheese is the same thing as bad milk. The aim in these Oriental methods of preserving eggs is to make a new product, using fresh eggs as the raw material, just as the dairyman uses fresh milk as his raw material in making cheese. Obviously the qualities of the finished product vary with the method of preservation. The term preservation is really a misnomer, for the processes are those of manufacture rather than of preservation.

In parts of India duck eggs are packed into a mixture of clay, brick dust and salt. They are allowed to remain in this pack for two or three months. When they are ready they are carefully cleaned, hard-cooked and served as a delicacy. For most of these types of preserved eggs, ducks' eggs are used because of their large size. Hens' eggs, which in the Orient are very small for the most part, are consumed fresh.

The Filipinos make a product called *balut*. Fresh duck or hen eggs are carefully packed with rice hulls in bamboo cylinders which are then warmed twice daily. Naturally a certain amount of incubation takes place under these conditions. At the end of eighteen days the eggs are unpacked, hard-boiled and sold as *balut*.

Still another method of preserving eggs consists in packing them in freshly burned wood ashes for three months. The alkalinity of the ashes causes changes to take place in the egg so that both the yolk and the white become quite firm. The yolk becomes similar in appearance to that of a hard-cooked egg, but the white remains transparent.

The Chinese use several different methods for preserving eggs. The product resulting from each method is quite different, just as brick cheese is different from cream cheese, although both are made from milk.

One Chinese method is to bury the eggs in the ground for a long time. This is the method of which we hear most in this country, yet it is least known among the natives of China. During the time the eggs are buried a sort of fermentation takes place, causing the formation of the odoriferous gas called hydrogen sulfide. But the gas bursts the shell and escapes, so that the eggs themselves are said to have neither a disagreeable taste nor an unpleasant odor.

Another type of preserved eggs is called *dsaudan.* It is made by combining salt, cooked rice and wort. The wort, which is essentially a dilute solution of sugar, causes fermentation. Since eggshell consists largely of calcium or lime salts which dissolve easily in even weak acids, the substances formed by fermentation naturally affect the shell. At the end of about six months the shell of these eggs has softened or entirely dissolved and the membrane just under the shell has become greatly thickened. The inside of the egg has changed from a liquid state to a texture resembling that of soft-cooked eggs, and the flavor and aroma have become wine-like.

Hulidan, also prepared by Chinese, is made by several different methods. The simplest way is to cover clean fresh eggs with a saturated solution of common salt and to leave them for about a month. When ready to be served they are hard-cooked. Except for a slightly reddish tinge which the yolk has assumed, the eggs resemble ordinary hard-cooked eggs in appearance. The flavor, however, is quite salty—usually too salty for people who are not accustomed to this food. "But," said a Chinese student, "Roquefort cheese is much too salty for me, yet many Europeans consider it a great delicacy."

The type of preserved Chinese egg that is probably most often seen in this country is that known as *pidan.* It is manufactured on a commercial scale in factories rather than in the home, as are *dsaudan* and *hulidan.* According to Chi Che Wang, a former student at the University of Chicago, *pidan* is prepared in the following manner: "One and a third pounds strong black tea is made and the leaves are strained out. To the infusion nine pounds of lime and then four and a half pounds of common salt are stirred in. Finally about one bushel of freshly burned wood ashes is added until the desired concentration is reached. This mixture is then put away to cool overnight. On the following day one thousand ducks' eggs of the best quality are first cleaned and then one by one carefully and evenly covered with the mixture. They are then stored away for a period of five months. At the end of the period they are brought out and covered further with rice hulls, and then with this outer layer fully a quarter of an inch thick they are ready for the market."

Pidan has a characteristic odor, though it is not that of bad eggs. The flavor is said to be "indescribable," as well as rather salty and a bit peppery. In texture *pidan* is quite different from fresh eggs. Both white and yolk are coagulated as if the egg had been cooked. The white resembles a clear coffee jelly in appearance and the yolk is greenish gray. Incidentally, a United States government bulletin reports that *pidan* is an excellent source of vitamin A, just as are fresh eggs.

Because these preserved eggs are quite different from our own idea of eggs, we are likely to look upon them as something quite inedible. We sometimes forget that some of the foods which to us are great delicacies may not appeal to Oriental peoples. Travelers in other lands often discover that once they have tasted these unusual foods they find them not only edible but occasionally quite desirable as well. From the nutritional standpoint it is fortunate indeed that the Orientals include eggs in various forms in their diet, for according to Dr. E. V. McCollum, "It is partly this extensive use of eggs by the Chinese people which makes their diet adequate."

FROM BROILER
TO FRICASSÉE

Chicken Dinner—Yesterday and Today

WHEN, as a bride, Grandmother served a chicken dinner, she literally followed the directions of the colonial cookbooks which directed the cook to "first catch your bird." She went out into the yard, looked over her flock with a critical eye, and selected the bird she wanted. Then either she or Grandfather applied the ax, or maybe she just grasped the bird by the head, gave it a few lusty swings through the air, and the chicken was dead. While the beheaded fowl flopped about the backyard making queer squawky noises, Grandmother dashed into the house for a teakettle full of water which she had thoughtfully put on a fresh fire just before she started out to the yard to catch her bird. She doused the chicken in a bucketful of scalding water and for a few busy minutes the feathers flew, or at least they flew as much as wet feathers can fly. Then came the tedious job of picking out the pin feathers, and finally the removal of head, feet and entrails. After a singe with a piece of burning paper and a thorough scrubbing, the cleaned bird was set in a cool place overnight, or at least for five or six hours, if possible. Sometimes, when unexpected diners appeared, the chicken had to be cooked at once. But the really good cook preferred to kill her chicken the day before she cooked it, because she knew that during the keeping the meat became tender.

But today the chicken dinner is quite a different story. Grandmother's chicken cookery varied with the season. In late spring and early summer she served broilers. By July and August the chickens had grown a little more and had transformed themselves into nice plump fryers. Throughout the great Corn Belt, which is really the poultry supply area of the United States, the chickens usually reached this stage about the Fourth of July. Farmers in this section always set two objectives for the Fourth of July: the corn must be knee high and the first fryers of the season must be ready for the holiday dinner.

355

By fall, the chickens that were left had developed into full-grown birds, meaty and plump. Now they were roasters, and were especially delicious stuffed and baked. Gradually, as the roasters matured still more, they became old cocks, good for soup making, while the hens developed into stewing fowls.

The seasons, of course, still exist, and the cycle of the poultry supply remains largely the same, even if in some sections of the country great chicken hotels have been built to turn out broilers the year around. But as we all know, the homemaker of today is not restricted by seasons in her choice of poultry for the table. She goes to the market and selects the bird that pleases her, and should she wish broilers in December or roasters in May, she may have them, because modern refrigeration has made these things possible.

The story of the birds before they come to the city market has been told in this book by Dr. Pennington—how they are milk-fed to become soft and white and delicate in texture, and then are killed, dressed, cooled, graded and packed, twelve to a box, in new boxes neatly lined with fresh parchment paper, and thoroughly chilled. These birds for the most part are not drawn. Some of them are sent directly to market, and some of them are put into large, clean, cold rooms to be frozen solid and kept so until they are needed.

Like any other food, frozen poultry must be properly handled. If the frozen birds are put into a refrigerator and allowed to defrost naturally and slowly, they will be of excellent flavor. If they are put into cold water, to hasten the defrosting unduly, as is sometimes done, the flavor suffers, just as does that of any other meat that is put to soak in water for several hours.

Poultry that is packed drawn goes through a similar preparatory process. But after the birds have been killed and dressed, the head, feet and entrails are removed, the birds are packed practically ready for the pan, and they are immediately hard-frozen.

Quick-frozen poultry is the latest market development for supplying the homemaker with chicken ready for the pan. This poultry goes through the same preparatory processes that the other poultry does. After drawing, each bird is submitted to the same careful, individual inspection the homemaker would give it in her own kitchen. Every pin feather is removed, every hair is singed off, and the bird is washed inside and out. Water sprayed under pressure reaches every crevice that needs washing. The cleaned bird is then packaged appropriately for its type and put into a quick freezer in which the temperature is so low that the bird is frozen as solid as a block of ice in the short space of about forty-five minutes. The frozen chickens are transferred to refrigerated holding rooms and released to the market as required.

Quick-frozen poultry is delivered to the homemaker in its frozen state, so that she may defrost it when she is ready to use it. She simply allows it to stand at room temperature or in a refrigerator until it has become defrosted, so that she can handle the bird for stuffing or other preparation. Stewing birds, which are already cut up, can be put directly into cold water and heat applied gradually. As the bird defrosts it also begins to cook, so no time is lost.

How to Select Poultry

In selecting poultry for cooking the first thing to consider is the method of cooking to be employed. A stewing bird would be quite unsatisfactory for frying, and a broiler stewed would be a great disappointment. As in other meats, the young tender kinds are most satisfactory for quick methods of cookery, such as broiling and frying, and the older birds are best for slower cooking methods which call for low cooking temperatures.

The reason for this lies in the natural structure of the meat. Every muscle is made of innumerable tiny strands, called muscle fibers. These fibers are held together in small bundles, and the bundles are in turn held together to make muscles. The substance that holds the fibers and bundles together is the connective tissue, or collagen. The older a bird gets, the stronger this tissue becomes and the less tender are the muscles.

High cooking temperatures make the connective tissue tougher, and therefore long, slow cooking is required to make older birds tender. These birds are, however, flavorsome and meaty. Moreover, often they are less expensive than the other types, and therefore they are economical to buy. They may be made into any number of delicious dishes for which the younger birds are quite unsuitable.

FROM
BROILER TO
FRICASSÉE

Market Classes of Poultry

The two terms most often used in connection with market poultry are market class and grade. Market class refers to classification of poultry according to type and size. The market classes are broilers, fryers, roasters, fowl, capons. The various classes with their sizes are listed in the table below. See also Book I page 241.

The grades indicate whether a bird is fancy, choice or standard. In poultry marketing these grades are used mainly in wholesale selling. On the retail market, grades of birds packed by different packers are differentiated by brand names, just as other foods are.

Whatever the class of chicken, whether it be broiler, fryer or roaster, the best grade birds in the class are meaty and plump. In young birds (broilers and fryers) the tip of the breast bone is pliable. The skin is smooth and fine-grained. Although birds with broken skins are not put into the fanciest class, since the fanciest class implies as near perfection as possible, they are often of excellent quality. The very fact that the skin is broken may indicate a tender, well conditioned bird.

MARKET CLASSES OF POULTRY

Class	Weight	Season	Method of Cooking	Am't. to Buy
Broilers _____	1 – 2½ lbs.	Apr.–July	Broiling	½ bird per person
Fryers _____	2½– 3½ lbs.	June–Sept.	Frying	¾–1 lb. per person
Roasters _____	3½– 6 lbs.	Sept.–Jan.	Roasting	½–¾ lb. per person
Stewing Fowl ___	2½– 7 lbs.	Year around	Stewing Steaming Braising	¼–½ lb. per person
Capons _____	6 –10 lbs.	Dec.–Jan.	Roasting	½–¾ lb. per person

FROM
BROILER TO
FRICASSÉE

The bulk of market poultry is marketed dressed, that is, with only feathers removed. That means that the head, feet and entrails, which constitute about one-third of the weight of the bird, are shipped to market before they are discarded. Tradespeople use the terms "dressed" and "drawn." A bird is dressed when it has been killed and picked. The entrails are still inside the carcass. When these have been removed the bird is drawn. In most markets the birds are drawn after the housewife has made her selection.

There is much discussion among consumers as to the desirability of purchasing poultry that has been drawn at the plant. There are good arguments in favor of such a plan. But for reasons that Dr. Pennington has pointed out, when poultry is full-drawn at the plant, the birds must be immediately frozen and they must be kept hard frozen until they are delivered to the consumer.

Chicken in Portions

Chicken cut up into portions, first tried experimentally, has grown greatly in popularity. The family of two, the woman or man who lives alone, finds it both convenient and economical to buy two drumsticks, or a breast and a thigh, or all backs and necks (for soup making). The choice meaty pieces are sold at a higher price per pound than the less choice ones, which for some uses are economical purchases. Modern refrigeration has made possible this plan of selling chicken and other poultry in parts.

In this method of selling poultry emphasis might be put on the importance of proper refrigeration. In order that the chicken be in good condition when the homemaker gets it, it should have been recently cut up and kept very cold in a good refrigerator. A package or pan of cut-up poultry on display without refrigeration not only means deterioration of the poultry, but it is actually dangerous to the consumer. Keeping such a perishable product as cut-up poultry under constant refrigeration is in line with the modern policy of keeping all perishables under refrigeration in order to assure safety of food supply to consumers and to reduce waste.

The Food Value of Poultry Meat

Because of its structure and delicate texture as well as its delicious flavor chicken meat, and broth made from it, are among the first meat foods served to children and those who require foods that are easy to digest. In general, the meat from even a fat roaster or fowl is not greasy if it has been properly prepared, for most of the fat in chickens accumulates around the digestive organs, rather than being distributed through the muscle tissue. Consequently the greater portion of the fat may be removed before cooking. Incidentally, chicken fat, especially when it is yellow, contains some vitamin A, the growth vitamin.

The chief food constituents of poultry meat, as of other meats, are proteins, the muscle and tissue builders. But not all poultry contains the same kind of proteins, nor in the same proportion. The meat of broilers, for example, contains a high proportion of proteins and protein-like substances called peptones and albumoses, which are easily soluble in water. Usually, the more easily a food dissolves, the more easily it is digested.

The white meat of chicken contains more of these soluble peptones and albumoses than does the dark meat. As Miss Pennington has explained in her discussion of how the chicken grows, the peptones and albumoses gradually change to other proteins, chiefly globulins. Globulins are not soluble in water, but they do dissolve easily and quickly in slightly salted or acidulated water.

The more mature a bird is, the more globulins are present in its flesh. By the time a bird has developed into a fowl or an old cock, there is a much greater quantity of globulins than of peptones and albumoses in the muscle. That is why most recipes for stewing chicken and for soup making tell the cook to simmer the bird in water to which a little salt or a mild acid, such as lemon juice, has been added.

The way the fat is distributed through the meat makes a difference in digestibility, too. Broilers use most of their food for growing, so their muscles contain very little fat. What little there is is mainly in the dark meat. As the chicken matures, more fat is distributed throughout the meat, until stewing fowls and old cocks may be quite high in fat. But in these, as in younger birds, there is less fat in the white meat than in the dark. The fat in the dark meat portions contributes much to the juiciness of these parts.

Still another factor that contributes to the ease of digestibility of both white and dark chicken meat is the shortness of the tiny individual meat fibers, which makes them easily used in the digestive processes.

The fuel value of poultry meat varies almost directly with its fat content, as the following table shows. Broilers, which are lowest of all in fat, yield only 290 calories per pound, while capons, which depend in part for their goodness on their fat content, yield 990 calories per pound. Similar conditions are true for other animals, such as beef and veal. The young animal has deposited practically no fat, since all of its food is required for growing. Veal cutlets yield only 625 calories per pound, while a pound of beef round yields 811, and a pound of Porterhouse yields approximately 1229 calories.

COMPOSITION AND FUEL VALUE OF POULTRY MEAT

	% Protein in edible portion	% Fat	Calories per pound calculated when bird is ready for cooking
Broiler _____	21.5	2.5	290
Roaster _____	21.2	8.5	592
Fowl _____	19.3	16.3	751
Capon _____	21.0	21.0	990
Duck _____	21.6	2.2	892*
Goose _____	15.7	29.9	1209
Turkey _____	22.2	17.3	970

[Figures from Lowe's Dietetic File]

---

* Although duck is low in fat content, it is higher in calories per pound when ready for cooking because the muscles are larger in proportion to the bones than are those of broilers.

BIRDS OF THE FESTIVE BOARD

THE meat of duck is darker in color than that of any other domestic bird. It is deliciously flavorsome, and for the diet which requires careful restriction of fat, it is an ideal meat. The proportion of meat to bone is somewhat low, and therefore duck is often considered something of a delicacy. It is particularly popular for service in hotels and restaurants.

The Delicate Duck

Because of the development of the duck-raising industry in the Long Island territory, the term Long Island duck has come to be almost synonymous with excellent eating qualities. Many fine ducks are produced in other sections of the country.

The methods for cooking ducks are similar to those for cooking chicken. Young duck may be broiled or fried. For roasting, ducks may or may not be stuffed. Traditionally, the duck is cooked without stuffing. The classic way to roast duck is to rub the inside of the bird with salt, and then put an apple, cut into quarters, and an onion, inside the cavity. After roasting, the apple and onion are removed and discarded. This method is still popularly used for cooking wild duck. Domesticated duck, however, is so delicate in flavor that stuffing put into the bird and roasted with it is quite delicious.

FRIED DUCK

A medium sized duck will cut into 6 good sized portions for frying. Put the pieces skin-side down into a hot skillet, letting the fat fry out quickly. Enough fat will fry out to brown the cut sides. Pour off any surplus fat. When well browned, roll each piece in flour and brown again. Season with salt and pepper, and cover the pan closely. Cook slowly for 30–35 minutes. When the meat is done, uncover and let cook for about five minutes to brown the meat thoroughly again, remove duck from pan, thicken drippings with flour, allowing 2 tablespoons flour for each cup of milk to be added. Add 2 tablespoons minced parsley.

362

ROAST DUCK WITH RIPE OLIVES AND ORANGES

Duck
12 large ripe olives
3 thin slices salt pork
3 navel oranges

6 slices bacon
1 c. sugar
¾ c. water for syrup

Lay strips of salt pork over breast of duck during roasting. Roll half a slice of bacon around each olive, fastening with toothpick. About 10 minutes before duck is done arrange the olives around duck in roaster and continue cooking. Peel and quarter oranges, and simmer gently in syrup made by boiling sugar and water together 5 minutes. When quarters are tender, remove from syrup and drain. Put duck on platter and garnish with olives and oranges and a sprig of parsley or watercress.

ROAST DUCK WITH ORANGE SAUCE

1 duck
2 tsp. salt
¼ tsp. pepper

3 tbsp. cooking fat
1 c. boiling water
2 tsp. finely minced onion

Rub duck with the melted fat. Bake uncovered in hot oven (475° F.) 15 minutes, then reduce heat to low (275–300° F.), add the hot water and minced onion, sprinkle with salt and pepper, and put cover on roaster. When done, use liquor in roaster for base of sauce.

ORANGE SAUCE

2 c. hot water (or liquor from pan with enough more water to make 2 c. liquid)
5 tbsp. flour

1 medium orange, skin and meat
2 tbsp. lemon juice

Make paste of flour with 4 tablespoons cold water. Add to boiling water and cook until smooth. Peel orange. Remove white under portion from peel. Cut the peel into thin slivers and parboil these 10 minutes. Add to flour paste, with lemon juice. Garnish bird with slices of orange.

ORANGE STUFFING

3 c. bread crumbs
½ c. hot broth or water
4 tbsp. melted fat
1 egg
½ tsp. salt

⅛ tsp. pepper
2 c. diced celery
Rind of 1 orange, grated
Pulp of 1 orange, cut up

Pour broth or water over bread and let stand for a few minutes. Add fat, egg, orange rind and pulp, seasoning and celery. Mix lightly but thoroughly and fill into bird.

PEANUT STUFFING

1 c. fine bread crumbs
½ c. evaporated milk
½ tsp. minced onion

½ c. finely chopped peanuts
2 tbsp. melted butter
Salt and pepper to taste

Blend all ingredients thoroughly.

363

WILD RICE STUFFING

2 c. steamed wild rice	Heart, liver and gizzard of duck
1 small onion, minced	1 tsp. salt
	⅛ tsp. pepper

Chop the heart, liver and gizzard and combine thoroughly with the rice. Add seasonings, blend and fill into duck.

The Fat Capon

Capons are male birds from which the organs of reproduction were removed when the birds were very young. They grow to much larger size than other chickens, and because they exercise less than other birds their meat is delicate and tender. Moreover, much of their feed is transformed into fat, so the meat is somewhat richer than that of roasting chickens. Although capons are usually more expensive per pound than roasting chickens, they are in reality quite economical, for they are meaty and there is little waste. The breast and thighs are especially meaty, and therefore capons are often used in hotels and restaurants where special uses require serving the meat in slices. And the statement of the cook of the sixteenth century Tudor days, that "fat Capons be ever in Season," is still true.

ROAST CAPON LOUISIANA

One 5 or 6 lb. capon	Salt
Nut stuffing	1 qt. milk
½ c. hot lard	

Clean, stuff and truss the capon. Place in roasting pan and pour the hot lard over the bird. Sprinkle lightly with salt. Cook uncovered in moderately hot oven (425° F.) for 20–25 minutes. When the bird is brown, pour a quart of hot milk over it, turn down the heat and baste the bird occasionally with the hot milk. When done, add a little flour paste to the hot milk, allowing 2 tablespoons flour for each cup of milk. Untruss the bird on a hot platter, garnish with watercress and serve.

CHESTNUT STUFFING

4 c. chestnuts	1 tbsp. lemon juice
2 c. bread crumbs	Grated rind of ½ lemon
¾ c. cream	Salt and pepper
6 tbsp. melted butter	

Blanche and shell chestnuts. Cook in boiling salted water until tender. Chop fine. Add lemon juice and rind to cream, and add to chestnuts. Mix in the crumbs, season to taste with salt and pepper, and stuff into bird.

364

Roasted turkey—symbol of American hospitality.

The Turkey—Royal but Democratic

France has *pâté de foi gras,* Russia has caviar, England has roast beef. But America has turkey.

"The turkey," wrote Benjamin Franklin, "is an American from head to tail. He is a bird of courage." The turkey was one of Franklin's suggestions to the Colonial Congress when that body was considering an emblem for a great seal that should be suitable for the newly independent American Colonies.

The turkey as an emblem would not have been new to European peoples, for by that time the great bird was well enough known and appreciated so that roasted turkey was served at the royal wedding feast of the French King Charles IX and Elizabeth of Austria.

In those early days the European method of preparing turkey was to parboil the bird, then stuff it with Spanish chestnuts and bake it. Priscilla, busily preparing the turkeys and other wild fowl for the first Thanksgiving dinner in her new American home, wished sorrowfully that she had a few Spanish chestnuts so that these wild birds might "seem more like their brothers across the sea."

Ever since that early Thanksgiving, when "Bradford, the good Governor, sent fowlers forth to snare the Turkey and the wild fowl, to increase the scanty fare," turkey has been the festival meat of America. It became the emblem of American plenty. Better than any other one dish, turkey expresses the spirit of American hospitality.

The turkeys of Priscilla's day, famous as they are, would in many   365 cases make rather a sorry showing if put beside one of the modern, scientifically fed and managed birds with its fine-grained, tender, fat-larded meat. Colonial cooks found it necessary to parboil their turkeys before roasting them. One old cookbook, written in 1661, gives the following directions "to bake a turkey": "Bone and lard your Turkey when it is parboiled, being seasoned with Pepper, Salt, with a little Cloves and Mace, put him in your Coffin prepared for it, lay on butter, and close it; put the head on top with your garnish; Indore it, bake it, and fill it with clarified butter when it is cold."

The "coffin" was a piecrust which was spread over the baking bird. "Indoring," or "endoring," was glazing the roast with egg yolk. Larding is the process of drawing narrow strips of fat salted pork or ham or bacon through the breast and other meaty portions of the turkey before baking the bird. Those wild fowl were somewhat dry, and the fat was believed to improve the flavor and add juiciness. Today larding is almost unheard of. Modern turkeys, specially prepared for market, are fed so that filmy deposits of fat are laid down throughout the muscles. When the bird is baked, the fat melts and the cooked meat is deliciously juicy.

With the coming of late fall the royal birds reach their prime, just in time to grace the Thanksgiving dinner. While cornfields are green and leaves still on trees these great birds grow and grow. If they are killed then their meat is somewhat stringy and not so juicy and pleasing as desired. But just as soon as the first frosty weather comes, when cornfields rustle in late fall winds and colored leaves have whirled to the ground, turkeys develop prodigious appetites. Golden corn is almost visibly transformed into meaty turkey breasts and drumsticks. It is then that the real turkey season has arrived.

Food lovers long ago regretted that turkey was available for such a short season each year. Gradually turkey came to be the Christmas meat, too. But food lovers still wished to extend the turkey season. Modern refrigeration methods have made possible the granting of this wish, and today we have turkey the year around, at least in our large markets. Some of the fanciest turkeys produced each year are frozen and held for high-class trade.

Selection of the Turkey

Turkeys range in size from 8 to 25 pounds, with most of them in the 12 to 16 pound group. Extremely large birds are the exception.

A half turkey,
ready to be
stuffed and
trussed.

Most of those weighing over 16 pounds go into the hotel trade where
large birds lend themselves to economical serving. Many connoisseurs
believe that the meat of large young birds is exceptionally fine in flavor.
But with the decreasing size of the family, and therefore of household
equipment, the demand for small turkeys—8, 10, 12 pounds—is
increasing. So breeders are giving much attention to developing
turkeys which will be small when mature.

Turkeys, like other young animals, do not begin to fill out until
they reach maturity. Until that time the birds are somewhat rangy
and therefore not so good for eating as after they begin to fill out.
It has been suggested that until small, mature, well filled turkeys are
developed in large enough quantities to supply the demand without
having to charge a premium for them, market men might split the large
turkeys in halves, just as broilers are split, and sell turkey in halves.
As yet this suggestion has met with little favor on the part of
most market men, although many Jewish shops have followed the practice successfully for a number of years.

The half birds lend themselves to stuffing and trussing and baking
just as a whole bird does, though the method of handling is somewhat
different. The stuffing is put into the cut side of the bird, then a
piece of parchment is laid over it, and the bird is trussed, the trussing
twine holding the stuffing in place. The roaster rack is placed over
the trussed bird, the whole is inverted and put into the roaster. Cooking is exactly as for the whole bird. The roasted half turkey is attractive and can be carved and served as satisfactorily as a whole bird. 367

There may be a time when the homemaker will commonly buy turkey
roasts—drumstick, or thigh or breast, just as she now buys cuts of veal
or lamb, and even cuts of chicken.

The size of the bird to be purchased is determined by the number of
people to be served. If the turkey is to be roasted, one-half to three-
quarters of a pound of turkey, purchasing weight, is allowed per person.

Various grades of turkey are available. Birds in the highest grade
must be young, with broad, full breasts, with fine-grained, soft meat,
and with backs, hips and pin or hip bones fully covered with fat. In
each succeeding grade these desirable qualities are slightly less prominent. All qualities are available in both frozen and freshly killed
birds. Both hen and tom turkeys are good, there being no noticeable
difference in quality of meat.

In a few markets turkeys that have been graded by government
appointees have been sold with a government certificate as to grade.
The practice is not yet general, however. A good many turkeys have
been so graded experimentally at country packing plants. Every
packer, of course, grades his birds and the practice of selling them by
brand name is increasing.

Trussing and Roasting

Trussing and roasting are the same for turkeys as for chickens. If
skewers are used in trussing, insert one long skewer through the wings
and through the body below the breast. Draw the thighs close to the

—And so stuff
your bird.

body and run a skewer through them to hold them in place. Tie the
ends of the legs together with a long piece of twine, bring the twine
down around the tailpiece to hold the legs down. Then bring the
twine down around the end of each of the thigh skewers, cross it over
the back of the bird, wind it around the end of the wing skewer and
tie across the back. Weigh the stuffed and trussed bird and compute
the time required for roasting. Allow 15 to 20 minutes per pound.
The smaller the bird, the longer the time per pound required.

Turkey, like chicken, may be cleaned and stuffed the day before it
is roasted. Prepare the bird for the oven and keep it in the refrigerator
until ready to cook. When the bird is very cold when put into the
oven, a slightly longer cooking time is required.

Basting is not necessary, although it is not objectionable. Thin
slices of bacon or fat salt pork may be laid over the breast during cooking, although if the bird has been properly fattened and managed it
contains enough fat to baste itself. Some cooks prefer to cook turkey
breast down, so that the juices run into the breast and keep it moist
throughout the cooking period. Hot cider or gingerale may be substituted for the water that is added to the pan at the end of the
searing period.

369

Broiled Turkey

For broiling, young turkeys are most desirable. Very young turkeys, called poults, are excellent for broiling and frying. They are appearing on the market in increasing numbers. An older bird may be broiled very satisfactorily if it is first steamed an hour.

Cut the bird into attractive pieces. The breast, thighs and drumsticks are especially good broiled. The other portions may be saved and cooked some other way for another meal, although they, too, may be broiled.

Brush each piece with melted fat, place on broiler pan and put under a hot flame (450°–475° F.) for 5 minutes. Turn and brown all sides. Then lower the flame (250°–275° F.) and cook for 30 to 45 minutes more, depending on the thickness of the pieces. Prepare gravy from the drippings and add the giblets which have been cooked and chopped. For the gravy use the liquor in which the giblets were stewed, allowing 2 tablespoonfuls of flour and 2 tablespoonfuls of fat for each cup of liquid used.

Fried Turkey

Fried turkey is as delicious as it is unusual. The one great precaution to observe is to cook it at a low temperature so that it will remain tender. Either young birds or older birds which have been steamed are excellent for frying.

After cutting the turkey into pieces suitable for serving, dip each piece into beaten egg and then into flour to which has been added 1 tablespoon salt and ½ teaspoonful white pepper for each cup of flour. Finely sifted bread crumbs may be substituted for the flour.

Brown the turkey in a half cup of cooking fat in a heavy skillet. Then lower the heat, cover the skillet and cook the turkey slowly until done.

For the gravy, simmer the giblets until tender in just enough water to cover. When the turkey has been removed from the cooking fat, thicken the fat with flour. Add the liquor in which the giblets were cooked and enough milk to make the required amount of gravy. Two tablespoonfuls of flour and two tablespoonfuls of fat for each cup of liquid makes a medium thick gravy.

From one-fourth to one-half cup of gravy per person is a good allowance.

Singe, clean and wash turkey. Rub inside with salt, stuff and truss. Bake for 20 minutes, uncovered in hot oven (475° F.). Then put 1 cup of boiling water into roaster, cover, and finish cooking in slow oven (275–300° F.). Allow 18–22 minutes per pound, depending on size of bird. The smaller bird requires the longer time per pound.

A 14 to 16 pound bird, as purchased, requires 9 to 10 cups of stuffing. A half cup of stuffing per serving is usually allowed. These recipes make enough stuffing to fill a 14 to 16 pound turkey. Quantities can be increased and the surplus stuffing baked in a separate dish.

GIBLET STUFFING

9 c. toasted bread crumbs
½–¾ c. water or milk
½ c. melted fat
3 tsp. salt
½ tsp. pepper

½ tsp. sage
3 medium onions, chopped fine
2 c. diced celery
Giblets, cooked and ground

Put giblets in small pan with just enough water to cover. Cook until tender, grind through a food chopper. Pour water over bread and let stand a few minutes. Add fat, seasoning, onion, celery and ground up giblets to bread crumbs. Mix thoroughly.

SOUTHERN STUFFING

Liver of turkey
3 large sweet potatoes
1 lb. chestnuts
¼ lb. pinenuts
½ lb. English walnuts

½ lb. almonds
1 stick cinnamon
20 cloves
¼ lb. butter

Put the liver, peeled sweet potatoes and nuts through the medium knife of the food chopper. Add pepper, salt, cinnamon, cloves and butter. Put into stewpan and cook ½ hour, stirring frequently. Fill into turkey and bake.

WILLIAM BRADFORD STUFFING

9 c. bread crumbs
1 tsp. sweet marjoram
2 large onions, minced

½ c. melted butter or turkey fat
Salt and pepper to taste
1 tsp. thyme

Combine all ingredients thoroughly. Add enough water or milk to moisten very slightly, about ¾ cup, and fill into turkey. This is one of the most popular as well as one of the simplest stuffigs for turkey. The original recipe is found in an old colonial recipe book.

371

CELERY ALMOND STUFFING

6 c. bread crumbs, toasted	1/4 c. turkey fat or butter
3 c. diced celery	1 1/2 tsp. salt
1/2 c. celery leaves, shredded	1/2 tsp. pepper
1 1/2 c. whole blanched almonds	1/2 tsp. poultry seasoning
	2 eggs, slightly beaten
	1/2 to 3/4 c. water or milk

Combine all ingredients thoroughly and fill into turkey.

CHESTNUT STUFFING

7 c. bread crumbs	1 1/2 tsp. salt
2 c. chestnuts	1/2 tsp. pepper
2 eggs, slightly beaten	3/4 c. milk
1/2 c. butter or turkey fat	

Shell the chestnuts and cook in boiling water until the brown skin can be removed easily. Remove the skins, shred or dice the white portion and brown in 2 tablespoons fat. Combine all the ingredients, blend thoroughly and fill into bird.

ORIENTAL STUFFING

1 1/2 c. brown rice	3/4 c. mushrooms
3/4 c. almonds	2 eggs, slightly beaten
1 No. 1 can water chestnuts	2 tbsp. soy sauce
1 No. 2 can bamboo shoots	1/4 c. turkey fat or butter
1 No. 2 can bean sprouts	2 tsp. salt
1 c. shredded celery	2 tbsp. minced onion
	1/8 tsp. pepper

Cook rice in boiling salted water until tender. Drain. Slice or shred vegetables and nuts. Brown vegetables and nuts in the fat. Combine with rice, adding the eggs, salt and sauce. Blend thoroughly and fill into bird. This stuffing has an excellent flavor and texture. It may also be baked in a casserole and served as an accompaniment to turkey instead of as a stuffing.

EGG AND MUSHROOM STUFFING

9 c. bread crumbs	3 hard cooked eggs, sliced
1 egg, slightly beaten	2 tsp. salt
4 slices bacon, broiled and diced	1/2 tsp. pepper
3/4 c. mushrooms	3/4 tsp. poultry seasoning
	3/4 c. milk

Brown the mushrooms in 2 tablespoons of the bacon drippings. Combine all ingredients thoroughly and fill into turkey.

8 c. bread crumbs

1 pt. oysters

1 tsp. salt

½ tsp. celery salt

¼ tsp. pepper

1 egg, slightly beaten

Wash oysters thoroughly. Blend all ingredients and fill into turkey.

1 14–16 lb. turkey

1 pt. cream or undiluted
   evaporated milk

1 pt. mushrooms

Salt

Pepper

2 tbsp. butter

Cut up turkey as for stewing. Rub each piece lightly with salt and pepper. Put in layers into large casserole or roaster. Pour cream over the meat and bake in moderate oven (350° F.) until meat is tender, about 1½ to 1¾ hours. When done, remove from baking dish, dilute the cream with a little hot water, thicken with flour and add the mushrooms which have been sliced and browned in the butter. Serve the thickened cream as a sauce for the turkey.

This method of cooking is excellent for a turkey which is a bit less tender than one likes for broiling, roasting or frying. It is also a delightful way to use up the odd pieces which are sometimes difficult to serve.

1 14–16 lb. turkey

7 carrots

2 onions

8 stalks celery

1½ tbsp. salt

½ tsp. thyme

½ tsp. marjoram

8 tbsp. cooking sherry

18 pistachio nuts, chopped

2 tbsp. gelatin

½ c. cold water

Cut up the turkey as for stewing. Put it into a large kettle and just cover it with boiling water. Add the vegetables which have been diced, the seasonings and the nuts. Bring to boil, then turn down heat and simmer gently until meat is very tender. Remove meat from stock, cook stock down to about one-half its volume. In the hot stock dissolve the gelatin which has been soaked in the cold water. Strain carefully through a cloth to make the broth clear. In a large oval mold, or in small individual molds, arrange alternate slices of dark and light meat. Pour the cooled stock over the meat and chill. When ready to serve, unmold and garnish with pimiento cups, truffles, sliced hard cooked eggs and watercress. Serve with mayonnaise to which 1 teaspoon horseradish per cup has been added.

373

TURKEY COMPOTE

¾ c. brown rice	1½ c. diced turkey
2 tbsp. fat	1 No. 1 can peas
2 tbsp. flour	¼ tsp. salt
1½ c. liquor from canned	⅛ tsp. pepper
vegetables	1 No. 1 can mushrooms
1 egg	

Cook rice in boiling salted water until tender. Make sauce of fat, flour and liquor. Remove from fire, add beaten egg and stir until well blended. Add turkey, peas and seasonings. Put rice in buttered baking dish. Over it pour the turkey mixture. Top with the mushrooms which have been dipped in a little melted butter. Bake in moderate oven (325° F.) until heated through and mushrooms are browned.

ESCALLOPED TURKEY WITH NOODLES

2 tbsp. butter	¼ lb. noodles
2 tbsp. flour	1 c. diced cooked celery
1½ c. milk	1½ c. diced turkey
1 tsp. salt	¼ c. grated cheese
⅛ tsp. pepper	

Cook noodles in boiling salted water until tender. Make white sauce of first 5 ingredients. Put alternate layers of noodles, celery and turkey into a buttered baking dish. Pour white sauce or left-over gravy over all. Sprinkle with grated cheese and set into oven until heated through and cheese is thoroughly melted.

TURKEY ITALIENNE

¼ lb. spaghetti	½ tsp. salt
2 tbsp. butter	3 tbsp. chopped green olives
2 tbsp. flour	¼ c. grated cheese
1 tbsp. minced onion	1½ c. diced turkey
1 c. milk	2 hard cooked eggs

Cook spaghetti in boiling salted water until tender. Brown the onions slightly in the butter. Add the flour, stir until smooth, and add the milk. Continue cooking, stirring until the sauce is smooth and thickened. Add turkey, olives and grated cheese. When ready to serve arrange spaghetti on platter, pour turkey mixture over it and garnish with slices of hard cooked eggs.

TURKEY CHOP SUEY

2 c. diced turkey meat
4 slices bacon, diced and broiled
1 No. 1 can mushrooms
2 tbsp. bacon drippings
2 tbsp. shredded onions
3 c. shredded celery
1 No. can 1 bean sprouts
1 No. 1 can bamboo shoots
4 tbsp. soy sauce
2 tbsp. flour
Salt and pepper
1 c. rice

Melt the bacon drippings in a deep pan. Add the onions and celery and brown. Add the liquor from the mushrooms, bean sprouts and bamboo shoots. If there is not enough liquid just to cover the vegetables, add a little hot water. Cover and simmer until vegetables are tender. Thicken with the flour which has been stirred to a paste with a little cold water. Add the bean sprouts and bamboo shoots which have been sliced very thin, soy sauce and salt. Blend thoroughly. Then add the bacon, turkey and the mushrooms. The flavor of this dish is improved if it is allowed to stand several hours and then is reheated just before serving. Steam rice or cook it in boiling water until tender. When ready to serve, put a mound of rice on each plate, cover with chop suey. Garnish with whole toasted almonds or chopped cashew nuts. Fried noodles may accompany this dish.

TURKEY ROULETTES

3 c. flour
4 tsp. baking powder
4 tbsp. shortening
3/4 tsp. salt
3/4 c. milk

Sift together the dry ingredients. Cut in the fat. Add the milk and mix lightly to make biscuit dough. Roll the dough 1/8 inch thick and cut into 3 inch squares. Spread each square with turkey filling, moisten edges with water, and roll jelly-roll fashion. Bake in hot oven (425°–450° F.) for 15 minutes. Serve with hot gravy or medium white sauce, allowing 2 roulettes per serving.

FILLING FOR TURKEY ROULETTES

1 c. finely ground turkey
1/2 tsp. salt
1/4 tsp. pepper
2 tbsp. cream or gravy

Cream all together until well blended and spread on biscuit squares.

TURKEY CRÉOLE STYLE

3 tbsp. fat
1 tbsp. chopped onion
2 tbsp. chopped green pepper
1/2 tsp. salt
3 tbsp. flour
1 c. milk
1/2 c. tomato pulp
1 tbsp. horseradish
1 tsp. lemon juice
1 1/2 c. diced turkey meat

Cook onion and green pepper in the fat until brown. Add salt and flour and stir until flour is cooked. Add milk and tomato pulp. Stir until the 375

mixture reaches the boiling point, then add horseradish, lemon juice and turkey.
Serve over hot hominy.

CRANBERRY CLOVE JELLY

2 c. water	1 qt. cranberries
¼ tsp. salt	1½ tbsp. gelatin
2 tsp. whole cloves	2 tbsp. cold water
1½ c. sugar	1 tsp. lemon juice

Cook cranberries, salt and cloves in the water until berries are soft. Put
through sieve. Add sugar to pulp and cook 3 minutes. Add lemon juice and
gelatin which has been soaked in cold water. Pour half this jelly into mold
which has been rinsed with cold water. When set, add layer of lemon jelly
and turkey.

TURKEY IN LEMON JELLY

1½ c. diced turkey meat	3 tbsp. cold water
1 c. finely diced celery	1 c. boiling water
½ tsp. salt	1 tbsp. sugar
1½ tsp. gelatin	4 tbsp. lemon juice

Soak gelatin in cold water for 5 minutes. Dissolve in boiling water. Add
sugar and salt and stir until dissolved. Cool, then add the lemon juice, turkey
and celery. Pour over layer of cranberry jelly in mold. When set, add
another layer of cranberry jelly. Chill and serve. Garnish with rosettes of
cream cheese which has been moistened with a little milk or water.

CRANBERRY TURKEY MOLD

In large fancy mold or in small individual molds arrange alternate layers of
cranberry clove jelly and minced turkey in lemon jelly. When firm, unmold
on platter, garnish with celery hearts and salad greens.

TURKEY MOUSSE

1½ tbsp. gelatin	½ c. chopped sweet pickle
2 tbsp. cold water	2 tbsp. chopped pimiento
2 eggs, separated	1 tbsp. chopped green pepper
1½ c. milk	4 tbsp. chopped stuffed olives
½ tsp. salt	6 tbsp. finely minced celery
⅛ tsp. white pepper	⅛ tsp. cayenne
1½ c. diced turkey	½ c. chopped almonds

Soak gelatin in cold water. Separate eggs. Beat yolks, add milk, salt, pepper
and cook in double boiler until creamy. Add gelatin and stir until dissolved.
Cool. When gelatin begins to congeal, fold in stiffly beaten egg whites. Then
fold in the other ingredients. Pour into large mold or into individual molds
and freeze. When ready to serve, unmold and garnish with tiny lettuce hearts
and rosettes of tartar sauce or mayonnaise.

376

1½ c. minced turkey   1 tsp. salt
2 eggs   ¼ tsp. pepper
1¾ c. milk   1 tbsp. butter
1 tbsp. flour

Separate the eggs. Beat yolks, add milk, flour, salt and pepper. Cook in double boiler until the mixture coats the spoon. Add the butter and turkey. Then fold in stiffly beaten egg whites. Bake in moderate oven (350° F.) about 20 minutes, or until egg is set. Serve at once.

MARINATED TURKEY

Cut pieces of left-over turkey meat into fillets about 2 inches long and an inch wide. Put into bowl and marinate for 2 hours with 4 tablespoons vinegar, 2 tablespoons oil, salt and pepper to taste. Drain and dry on brown paper. Dip each piece of meat into frying batter and fry to golden color in deep fat at 385° F. At this temperature a cube of bread browns in 40 seconds. Garnish with parsley. Serve with left-over gravy or tomato sauce.

TURKEY DIPLOMAT, WITH CRANBERRY GARNISH

2 c. cooked turkey meat, diced
1 c. diced celery
6 stuffed olives, sliced
1½ c. mayonnaise
½ tsp. salt
¼ tsp. paprika
1 pkg. lemon gelatin
2 c. boiling water
2 hard cooked eggs, chopped
1 c. white cherries, drained and cut up
½ c. nutmeats, broken
2 tsp. Worcestershire sauce
¼ tsp. pepper
2 c. chopped cranberries
½ c. sugar

Cook cranberries in boiling water until tender. While hot add sugar and the lemon flavored gelatin. Pour into a shallow pan to the depth of one inch. Set aside to chill. Combine the turkey, eggs, celery, cherries, nuts, olives. Add the Worcestershire sauce and paprika to the mayonnaise. Add to the salad mixture and toss lightly together. Mold each portion of salad in a custard cup and turn out on a bed of salad greens. With a vegetable cutter cut little balls or fancy shapes from the cranberry jelly and place around each salad. Serve with toasted wafers.

APPLE AND TURKEY SALAD

Select large red apples. Remove cores, making rather large openings. Slash skin of apple in 5 slashes from blossom to stem end. Stuff with chopped turkey to which has been added salt and pepper and a few fine bread crumbs. Bake in slow oven (350° F.) until apples are done. Chill. Set each apple in lettuce cup, peel back the skin to make garnish and serve with mayonnaise.

GLACÉ ORANGES

Peel and quarter navel oranges. Simmer in a syrup made by cooking 1 cup sugar with ¾ cup water 5 minutes. When quite tender and almost clear, remove and drain the quarters. Serve turkey on platter with olives and oranges alternated about it as a garnish, with sprigs of watercress between.

WRAPPED OLIVES

Roll ripe pitted olives in strips of bacon. Fasten strip with toothpick. Put into pan with turkey the last 10–15 minutes of cooking, or cook on broiler pan or in skillet until bacon is done, but not crisp.

BROWNED CHESTNUTS

Take outside shell off chestnuts. Boil them in salted water until brown skin can be removed. Put some butter in saucepan, salt and pepper lightly. Shake chestnuts in pan over fire. When delicately browned, set in dish and pour a little turkey gravy over them.

ORANGE AND CRANBERRY RELISH

On platter arrange slices of orange, ⅛ to ¼ inch thick. In center of each slice place cube of cranberry jelly. Garnish with sprig of mint or parsley.

STEAMED WILD RICE

Wild rice, steamed until almost done and then tied in cheese-cloth bag and set into roasting pan so it can absorb juices, makes a delicious accompaniment to turkey.

CRANBERRY SAUCE

4 c. cranberries   1½–2 c. sugar
2 c. water

Boil sugar and water together 5 minutes. Add cranberries and cook without stirring 5 minutes, or until skins pop. Remove from fire and cool.

The Stately Goose

A trip through a market that specializes in fancy foods might lead one to think that the parts of the goose were more popular than the whole bird. There are such tempting specialties as smoked breast of goose, *pâté de foi gras,* stuffed goose neck, and goose-liver sausage. And, say the food purveyors, these delicacies are much more popular with foreign-born peoples than with Americans. Europeans have always appreciated the goose as a special delicacy. Where the American housewife thinks of goose as a greasy meat, the European cook knows well how to cook goose so as to have tasty meat and to save and use every bit of the soft, creamy fat. For goose fat, like chicken

378

fat, makes excellent shortening for pastries and many a special dainty, to say nothing of its traditional "medicinal" uses.

Although, thanks to modern refrigeration, geese are available the year around, the traditional time for serving roasted goose is near Christmas. The richness of the meat may have something to do with the fact that goose is more popular in winter than in summer. The real goose season comes in late fall. Catherine Frances Frere, in her "Proper Newe Booke of Cookery," written in the sixteenth century, advises housewives that "A goose is worste in midsommer mone (months) and beste in stubble tyme, but when they be yong grene geese, then they be beste."

The term "green geese" is still an accepted market term used to describe young birds that are at the choice stage for cooking. Green geese correspond to roasting chickens. Incidentally a "green goose" is always a gander rather than a goose, just as a roaster is a cock rather than a hen.

Geese vary in size from the small eight-pound birds to the large ones weighing twelve pounds or more. Young geese, which are most desirable, are spoken of as "green" geese. The identifying qualities of green geese are a soft, pliable bill and soft feet. The presence of many pinfeathers used to be considered sure evidence that the goose was young, but modern dressing methods turn out a clean, well plucked bird.

The thick pieces of meat lying along each side of the breast bone of the goose are the choice portions. Often they are taken out, rolled and smoked. The cured meat is sliced very thin and used for sandwiches, cold platters and appetizers. The thighs and drumsticks are sold fresh, for roasting or frying. The rest of the carcass is cut up and sold in neighborhoods where the population is largely foreign, for these women understand well how to make delicious dishes of this inexpensive meat.

Another delicacy made from goose, better known in Europe than in America, is stuffed goose neck. The skin is removed from the neck in one unbroken piece and filled with a highly seasoned stuffing. The ends are tied and the "sausage" is baked. When cold, it is served sliced thin.

Goose liver, soft and rich, is a popular basic ingredient for many special dishes. Its most famous use is in the manufacture of *pâté de foi gras,* a paste made from the livers of geese which have been carefully hand fed. *Pâté de fois gras,* as usually made by its inventors, is among the recipes at the back of the book. During the feeding period the geese are kept closely confined, so that lack of exercise will make them grow enormously fat, and the livers grow to huge size. In some sections of Europe, and in one small section of the United States, geese are noodled. That is, a fattening cereal mixture, cooked and then shaped into long, noodle-like strips, is hand fed to the geese.

In preparing goose for baking, a stuffing which contains some mild acid serves to counteract the rich flavor of the meat. German cooks frequently stuff the bird with sauerkraut. Many an old English cookbook mentions the celebrated roast goose stuffed with apples and raisins. Apricot dressing or prune dressing have the same effect. Cooks of Czecko-Slovakia rub the inside of the goose with caraway seed, and omit dressing.

Some of the fat may be drained off if the goose, without stuffing, is heated for thirty minutes in a moderately hot oven (425° F.). The fat that fries out of the goose during this time is drained off, the goose is stuffed, and the roasting is completed.

The legs of a goose are too short to allow of trussing like chicken and turkey are trussed. Tie the trussing twine around one leg and then around the other, leaving about 1½ to 2 inches length of string between legs. Bring ends of twine under back and tie securely.

ROAST GOOSE, GERMAN STYLE

1 large goose
1 lb. apples, peeled and diced
¼ lb. raisins

1 tbsp. brown sugar
3 c. bread crumbs
Salt

Mix apples, raisins, sugar and bread crumbs. Add a little salt. Fill into goose after the bird has been rubbed with salt. This dressing seems somewhat dry but becomes moist as the apples cook. Truss goose and put breast down on rack in roasting pan. Pour 2 cups boiling water over it. Put an onion into the pan. Bake for half hour in moderately hot oven (375° F.) and then turn the goose. Prick the skin around the legs and wings to let fat run out. Reduce heat to 300° F. and bake 2–2½ hours. If more water is necessary, add ½–¾ cup boiling water at a time. To make skin crisp, 5 minutes before removing from oven pour 2 tablespoons cold water over goose and let cook uncovered for 5 minutes.

APRICOT DRESSING

½ lb. dried apricots   ¼ c. butter
3 c. soft bread crumbs   ¼ c. celery
1 c. cracker crumbs   1½ tsp. salt
Pepper

Wash apricots, add just enough boiling water to cover them and simmer until tender, but not mushy. When cool, cut into small pieces. Combine apricots, bread crumbs, cracker crumbs, butter and celery. Season with salt and pepper. Mix thoroughly and stuff into goose,

APPLE STUFFING

5 green apples, quartered   2 c. bread crumbs
1½ c. seedless raisins   ½ tsp. cinnamon
2 eggs, slightly beaten

Blend all ingredients thoroughly and fill into goose.

CHESTNUT STUFFING

1 goose liver, parboiled   ½ tsp. pepper
   and chopped   ¼ tsp. cayenne pepper
1 c. minced cooked pork   1 tbsp. minced parsley
2 c. bread crumbs   3 tbsp. lemon juice
½ tsp. salt   1 qt. chestnuts, roasted
1 tsp. sage

Mix and fill into goose.

APPLE AND PRUNE STUFFING

25–30 prunes   1 tsp. brown sugar
6 green apples   ½ tsp. cinnamon
2 tbsp. butter   1 c. dried bread crumbs
Grated rind of 1 lemon

Cook the prunes until tender, letting the liquor on them cook down until quite thick. Peel and core the apples and cut them into quarters. Put the butter into a skillet, and add the other ingredients. Blend thoroughly and fill into goose.

NOODLES AND PÂTÉ DE FOIE GRAS

6 oz. noodles   ¼ tsp. nutmeg
1 can mushrooms   ¼ tsp. pepper
2 tbsp. butter   ½ tsp. salt
1 onion   1 sweetbread
½ tsp. prepared mustard   1 can pâté de foie gras
1 egg

Cook noodles in boiling, salted water until tender. Drain. Drain mushrooms, put butter in pan. When hot add noodles and mushrooms. Add   **381** minced onion and cook until tender. Add seasonings. Soak sweetbread in cold salty water, then in fresh water. Cover it with cold water, slightly salted. Let come to boil, drain and fry a few minutes in butter. Mix all ingredients well in bowl, including egg. Put in greased pan, brush with egg yolk. Fry a few drained noodles for the top and sprinkle with bread crumbs. Set pan in boiling water and bake 25 minutes. Serve with this sauce:

2 tbsp. butter	6 chopped olives
1 tbsp. flour	1 tbsp. lemon juice
2 c. canned soup, mush-	1 tsp. salt
room liquor or water	$\frac{1}{8}$ tsp. pepper
12 chopped mushrooms	

Blend butter, flour and canned soup. Add seasoning and other ingredients. Let come to boil, stirring.

GOOSE LIVER LOAF

1 uncooked goose liver, salted	3 eggs
	2 onions, browned in butter
1½ c. milk	4 tbsp. butter
1 small loaf white bread	Salt

Soak the goose liver in rum overnight. Dry and mince it. Soak the loaf of bread in the milk, press it dry, and add to it the eggs, onions, butter and seasoning. Then add the minced liver. Put mixture into a well buttered baking dish and bake at a moderate temperature (350°–375° F.) until done, about 1 hour.

HOW'S AND WHY'S

IN COOKING POULTRY

The Broiling Chicken

B ROILERS are, so to speak, the tender cuts of chicken. They are the very young birds only four weeks to two months old. Their muscles are small, delicate and tender. There is no accumulation of fat, so that fat is usually added in cooking. Because the meat is so tender, broilers can be cooked quickly, and because the connective tissue is so thin, it is not appreciatively toughened even when submitted to rather high cooking temperatures, as it is in broiling. The flavor is so delicate that the only seasoning needed is a little salt and pepper, with melted butter. Accompaniments for broiled chicken should be the milder-flavored vegetables and salads.

Oven and Pan Broiling

For broiling, the chicken is split into halves, lengthwise. The back-bone may or may not be removed. Serving and eating are somewhat simplified if it is taken out before cooking. The pieces are rubbed with fat and they may be salted lightly before cooking. Then, for oven broiling, the pieces are laid skin side up on the broiler rack and placed under a hot flame to brown. This requires from five to seven minutes. Then the pieces are turned, without, however, puncturing the meat, lest the juices run out.

When the cut side has browned, the flame is turned low and the meat is cooked for about ten to fifteen minutes more, depending on the size and thickness of the pieces. The high initial heat browns the meat, and the lower heat finishes the cooking without drying it out or toughening it. Browning the skin side first and then finishing the cooking with the cut side up catches the juices in the tiny hollows and allows the meat to absorb them instead of letting them drip into the broiler pan. It also keeps the skin tender and soft. Just before serving, the pieces are brushed with melted butter.

Pan broiling is similar to oven broiling. The pieces of chicken, brushed with fat, are put into a hot skillet which has also been brushed

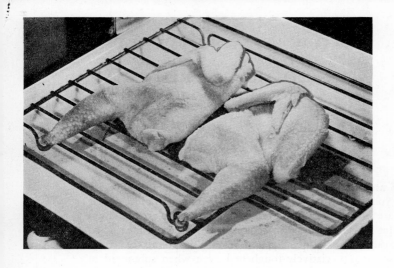

"Just split 'em down the b a c k and broil 'em."

with fat. After the pieces have been browned, the flame is turned down so that the actual cooking is not too fast, lest the outside scorch before the inside of the muscles is entirely cooked.

CHICKEN LÉONY

Cut a 2 pound broiler into quarters. Season with salt and pepper and brown in butter. Add ½ teaspoon minced onion, 2 tablespoons cooking sherry and 5 tablespoons blanched spinach. Add 1 cup cream and 1 cup chicken broth or water, cover and let cook gently until chicken is done.

BROILED CHICKEN WITH TOMATOES

While chicken is broiling, broil also thick slices of ripe tomatoes. The tomato slices are put into the broiler when the chicken is turned the first time, else they will be over cooked.

SOLARI'S CHICKEN, Country Style

2 broilers, cleaned and Flour
    split 1 c. cream
1 pt. milk Butter

Soak the broilers in milk for several hours. When ready to cook, dry, season and dust with flour. Brown in butter and then cook slowly in a moderate oven (325°–350° F.) until tender. Remove chicken from pan, add the cream to the drippings, blend thoroughly and serve.

384

1–3 lb. broiler
2 bouillon cubes
2 c. boiling water
2 tbsp. flour
2 tsp. Worcestershire
  sauce
1 tsp. sugar

¼ tsp. pepper
1 tsp. mustard
2 tbsp. butter
2 onions
2 tbsp. tomato paste
1 tbsp. minced parsley

Sprinkle chicken with ½ teaspoon salt and ⅛ teaspoon pepper. Place on broiler under flame, being careful to turn so that all parts brown evenly. Place on hot platter and serve with following sauce:

Melt butter, add chopped onions, cook until light brown. Add flour, bouillon cubes dissolved in boiling water, mixed with the other ingredients. Cook 10 minutes, stirring occasionally.

And This Is Fried Chicken

When a chicken grows about two or three months beyond the broiler stage, it becomes a fryer. The muscles get larger and meatier, and they contain traces of fat here and there. Because the muscles are thicker, the pieces of meat take a little longer to cook than the halves of broilers. But the fryer is still a very young chicken, and therefore tender.

Everywhere a favorite, fried chicken means different things to people in different parts of the country. The difference, however, is in the method of cooking, not in the bird itself. One cook rolls the pieces of chicken in flour, another prefers cracker crumbs, another uses corn-meal, still another dips the pieces into a batter, and others want the chicken just as it is, not dipped in anything, but dropped directly into hot fat and fried to golden brownness.

As for the actual frying, some use only a little fat in the frying pan, some use a large amount, some fry in deep fat in the French manner. Sometimes the fat is lard, sometimes butter, sometimes half of each, and sometimes one of the vegetable fats or oils.

Whatever the method used, the finished product should be golden pieces of tempting tenderness, fit for the rhapsodies of a poet.

In all of the methods for frying chicken, except in French frying, the chief rule to observe is: high temperature at first, for a short time, to brown the surface, followed by low temperature to finish cooking and to keep the meat tender. The browning is done with the pan uncovered, while the remainder of the cooking may be done with or without a cover. If a cover is used, steam collects and drips down

Fried chicken,—w h a t
more need be said?

on the pieces, making them deliciously tender and keeping the golden
surface soft. Without a cover the crust tends to remain quite crisp.
When a large quantity of chicken is fried at one time the easiest way
to cook it is to brown it over the open flame or in a hot oven, and
finish cooking it in a moderate oven (350° F.).

When done, the chicken is removed from the pan and the drippings
are used to make the cream gravy which is the final touch to real fried
chicken as connoisseurs know it.

For each cupful of gravy, use two tablespoonfuls of the drippings
and two level tablespoonfuls of flour. Blend them thoroughly above
a low flame. Stir until the flour thickens and then add a cupful of
milk, still stirring. Let the gravy come to a boil, season with salt
and pepper, and serve, either as a sauce over the chicken, or in a
separate dish.

In order to accomplish the crisp golden crust that can easily be
removed from pieces of chicken, the pieces are dipped into slightly
beaten egg, then into sifted crumbs, into the egg once more and finally
again into the crumbs, and then fried. Or the pieces are dipped into
a thin batter and then fried in deep fat.

The easiest way to "crumb" pieces of chicken is to put the crumbs
or flour, mixed with the salt, into a bag. Put the pieces of chicken in
386 and shake.

A good batter for coating chicken for frying is made of

        1 c. flour
        1 egg
        1½ tsp. salt
        ¾ c. milk

Combine all the ingredients and beat until the batter is smooth. Dip each piece of chicken into the batter and fry in a skillet, omitting the water, or in deep fat.

In deep fat or French frying the secret of success lies chiefly in the temperature of the fat. It must be hot enough so that it browns the crust in just the time that is required to cook the meat. If it is too hot, the surface of the pieces browns too soon, and the inside remains partly cooked. If it is not hot enough, the coating absorbs fat and the meat does not cook satisfactorily. A temperature of 375° F. gives good results. This is the temperature at which a cube of bread will brown in 45 seconds when dropped into the fat. The thicker pieces of chicken—the drumstick, thigh and breast—cook in 12 to 17 minutes. The thinner pieces require less time.

To Cut Up Chicken for Frying

Chickens large enough for frying are meaty enough to be cut up to facilitate cooking and serving. A sharp knife is essential to satisfactory results. Poultry shears are helpful. As in preparing cuts from any other animals, the cuts from chicken naturally follow the joints.

First, remove the leg, cutting through the skin on the inner side of the thigh, next to the body. Remove this piece at the hip joint. Separate the thigh from the drumstick. Next remove the wings, cutting through the joint. Next make a short incision just above the vent. Cut around the vent. From this point, with the knife blade inside the body cavity, cut along the side of the carcass to the wing joint, cutting through the small joints in the ribs. When this cut has been made at each side, snap back the breast piece and separate. This exposes the entrails lying in the body cavity. Divide the breast in halves, cutting lengthwise. Remove the entrails. Cut the back piece in halves, cutting down just behind the ribs, to the backbone. Each of the resulting pieces may be cut into halves. Break the ribs back at the backbone joints, insert the point of the knife under each small rib and pull it out. Removing the ribs makes the pieces easier to handle, both in cooking and in serving.

FRIED CHICKEN

(As cooked in Maryland as early as 1639)

Clean and divide chicken into about 12 pieces, splitting breast and back. Dip into seasoned flour, then into egg beaten with 2 tablespoons water, and then into sifted bread crumbs.

Cut salt pork into tiny cubes and fry out the fat, or use drippings. When hot, put in the chicken and let it cook slowly for about an hour, turning often to cook the chicken evenly all over. *It must be cooked slowly,* else it will be dry.

When chicken is done, add to the 3 tablespoons fat in the pan 2 tablespoons flour. Blend fat and flour and then add 2 cups cream, not milk, but cream. Stir this in gradually. Season. Serve with corn fritters.

COUNTRY FRIED CHICKEN AND CREAM GRAVY

(As President Franklin D. Roosevelt likes it)

1 frying chicken, cut into serving pieces	
1 c. flour	Fat for deep frying
1 tsp. salt	Parsley

Roll the chicken pieces in salted flour and drop into hot, deep fat (375° F.). Fry to golden brown and serve on hot platter garnished with parsley. Make gravy of 4 tablespoons flour, 4 tablespoons fat and 2 cups milk. Season to taste.

VIRGINIA FRIED CHICKEN

Cut up 3 lb. spring chicken. Sprinkle pieces with salt, pepper and flour. Put into skillet containing lard that has been highly heated. Allow 6 tablespoons lard. Brown on all sides, then reduce heat, cover and cook gently until done, 35 to 40 minutes.

FRIED CHICKEN, Southern Style

2 broilers, about 1½ lb. each	½ c. butter
2 eggs	2 onions, sliced
2 tsp. salt	4 tbsp. flour
⅛ tsp. pepper	1 pt. heavy cream
Flour	1 pt. milk

Cut the chickens into fourths. Beat the eggs, adding salt and pepper. Dip the chicken first in this and then in flour. Melt the butter in a heavy frying pan and when sizzling hot put in the chicken and let it brown. Sprinkle the sliced onions over the chickens. Cover tightly and let simmer for an hour. Remove the chicken from the pan and to the drippings add 4 tablespoons flour, the cream and milk. Let boil up, stirring constantly. Season with salt and pepper. Pour over chicken or serve in gravy bowl.

FLORENTINE FRIED CHICKEN

1 3 lb. frying chicken, cut up
2 egg yolks
2 tbsp. water
2 tbsp. lemon juice

¼ lb. grated cheese
1 c. sifted bread crumbs
½ c. cooking oil
½ tsp. salt

Beat egg yolks with water, lemon juice and salt. Dip each piece of chicken into this liquid, and then into the bread crumbs which have been mixed thoroughly with the cheese. Fry slowly in the cooking oil, being careful to keep the temperature low so that the cheese will not become stringy. A dry cheese, such as Parmesan, is especially good.

SMOTHERED CHICKEN

1 chicken, cut up as for frying

2 c. cream
Salt, pepper to taste

Into a heavy skillet put 1 cup cream. Put in the pieces of chicken which have been seasoned slightly. Cover and cook until well browned, adding more cream as needed. Remove to hot platter and pour over the chicken the cream which has been thickened slightly with a tablespoon of flour.

CHICKEN A LA LÉON d' ORO

1 fryer, cut up
Salt and pepper
Sliver of garlic
2 tbsp. salted cooking sherry
1 small can button mushrooms

½ tbsp. butter
3 tbsp. olive oil
1 green pepper, chopped
Pinch of sage
1 small can Italian tomato paste
1 tsp. sugar

Brown the chicken in the olive oil. Season with salt and pepper. Add all the other ingredients, in order, except the butter, and simmer for 10 minutes. Just before removing from the pan add the butter and serve at once on a hot platter.

SPANISH FRIED CHICKEN

3 frying chickens (2 lb. each)
¼ c. olive oil
2 lemons

½ c. butter
2 eggs
½ c. flour

Cut up the chickens as for frying. Pepper and salt each piece, then roll in the flour, and dip into the slightly beaten eggs. Heat the oil in a frying pan and add ¼ cup butter. Brown the pieces of chicken, browning them on the skin side first. Turn the pieces and finish cooking, keeping the heat low so the meat will cook slowly. Remove the chicken to a hot platter. Brown the remainder of the butter, add the juice of half a lemon and pour over the chicken. Cut the remaining lemon into pieces and serve on platter with chicken.

PECENE KURE (Baked Frying Chicken with Cream)
(Czecko-Slovakian)

1 frying chicken	Flour
Salt and pepper	2 tbsp. butter
1 c. sweet cream	

Cut up chicken as for frying. Roll in salted flour. Melt the butter in a pan. Put in the pieces of chicken, pour the cream over, cover and bake or cook slowly on top of range until meat is tender and nicely browned, about one hour. If the gravy is too thick, thin it slightly with a little boiling water.

GARNISH FOR FRIED CHICKEN

Roll marshmallows in flour, dip into beaten egg yolks and then roll in sifted bread crumbs. Fry quickly in deep fat (375° F.) until brown. Drain and use as garnish.

Roasting to a Turn

For a golden brown bird, juicy and tender, cooking temperatures must be watched. High temperatures for a long time may transform the most tender roasting chicken into a tough, dry bird. A simple method has been worked out for getting the most satisfactory results.

The trussed bird is put on a rack in the roasting pan, brushed lightly with melted lard or chicken fat and put uncovered into a hot oven (475° F.). Butter is not satisfactory for this use, for the salt and water in the butter cause the skin to blister. The rack is not essential, but it is desirable, for it holds the bird up out of the drippings during the cooking period.

At the end of twenty minutes in the hot oven, the bird will have browned almost as much as it will brown during the entire cooking period. Now the heat is turned down so the oven temperature will be low (275°–300° F.), a fourth cupful of boiling water is put into the pan, the pan is covered and the bird is allowed to cook, without basting, until it is done. If a crisp skin is preferred, the little steam vents in the pan are left open. If a soft, tender skin is preferred, the vents are left closed.

The time of cooking depends on the size of the bird. From 22 to 30 minutes per pound are required—the smaller the bird, the longer the cooking time per pound. The most accurate way to judge cooking time is to weigh the bird when it is stuffed and ready for the pan, and from the weight figure the approximate time of cooking. A four or five pound roaster requires about 22 to 25 minutes per pound, while a

2½ to 3 pound bird requires about 30 minutes per pound.

Much of the attractiveness of a roasted bird depends upon careful preparation before it goes into the oven.

Preparing the Bird for Roasting

The steps in the preparation of chicken for roasting fall naturally into the following divisions: removal of pin feathers, drawing, removal of head and feet, singeing, washing, stuffing, trussing.

In the new packing methods which prepare chicken for the pan, all of these steps except the stuffing and trussing are done at the poultry packing plant. Such poultry is, however, available to date in a limited number of markets.

At one time it was thought that the presence of pin feathers indicated that the chicken was young. Today, with new and improved dressing methods, every effort is made to remove as many of the pin feathers as possible. The number of pin feathers present is taken into consideration in grading poultry for the market.

Pin feathers should be removed before the bird has been wet. The easiest way to remove them is to use a strawberry huller.

If the market man has not removed head, feet and entrails, this is the next step. Using a sharp knife or poultry shears, cut the feet off at the joint. Very particular cooks remove the leg tendons before cutting off the feet. This is done by inserting the tines of a strong fork, or a heavy skewer, into the joint in such a way that the tendons or cords are held away from the bone. When the skewer or fork is twisted and then pulled, the tendons come out quite easily. If the roaster is young, 391 and if it is properly cooked, the presence of the tendons is not objectionable.

To draw the bird, cut around the vent and make a slit almost up to the tip of the breast bone. It is better not to make a cut from leg to leg, since this type of cut makes the bird less attractive after cooking. Insert the hand into the opening and carefully loosen the organs from the sides and back of the carcass. Pull out the entrails, making sure that the lungs and windpipe are included. No cut is necessary at the breast. If the windpipe does not come out with the removal of the entrails, the skin of the neck may be pushed back and the windpipe removed at the neck.

Separate the gizzard, heart and liver, being extremely careful not to break the gall bladder, the tiny greenish gland that lies almost imbedded in the liver. If this is broken it spoils the sweet flavor of the liver. To clean the gizzard, cut through the heavy outer muscle, cutting just to the tough inner lining, but not through it. This inner lining, forming a sort of sac, may be pulled out without breaking. Trim. Cut the blood vessels from the top of the heart.

When the bird has been drawn it is ready for singeing, although it may be singed before drawing. Singeing removes the tiny hairs and downlike feathers that may be present. It also tightens the skin. Hold the bird over a direct flame, turning it quickly and spreading each wing so as to singe off the tiny hairs in the angle of the wings and at their tips. The back also needs careful singeing.

Remove the oil sac, the small fatty gland at the base of the tail. Push the skin of the neck back to the body and cut off the neck, leaving the skin unbroken.

Wash the bird inside and out, using cool or cold water. Baking soda rubbed on the outside of the bird with a cloth and then thoroughly rinsed off makes the bird look white and clean. The soda combines with some of the oil in the skin to make a sort of natural soap which has a cleansing effect. The inside is rinsed only with cold water, as are also the giblets (heart, gizzard, liver). Drain the bird and wipe away the surplus water. If the inside of the bird is left quite wet, the stuffing may become soggy.

Fill the cavity with stuffing. The inside of the bird may be rubbed lightly with salt before the stuffing is put in, though this is not necessary. Fill the stuffing in quite firmly, but do not pack it. If it is too loosely put in, the bird looks shrunken. If too tightly packed, the baked dressing is too solid to serve attractively. For a bird weighing three to four and one-half pounds, four cups of dressing fill the cavity nicely.

Sew up the opening and truss the bird. White twine and a needle may be used for closing the opening, or small aluminum skewers may be inserted across the opening and the twine laced around them. The latter method has the advantage that the skewers are easy to insert and equally easy to remove. When the bird is cooked, the skewers are pulled out and the twine is lifted off.

Steps in Trussing

The purpose of trussing is to form the bird into as compact a mass as possible, so that during cooking the thinner portions, such as the wings and the ends of the drumsticks, will not be overcooked before the heavier pieces, the thighs and the breast, are done.

The steps in trussing are as follows:

1. Fold the skin of the neck back over the bird's back and skewer it down, using preferably one of the small aluminum skewers.

2. Fold the wings back so that their tips are held against the back of the bird—a sort of "arms akimbo" position. Or the wings may be placed flat against the sides of the bird, where they are held in place by the trussing twine. The advantage of the first method is that when the cooked bird is placed on the platter the wings help to hold it in an upright position and to steady it for carving.

3. With a long twine tie the ends of the legs together, fastening securely.

4. Bring the twine from the legs down around the tailpiece, drawing the legs down so that they are held close to the body.

5. Bring the twine forward, over the front of the wings, then over their tips, and across the back of the bird. Tie tightly, so as to hold wings as close as possible to body. If the neck has not been skewered down, the string may be fastened around it to hold it in place.

This method of trussing is satisfactory for other types of poultry as well as for chicken. It does away with the need for large skewers which puncture the meat and tend to make it unattractive.

ROAST CHICKEN

Stuff and truss roasting chicken. Put uncovered into hot oven (475° F.) for 20 minutes. Reduce heat to 275° F., put ½ cup boiling water into roaster, cover and bake until chicken is done. Allow 22–25 minutes per pound.

CHICKEN ALMOND

1 3 lb. roaster	1 c. mushrooms, sliced
1 c. almonds, blanched and chopped	¼ c. water
2 tbsp. butter	1 tsp. cornstarch
1 onion, chopped	1 tsp. soy sauce

Cut the raw meat from roasting chicken. Cut meat into cubes. Fry almonds for 5 minutes in the butter. Remove almonds from pan, and put in chicken meat, onions, mushrooms and water. Cook gently for 25 minutes. Add almonds and thicken with cornstarch which has been mixed with soy sauce and 2 teaspoons cold water. Serve very hot.

BAKED CHICKEN EXTRAORDINARY

Split slices of pineapple. Put pieces of boned chicken between. Top each sandwich with a one inch slice of sweet potato a little smaller around than the pineapple slice. Sprinkle each with 1 tablespoon brown sugar. Cut bacon strips in half and arrange criss-cross on top of all. Put on rack in roasting pan and bake uncovered in moderate oven (375° F.) for 45–60 minutes. Garnish and serve.

STUFFED CHICKEN LEGS

Remove the legs from roasting chickens, bone them and fill the cavity with bread dressing. Put in baking dish, cover with chicken stock and cook slowly until thoroughly tender. Thicken the stock and serve over the legs.

DIXIE ROAST CHICKEN

4–5 lb. roasting chicken	1 qt. hot milk
½ c. hot lard or butter	4 tbsp. flour
Salt	Stuffing

Stuff the fowl, truss and place in roasting pan. Pour the hot lard or butter over the bird. Sprinkle with salt. Roast for 20 minutes uncovered in fairly hot oven (425° F.) until brown. Turn down heat, pour the hot milk over the bird, cover pan and continue roasting in moderate oven (350° F.). Baste occasionally with milk. Time of cooking will be about 90 minutes. Brown the flour in a little butter, add this to the milk in which the fowl was roasted. Garnish platter with watercress or parsley.

BAKED DRUMSTICKS

Drumsticks, thigh, or breast may be cooked this way or all of them may be cooked together.

Dip each piece of meat into milk and then roll in flour or cornmeal to which a little salt has been added. Melt 3 or 4 tablespoons fat in a casserole, roasting pan, or heavy skillet and put in the pieces of meat. Cook uncovered in hot oven (450° F.) for 15 minutes. Add ¼ cup boiling water, cover the pan, reduce oven temperature to slow (300°–325° F.) and cook until tender, about 1 hour.

CHICKEN ROAST IN CASSEROLE

1 stewing chicken
Salt and pepper
½ c. butter

3 c. canned tomatoes
3 c. water
2 tbsp. olive oil

Cut up the chicken as for stew. Season the pieces. Heat the butter and olive oil in a large kettle or baking dish. Brown the chicken on all sides. Add the tomatoes which have been put through a strainer to remove seeds. Add the water. Simmer until chicken is tender. When the chicken is done there should be enough tomato sauce for gravy to serve with the chicken and perhaps an extra spoonful or two to add to the peas and noodles which are often served with this dish.

MO GOO GAI PEN (Chinese)

¾ c. canned or ¾ lb. fresh mushrooms
2¼ c. sliced celery
½ lb. bean sprouts
½ lb. water chestnuts

1 tbsp. salt
¼ lb. bamboo shoots
3 lb. young roasting chicken
4 tbsp. lard or peanut oil

Slice celery and bamboo shoots into very thin pieces about 1 inch long and ½ inch wide. Peel and slice water chestnuts. Remove skin and bones from chicken and cut meat into thin slices. Put the fat into a heavy skillet and melt. Add the chicken and cook 3–4 minutes. Add the vegetables and cook about 3 minutes, stirring constantly. Add 3 cups meat stock or water. Stir vigorously and then simmer, letting the mixture simmer gently for 10–12 minutes. Make a paste of 2 tablespoons cornstarch, ½ teaspoon sugar, and 2 tablespoons soy bean sauce. Add to the vegetable-chicken mixture and stir until thickened.

BREAD STUFFING

4 c. bread crumbs, toasted
¼ tsp. pepper
½ tsp. poultry seasoning
2 tbsp. melted butter or chicken fat

2 tsp. salt
1 egg slightly beaten
¼ tsp. minced onion
⅓ c. boiling water

Mix in order given, blending lightly but thoroughly. If a dry, crumbly dressing is preferred, the water may be omitted. If moist dressing is desired, the addition of 2 teaspoons baking powder will prevent sogginess.

MUSHROOM STUFFING

1 c. mushrooms
2 tbsp. butter
3 c. fine dry bread crumbs
½ tbsp. minced parsley

1 tsp. minced onion
¾ tsp. salt
½ tsp. poultry seasoning
½ c. hot water

Brown mushrooms in butter. Add to the other ingredients which have been thoroughly blended, and fill into bird.

395

GIBLET STUFFING

Simmer giblets until tender. Chop and add to bread stuffing.

CELERY STUFFING

3 c. soft bread crumbs
2 c. diced celery and
chopped celery leaves
1 c. well drained peas
½ tsp. pepper
2 tbsp. melted butter

½ c. finely chopped onion
1½ tsp. salt
¼ tsp. celery salt
1 tsp. poultry seasoning
Cold water to moisten

Force the peas through a fine sieve. Heat the butter in a frying pan, and brown the onion. Combine all the ingredients using only enough water to moisten.

EGG AND MUSHROOM STUFFING

3 c. bread crumbs
1 egg, slightly beaten
4 slices bacon, broiled
and diced
½ c. mushrooms

¼ c. milk
2 hard cooked eggs, sliced
½ tsp. salt
⅛ tsp. pepper
¼ tsp. poultry seasoning

Brown the mushrooms in 2 tablespoons bacon drippings. Combine all ingredients thoroughly and fill into bird.

WATERCRESS STUFFING

3 c. fine dry bread crumbs
1½ c. finely cut watercress,
leaves and stems
1½ tsp. chopped onion

6 tbsp. butter
3 tbsp. chopped celery
¾ tsp. salt
⅛ tsp. pepper

Cook the onion and celery in half the butter for 2 minutes. Then add the watercress and seasoning. Allow liquid to evaporate. Add the remaining butter and stir in the crumbs. When the crumbs have absorbed all the butter, fill dressing into fowl.

POTATO STUFFING

1 c. mashed potatoes
2 eggs, slightly beaten
4 tbsp. melted butter
½ tsp. salt
2 tsp. minced onion

2 c. very dry bread crumbs
1 c. milk
6 slices bacon, broiled and diced
⅛ tsp. pepper

Brown the onion in a little of the bacon drippings. Mix the crumbs with the potatoes, and then add the other ingredients. Mix thoroughly and stuff lightly into bird. This stuffing must not be packed tightly into the fowl.

PRUNE AND APPLE STUFFING

3 c. bread crumbs
1 tsp. salt
⅛ tsp. pepper
½ c. broken nut meats

¼ c. melted fat
1 c. apples, pared, diced and stewed
½ c. stewed and stoned prunes

Blend all ingredients and fill into bird.

PRUNE STUFFING

¼ lb. macaroni
⅛ tsp. pepper
2 c. stewed prunes, chopped

2 tsp. salt
½ tsp. poultry seasoning
2 tbsp. dry bread crumbs

Cook macaroni in boiling salted water for 10 minutes. Drain, and blanche by letting cold water run over it for a few moments. Add the other ingredients and mix thoroughly. If dressing is too dry, moisten slightly with some of the prune juice.

CHESTNUT STUFFING

1 qt. chestnuts
4 tbsp. fat
1 small onion, minced
2 c. dry bread crumbs
4 tbsp. chopped parsley

½ c. milk
1 tsp. salt
¾ tsp. poultry seasoning
⅛ tsp. pepper

Cook chestnuts in boiling salted water until tender. Cool, remove shell and skin. Chop. Brown the onion in the fat in a skillet. Combine all of the ingredients, and fill into bird.

ORANGE STUFFING

3 c. dry bread crumbs
1 c. diced apples
4 tbsp. melted butter

⅔ c. orange juice
½ c. seedless raisins
4 tbsp. sugar
Salt and pepper

Mix all ingredients and stuff into fowl. If more moisture is needed, add a little hot water.

CRACKER CORN STUFFING

4 doz. small soda crackers
2 c. canned corn, or cooked fresh corn
2 tbsp. chopped celery leaves
⅛ tsp. pepper

1½ tsp. salt
1 c. milk or broth
¼ c. chopped celery
2 tbsp. green pepper, chopped
⅛ tsp. mace

Combine all ingredients and blend thoroughly.

CHEESE STUFFING

4 c. bread cubes
2 tbsp. chopped parsley
1 egg, slightly beaten

4 tbsp. melted fat
½ c. grated American cheese
Milk to· moisten

Combine all ingredients, add enough milk to moisten, and add salt if needed. Nippy cheese may be substituted for the American.

OYSTER STUFFING

1 pt. oysters
4 c. dry bread crumbs
⅛ tsp. pepper

¼ tsp. celery salt
½ tsp. salt

Mix all ingredients and stuff into fowl.

SAUSAGE AND APPLE STUFFING

½ c. fresh sausage
½ c. chopped tart apple
2 c. cracker crumbs
½ c. hot water

¼ tsp. minced onion
¼ tsp. salt
⅛ tsp. pepper

Cook the sausage by putting it into a warm skillet and stirring occasionally. Drain off the surplus fat, add apples, seasonings and cracker crumbs. Add hot water, blend thoroughly and fill into bird.

VITAMIN STUFFING

2 c. raw spinach
4 sprigs parsley
1 large carrot
¾ green pepper
¾ small onion
3 large stalks celery

2 tbsp. butter
1 egg, beaten
26 small soda crackers, rolled
⅛ tsp. pepper
½ tsp. salt
½ c. milk

Pack the spinach tightly in the cup when measuring. Put the vegetables through the medium cutter of the food chopper. Fry lightly in butter. Add the beaten egg, the seasoning, the crumbs and the milk. Mix thoroughly and fill into fowl.

NUT STUFFING

1 c. fine dry bread crumbs
2 tbsp. melted butter
½ tsp. minced onion
½ c. evaporated milk

½ c. finely chopped peanuts, almonds or other nuts
½ c. diced celery
Salt and pepper

Brown celery in butter. Add to other ingredients and combine lightly but thoroughly and fill into fowl. Chestnuts may be substituted for the peanuts. Remove outer hull of chestnuts, blanch in hot water, and brown in butter before adding to the dressing.

2 c. cooked rice
Heart, liver and gizzard
   of fowl, stewed and
   chopped
1 small onion, minced

3 tbsp. melted butter
1 tsp. salt
½ c. minced celery
⅛ tsp. pepper

Combine all ingredients and fill into fowl.

CRACKER PEANUT STUFFING

2 c. shelled roasted pea-
   nuts, finely chopped
4 tbsp. melted butter
2 c. hot milk

72 small square soda crackers,
   crumbled
2 egg yolks
1 tsp. salt

1 tsp. pepper

Soak cracker crumbs in milk until they have absorbed it. Combine all ingredients and fill into bird.

CEREAL STUFFING

5 c. crisp ready-to-eat
   cereal
Chopped chicken liver

1 egg beaten with ¼ c. cold
   water
½ c. nut meats
Salt and pepper to taste

Combine all ingredients and blend thoroughly.

FRUIT STUFFING

2 medium oranges
¼ c. whole pecan or wal-
   nut meats
4 c. bread crumbs

1 egg, beaten
6 prunes, cooked and chopped
6 apricots, cooked and chopped
1 tsp. sugar

Combine all ingredients, adding beaten egg last. Season with salt and pepper.

NOODLE STUFFING

6 c. cooked noodles, cut
   into inch pieces before
   cooking
½ tsp. sage
¼ c. butter
1 tbsp. chopped onion
1 clove garlic

1 tsp. salt
1 c. shelled and blanched
   chestnuts
½ c. chopped celery
½ c. chopped stuffed olives
2 hard-cooked eggs, chopped
½ c. water

Melt butter, add onion and garlic and fry golden brown. Add noodles, chestnuts, sage, celery, olives and eggs with ½ cup water. Blend well. Stuff into fowl.

399

MACARONI STUFFING

½ lb. macaroni	½ lb. mushrooms
4 tbsp. melted butter	1 c. prunes
3 apples	Salt and pepper
½ lb. chestnuts	Sage
1 egg	

Cook macaroni in boiling salted water until tender. Drain. Cook and stone prunes, cut into quarters. Pare, core and chop apples. Parboil chestnuts, remove hulls and cut into quarters. Mix macaroni, prunes, apples and chestnuts, melted butter and beaten egg. Season with salt, pepper and sage. Stuff mixture into chicken.

NOODLE FRUIT STUFFING

¼ lb. noodles	1 c. seedless raisins
1 c. soft bread crumbs	1 tsp. chopped onion
1 c. chopped apples	1 tsp. salt
⅛ tsp. pepper	2 tbsp. butter
½ tsp. poultry seasoning	¾ c. hot water

Cook noodles in boiling, salted water until tender. Drain. Mix noodles, bread crumbs, apples, raisins, onion, salt, pepper and poultry seasoning. Melt butter in hot water and add, mixing thoroughly.

Persuasive Ways With Fowl

For stewing, mature birds are most satisfactory. The muscles and tendons are completely developed, and the connective tissue between the muscle fibers has thickened. Consequently the meat is less tender, and because it *is* well developed it is more flavorsome than that of young birds. Moreover, it is precisely the thickened connective tissue and the well developed tendons that give body and character to chicken soup, and it is the absence of this well developed connective tissue that makes very young birds unsatisfactory for making soups.

If through a microscope we could watch what happens when heat is applied to connective tissue we should see the explanation of the reasons for the methods used in cooking stewing birds. If high, dry heat is applied, the connective tissue thickens, shrivels up and becomes tougher than it was before. If, however, a piece of the connective tissue is put into a little warm water and heated gently, it first softens and then gradually dissolves in the water, making the base for what we call chicken stock. When the stock cools, it jellies. In other words, the gentle heating in the water actually transforms the tough connective tissue into delicate, quivery gelatin.

But it is not only the connective tissue that is important. Flavor is to be considered, too. The flavor of chicken meat is due to the presence of substances called "extractives." It is these extractives that are used in making bouillon cubes and meat extracts which give such delicious flavor to soups and gravies.

The quantity of the extractives in the muscle increases as a bird matures, and it increases also in the muscles which are most used. That is why the thighs and drumsticks are the most flavorsome of all the parts of chicken, while at the same time the breast, which contains the least used muscles, is most delicate in flavor. In many wild fowl, particularly in wild duck, the opposite is true. These birds use their wings, and therefore also their breast muscles, much more than their legs. So the meat from the breast is darker in color and more flavorsome than that from the legs.

Before stewing a fowl, rub the entire surface of the bird with a cut lemon. This keeps the meat white, and is especially desirable when the meat is to be used in chicken pies or in salads.

Another way to accomplish this is to wrap the bird in a white cloth, which is then tied. The cloth also serves the purpose of holding the bird in shape during the cooking period.

When the fowl has been put into the stewing pan, cover it with water. Bring the water gradually to a boil, then turn down the heat so that the water just simmers. Cook for 1½ to 2½ hours, depending on the size of the bird. When the bird has cooked for about an hour, add one or two teaspoonfuls of salt. Spices or other seasoning added to the cooking water are easily absorbed by the meat, so care must be used to add only those which blend nicely. Vegetables may be added during the last 30 or 45 minutes of the cooking period.

Fricassée Chicken

Fricassée chicken is the same as fried chicken. The term is somewhat loosely used, as it is applied to methods of cooking older birds as well as to the regular frying process. When stewing birds are fricasseed, they are first stewed until they are almost done and then they are rolled in flour or cornmeal and fried in fat.

Braised Chicken

In his "Royal Cookery, or the Compleat Court Cook," Patrick Lamb, for fifty years cook to English royalty, including King Charles II, James II, King William and Queen Mary, and Queen Anne, says, "Braise is a certain Way of stewing most Sorts of Fish as well as 401

Flesh, which extreamly heightens the Taste of them, and is very much in Vogue."

Braising is a good way to cook a bird that has passed the best stage for roasting. The bird, whether whole or cut up, is first browned thoroughly, then a small amount of liquid, usually water, is added, the container is covered tightly and the meat is cooked at an even, low temperature.

CHICKEN WITH DUMPLINGS

Stewing chicken	Pinch of salt
1½ c. flour	¾ c. milk
1 egg	2 tsp. baking powder

Barely cover chicken with hot water and simmer until tender. When done, remove from broth and cook dumplings. To prepare dumplings: Sift dry ingredients together. Beat egg slightly and add it to the milk. Combine the liquid and the dry ingredients and mix lightly. Drop by spoonfuls on boiling broth. Cover closely for 5 minutes, then uncover and cook until done. Arrange around chicken on hot platter. Garnish with parsley.

CHICKEN FRICASSÉE

1—3 lb. chicken	2 tbsp. butter
1 c. chicken stock or water	1 tbsp. flour
½ c. milk	1 egg yolk
3 cloves	1 bay leaf
3 whole allspice	Salt and pepper

Cut up the chicken as for stewing. Brown in pan with butter. Cover with chicken stock or water, add seasonings. Simmer until the fowl is tender, about an hour, strain, and to the cooking liquor add the flour mixed to a paste with a little cold water. Add milk and cook until thickened, stirring constantly. Add the beaten egg yolk which has been mixed with 2 tablespoons cold milk. Heat and pour the sauce over the chicken and serve.

BOILED FOWL ENGLISH STYLE

1—4 lb. stewing chicken	1 clove
3 carrots, diced	3 turnips, diced
2 leeks	Marjoram
1 bay leaf	2 large potatoes, diced
3 small onions	1 small head cauliflower
Salt and pepper	

Place trussed chicken in pan with just enough hot water to cover and cook gently for 20 minutes. Add the spices and herbs tied in a cloth, and cook for 50 minutes. Then add the vegetables, except the cauliflower, and cook 20 minutes more. Cook the cauliflower separately in boiling salted water. Untruss the chicken on hot platter, arrange vegetables in groups around the bird and serve.

CHICKEN LOAF

3 c. cooked chicken
3 sprigs parsley
1 small onion
1/8 tsp. pepper
2 eggs

1/4 c. bread crumbs
Salt
1 c. milk
2 hard cooked eggs

Chop chicken, onion and parsley. Add beaten eggs, crumbs, pepper and milk. Pack in greased pan. Bake in hot oven (400° F.) for 40 minutes. Turn out on platter and garnish with hard cooked eggs. May also be baked as individual loaves in small pans. Excellent served cold.

NOODLE RING FILLED WITH CHICKEN A LA KING

Chicken a la King

3 tbsp. butter or chicken fat
5 tbsp. flour
1 c. chicken stock
1 c. cream or evaporated milk
1/3 c. chopped ripe olives, seeded

1 tsp. lemon juice
1 tsp. salt
Paprika
2 c. diced cooked chicken
1 c. chopped mushrooms
2 tbsp. chopped pimiento
2 egg yolks, beaten

Make sauce of the butter, flour, stock and milk. Season. Add the chicken, mushrooms, olives, pimiento and lemon juice. Heat for 5 minutes and add the beaten egg yolks to which has been added 2 tablespoons cold water. Cook slowly for 2 minutes.

Noodle Ring

1/4 lb. noodles
1 qt. boiling water
1 tbsp. butter
3 eggs

1/2 c. evaporated milk
Pepper
1 tsp. salt

Drop noodles into boiling salted water. Boil briskly 10 minutes. Drain, rinse in cold water and drain again. Add eggs beaten lightly, milk and pepper. Turn mixture into buttered ring mold, dot with butter. Put mold into pan of boiling water and bake in a slow oven (325° F.) until set, but not brown, about 3/4 hour. When done, turn out on large plate, and fill center with chicken à la king.

CHICKEN PUFFS

1 egg
1/2 c. diced chicken
1 tsp. baking powder

1 c. flour
1/2 c. milk
Salt and pepper

Beat eggs. Add milk. Sift together flour, baking powder and seasonings. Add milk and eggs to dry ingredients. Then add chicken. Beat well. Drop by spoonfuls into hot fat and fry until golden brown. Serve with tomato-olive sauce.

CHICKEN CHOW MEIN

1—3 to 4 lb. stewing chicken
2 large onions
1 tbsp. cornstarch
1 c. diced celery
½ c. diced green peppers
½ c. butter
1 c. fresh or 1 small can of mushrooms
5 tbsp. Worcestershire sauce
2 hard cooked eggs

Cook the chicken slowly in a small amount of water until tender. When cool, remove meat from bones, putting aside some of the breast meat for garnish. Simmer the vegetables in the butter for 30 minutes. Add the cornstarch mixed to a paste with a little cold water, and the Worcestershire sauce. Add the diced chicken, heat and serve with fried noodles. To prepare the noodles, drop them into boiling salted water and cook until tender. Drain and fry them in deep fat until brown. Garnish the chow mein with slices of hard cooked eggs and breast meat.

CHICKEN SHORTCAKE

2 c. flour
½ tsp. salt
¾ c. milk
4 tsp. baking powder
4 tbsp. shortening
1 c. diced cooked chicken
½ c. diced celery
2 tbsp. butter
1 c. chicken stock
2 tbsp. flour
1 tbsp. butter
Salt and pepper

Make biscuit dough of first five ingredients. Roll out to ¾ inch thickness and cut with small round biscuit cutter. Bake in hot oven (450° F.) for 12 minutes. While the biscuits are baking, make sauce of 2 tablespoons flour, 1 tablespoon butter and chicken stock. Brown the celery in 2 tablespoons butter, add the chicken and heat thoroughly. Break open each biscuit, put some of the chicken mixture on lower half, put the top back on and put a spoonful of the chicken mixture over all.

CHICKEN PUFFS ROYAL

1 c. cold ground chicken
4 egg whites beaten stiff
¼ tsp. pepper
4 egg yolks, beaten
½ tsp. salt
¼ tsp. celery salt

Combine the meat, egg yolks, and seasonings. Fold in the stiffly beaten whites and drop by spoonfuls into hot fat. Drain on brown paper and serve at once.

CHICKEN SAVOYARD

2 c. cooked chicken
1 c. gravy or broth
½ c. chopped mixed pickle
½ tsp. salt
1 pimiento, chopped
Buttered toast or patty shells

Into the top of a double boiler put all the ingredients except toast. If broth requires thickening, add a little flour. Heat 20–25 minutes, stirring frequently. Serve on toast or in patty shells.

404

PINEAPPLE CHICKEN IN TIMBALE CASES

¾ c. pineapple tidbits   1½ c. medium white sauce
1½ c. diced cooked chicken   6 timbale cases

Drain the tidbits. Put six of them aside, and combine the remainder with chicken and white sauce, heating in the top of the double boiler. Heat the timbale cases in slow oven (300° F.) for 1 minute. Place the timbale cases on serving dishes, and fill each with the creamed mixture. Garnish each case with a tidbit surrounded with parsley.

BROWN FRICASSÉE OF CHICKEN

1 fat fowl, jointed   Flour
4 tbsp. chicken fat   ½ tbsp. chili powder
Clove of garlic   4 c. hot water

Salt pieces of chicken, allowing ½ teaspoon salt per pound of meat. Rub each piece with cut end of garlic clove, and roll in flour. Brown in hot fat. When brown, remove from skillet, add 4 tablespoons flour and chili powder and blend with fat in skillet. Add water gradually, stirring constantly. Let come to boil. Put in chicken and simmer slowly until done, about 1½ hours.

CHICKEN IN COCOANUT

1 stewing fowl   1 c. tomatoes
¾ c. corn   4 fresh cocoanuts
4 tbsp. diced bacon,   1 small onion, sliced
   browned   1 green pepper, chopped

Stew chicken until tender and remove meat from bones. Saw tops off cocoanuts, drain out the liquid and scrape out about half of the meat, shredding it out with a fork. Combine 3 tablespoons cocoanut and the corn. Add onion to bacon in skillet, add pepper, and tomatoes. Season with salt and pepper and combine with corn-cocoanut mixture. Add chicken meat. Fill mixture into cocoanut shells. Put the top back on as cover and seal with flour paste. Set in pan of hot water and bake for 1 hour in moderate oven, basting occasionally to prevent cocoanuts from scorching. Serve hot. This is a good way to prepare chicken for a picnic, since it keeps hot 4–5 hours.

ESCALLOPED CHICKEN

Cook stewing chicken in small amount of water until tender. Remove the bones. Run skin through food chopper and dice the remainder of the meat. Mix the skin and meat, season with salt, pepper and a little poultry seasoning. Skim fat from broth and mix lightly with 1 cup bread crumbs. In a buttered casserole arrange a layer of chicken and then a layer of crumbs until dish is filled. Top with a layer of chicken. Cover with gravy made from chicken stock. Bake 25 minutes, or until brown.

405

CHICKEN BAKED IN SOUR CREAM

1½ c. sour cream	2 tsp. salt
¼ tsp. pepper	1 stewing chicken

Rub seasoning on fowl which has been cut up as for stewing. Place chicken in casserole and pour sour cream over it. Bake in moderate oven until fowl is tender, about 2–2½ hours.

CHICKEN KROMSKIS

1 c. finely minced cooked chicken	1 tbsp. butter
	Bacon slices
4 tbsp. milk	Batter
1 tbsp. flour	Fat for frying

Make thick white sauce of milk, flour, and butter. Add chicken and season. Spread out mixture on platter and cool. Shape into small cylindrical croquettes. Remove rind from bacon, cut each slice into halves. Roll each croquette in a piece of bacon, dip into batter and fry in deep fat. Arrange on platter and garnish with parsley.

Batter

1 c. flour	6 tbsp. lukewarm water
Pinch of salt	1 egg white
1 tbsp. butter	

Sift flour and salt together. Make hollow in center. Mix melted butter and water and add to flour. Beat well and let stand 1 hour. Fold in stiffly beaten egg white.

SUPREME OF CHICKEN

Chop very fine the breast of a raw chicken, and beat into it one at a time 4 eggs and ½ pint cream. Season with salt and pepper. Butter small moulds, fill with the chicken mixture, and bake 20 minutes standing in hot water covered with a buttered paper. Do not let the water boil. Serve with Bechamel or mushroom sauce.

CHICKEN CROUSTADE

1 4 lb. fowl	3 tbsp. butter
2 bouillon cubes	3–4 potatoes, cubed
2 c. boiling water	6 small onions
2 tbsp. flour	3–4 carrots, cubed
2 tbsp. shortening	3–4 small turnips, cubed

Cut the fowl as for stewing and brown in skillet with shortening. Melt butter, add flour and brown. Add the cubes dissolved in boiling water, and cook until thickened. Put vegetables in layers in bottom of casserole, put chicken on top of vegetables, and pour sauce over all. Bake in moderate oven (350° F.) until chicken is tender.

406

CHICKEN AND CORN CASSEROLE

2 c. diced cooked chicken
1 onion
2 stalks celery
2 tbsp. chopped green
   pepper
1 egg

1 No. 2 can corn
½ c. milk
½ tsp. salt
⅛ tsp. pepper
2 tbsp. chopped pimiento

Beat the egg slightly and add to it the milk. Combine the other ingredients in the order given. Put into a buttered casserole, sprinkle top with crumbs, dot with butter and bake 40 minutes in moderate oven (350° F.).

CHICKEN PIE

1 fowl
½ tsp. salt
Water
4 tbsp. shortening

2 c. flour
½ tsp. salt
4 tsp. baking powder
⅞–1 c. milk

Cut up fowl as for stewing. Place in a kettle and cover with hot water. Cover tightly and simmer until tender. When done, place chicken in casserole and make a gravy of the chicken broth using 2 tablespoons flour for every cup of broth. There should be at least 2 cups of gravy to pour over the chicken. Make a soft biscuit dough of flour, shortening, salt, baking powder and milk and lay dough on top of chicken and gravy. Bake in a hot oven (450° F.) 20–25 minutes. Serve with additional gravy .

CHICKEN AND HAM PIE

Cook a fowl until tender. Remove meat from bones. Thicken the liquid in which the fowl was cooked, allowing 1½ tablespoons flour for each cup of liquid. Line a deep baking dish with pie crust, put into the dish alternately very thin slices of boiled ham and layers of chicken meat. Pour the gravy over all. Cover with crust and bake in hot oven (450° F.) about 15 minutes, or until crust is done.

MONTE CARLO CHICKEN

1 stewing chicken, cut up
2 tbsp. butter
2 carrots
2 small onions, diced
2 bay leaves
Salt and pepper

2 c. water
2 tbsp. cooking sherry
1 doz. potato balls
1 doz. button mushrooms
1 tbsp. parsley, chopped

Melt butter in a casserole. Put in the chicken, leave uncovered and cook at 475° F. for 20 minutes or until chicken is browned. Then add the carrots, onions, potatoes, bay leaves, seasonings and water. Cover tightly. Reduce heat to 325° F. and cook 1 hour or until tender. Add the sherry, mushrooms and chopped parsley. Cook 5 minutes more and serve.

407

CHICKEN AU GRATIN

3 c. diced cooked chicken meat	½ c. grated cheese
⅓ c. chopped sweet peppers	4 tbsp. flour
	3 tbsp. butter
½ c. milk	Salt
	Nutmeg

Combine chicken meat and peppers. Add milk and let simmer 5 minutes. Make paste of flour and water or a little of the milk. Add to the chicken mixture and cook until it thickens, stirring constantly. Season with salt and nutmeg. Add butter. Pour into buttered baking dish, putting in a layer of the chicken mixture, then a layer of grated cheese, until both are used. Top layer should be of cheese. Bake in a moderate oven (350° F.) for 15–20 minutes, until cheese is melted and top is golden brown.

BAKED STEWING CHICKEN

Disjoint the fowl, salt and pepper the pieces and dredge with flour. Into a baking pan put 2 tablespoons butter, or, if the fowl was fat, use the rendered fat from it. Put the pieces of chicken into the pan, pour a cupful of sweet cream and one of water over it. Cover. Bake in a moderate oven (350° F.) until the meat and gravy are nicely brown and the chicken is tender. If the gravy is too thick, add a little hot water or hot milk before serving. If desired, milk may be substituted for the cream and water.

CHICKEN AND CELERY AU GRATIN

1½ c. medium white sauce	1½ c. cooked chicken meat
½ c. diced celery	¼ tsp. paprika
¼ c. grated cheese	Buttered crumbs

Combine the chicken, celery, white sauce and 2 tablespoons cheese. Pour the mixture into buttered baking dish, sprinkle crumbs and remaining cheese over all, and bake in a moderate oven (375° F.) until crumbs are brown.

CASSEROLE OF CHICKEN TAMALES

1 can chicken tamales	¾–1 c. chopped cold chicken
1 small can creamy corn	½ c. chopped sweet pickles
Salt and pepper	1 tsp. Worcestershire sauce
2 tbsp. butter	¼ c. grated cheese

Combine all the ingredients except butter and cheese. Put mixture into a buttered casserole, dot with butter and sprinkle with grated cheese. Bake in moderately hot oven (400° F.) for 20 minutes.

CHICKEN CASSEROLE

1 4 lb. stewing chicken
1 c. diced celery
1/4 c. minced onion
1 c. hot water
1 green pepper, chopped

2 c. diced carrots
4 tbsp. fat
Salt and pepper
Flour
1 c. milk

Cut up chicken. Dredge each piece in flour and brown in hot fat. Season. Place in casserole or roaster. Add water and cover. Cook slowly in a moderate oven (350° F.) 1½ hours. Then add the vegetables and continue cooking until chicken is done and vegetables are tender, about an hour. Remove chicken from broth, thicken the liquid, and if desired, add the milk to make a rich gravy.

JELLIED CHICKEN BELLEVUE

1 5 lb. fowl
1 small onion
1 carrot
2 stalks celery
Salt and pepper

4 tsp. sherry flavoring
2 tbsp. chopped pistachio nuts
1 hard cooked egg
Parsley

Just cover the chicken with boiling water. Add other ingredients, except the egg and parsley. Let simmer until the meat is tender enough to drop from bone. Remove meat and let stock cook down to half its quantity. Slice chicken and arrange in light and dark layers in mold. Strain stock over chicken. Chill until firm enough to slice. Unmold on bed of crisp lettuce. Garnish with sliced egg and sprigs of parsley.

CHICKEN VEGETABLE CASSEROLE

In buttered baking dish arrange alternate layers of raw, sliced potatoes, diced chicken and canned peas. Season with ½ teaspoon chopped onion. Season each layer with salt and pepper. Over all pour the following liquor:

1/4 c. liquor from peas
1 beaten egg
1 c. milk

1/2 c. chicken stock
2/3 tsp. salt
1 tbsp. butter

Bake in moderate oven (350° F.) 45 minutes.

CASSEROLE CHICKEN

1 4 lb. fowl
1 c. water
2 tsp. salt
1/2 c. flour
6 or 8 carrots
4 or 5 potatoes

1/2 c. seedless raisins
1 c. mushrooms
2 c. evaporated milk
Pepper
2 c. celery cut in 2 inch strips
1 c. liquid from giblets

Parboil giblets 20 minutes. Wash raisins in hot water and drain. Cut chicken as for frying. Salt, pepper and roll pieces in flour. Fry in hot fat until a light brown. Place in a baking dish, add celery, giblets, liquid from

409

CHICKEN ASPIC

1 qt. chicken stock	1 tbsp. chopped parsley
2 stalks celery, diced	1 tsp. shredded lemon peel
1 small onion	3 tbsp. gelatin
1 clove	1 c. cold water

Bring the chicken stock to boil and dissolve in it the gelatin which has been soaked for 5 minutes in the cold water. Let stand on back of stove or in warm place ½ hour and strain. Sliced chicken or shredded vegetables may be incorporated into the gelatin.

GALANTINE OF CHICKEN

1 large fowl	1½ tsp. salt
¼ tsp. pepper	Pinch of sage
Sprig of parsley	1 stalk celery

Bone fowl and rub lightly with salt. Roll the meat tightly, keeping skin side out. Place in stewing kettle, cover with hot water and bring gradually to boil. Add the seasonings and vegetables. Reduce heat so that broth just simmers. Cook 4 hours. Strain the broth through a double thickness of cheese-cloth, pour over the rolled meat and set in cold place to chill. Serve cold in slices.

MOUSSE OF CHICKEN

2 eggs	1 c. diced chicken
1½ c. milk	1 c. whipping cream or evaporated milk
1½ tbsp. gelatin	orated milk
¼ c. cold water	Salt and pepper
½ c. hot chicken broth	

Beat eggs, add milk and cook in double boiler until mixture coats spoon. Add the gelatin which has been soaked in cold water and then dissolved in the hot broth. Add the chicken, season and cool. When cold, fold in the whipped cream or whipped evaporated milk. Freeze in refrigerator tray 4–5 hours.

CHICKEN MOUSSE IN TOMATOES

1 tbsp. butter	1½ c. diced chicken
1 tbsp. flour	½ c. diced celery
1 c. milk	¼ c. whipping cream
2 tsp. gelatin	¼ c. mayonnaise
1 tbsp. cold water	8 tomatoes
1 tbsp. lemon juice	

Melt butter, add flour and mix to smooth paste. Add milk gradually and cook until thickened, stirring constantly. Add gelatin which has been softened in cold water, and the chicken. Season to taste with salt, pepper and paprika. Cool. Whip cream and fold it into the mayonnaise. Fold this mixture into the cold chicken mixture and add lemon juice. Peel tomatoes, cut a slice off the stem end and scoop out the soft portion. Fill with chicken mixture and chill thoroughly.

412

CHICKEN MOUSSE IN GREEN PEPPERS

Prepare Chicken Mousse as in preceding recipe and fill into green peppers from which the seeds have been removed.

SMOTHERED CHICKEN AND OYSTERS

1 stewing chicken	¼ c. shortening
1 pt. oysters	1 c. cream or evaporated milk
¼ c. melted butter	Cracker meal

Disjoint chicken, roll in cracker meal and season with salt and pepper. Brown in fat and transfer to baking dish. Roll oysters in cracker meal and fill spaces between chicken pieces with oysters. Pour on the cream or evaporated milk and bake until chicken is tender. Add more milk as necessary to keep from sticking.

PARSLEY CHICKEN (Jewish)

1 5 or 6 lb. hen	Salt
1 bunch parsley, chopped	Pepper
Flour	Fat from chicken

Cut up the chicken as for fricassee. Roll in flour and dust with salt and pepper. Fry out chicken fat in deep kettle, put in the chicken and cook to golden brown. Add the chopped parsley, wilting it in the hot fat. Pour in enough hot water just to cover the chicken. Cover closely and let simmer gently for several hours, or until tender. Add a little boiling water if necessary. When chicken is tender, thicken gravy and pour over chicken on platter.

CHICKEN TAMALE

Corn husks, for wrapping	1½ tsp. chili powder
¾ c. cornmeal	¼ c. chicken broth
½ tsp. salt	1 clove
1 c. boiling water	½ bay leaf
1 c. cooked chicken meat	½ tsp. salt
½ small onion	⅛ tsp. pepper
½ small Spanish pepper	

Soak husks in warm water. Add boiling water to cornmeal, with ½ teaspoon salt and cook to make a thick paste. Cook or steam until cornmeal is done. Cut the chicken, onion, and pepper into small pieces. Add the seasonings and the broth and simmer for a few minutes. If the mixture is too thin thicken with a little cornstarch.

Spread out 2 large husks, letting them overlap. Cover the center of the husks with a layer of cornmeal ¼ inch thick. Put about 2 tablespoons of the meat mixture in the center, on the cornmeal layer. Roll up, with husks on the outside. Tie the ends tightly and steam for an hour.

FLORENTINE FRIED CHICKEN

1 3½ to 4 lb. stewing chicken
1 pt. water
2 egg yolks

Bread crumbs, browned
½ lb. grated cheese
Juice of 1 lemon

Clean and cut up chicken. Cook in 1 pint of water until tender. Remove chicken and reduce stock to 1 cup. Add the yolks of 2 well beaten eggs and the lemon juice. Strain, dip the chicken into the sauce, then into a mixture of bread crumbs and grated cheese. Fry a golden brown. If any sauce remains, serve in a bowl.

VIENNESE FRIED CHICKEN

1 stewing chicken
Olive oil—enough to cover
1 tbsp. lemon juice
1 bay leaf
1 c. chicken stock
1 tbsp. parsley

Salt and pepper
2 eggs, well beaten
Bread crumbs, browned
1 egg yolk
1 c. milk
10 small mushrooms

Clean and cut up chicken. Cover with a mixture of lemon juice and olive oil. Add parsley, bay leaf, salt and pepper. Cook for three hours, or until done. Drain, dip each piece in egg and then in bread crumbs and brown. Mix the chicken stock, milk, egg yolk, seasoning and heat thoroughly. Just before removing from the fire add the mushrooms. Pour sauce around the chicken. Garnish with slices of lemon and a few sprigs of parsley.

CHICKEN A L'ANDREA

4 large breasts of chicken
4 eggs
1/5 lb. almonds
1 small loaf bread

6 ripe olives
2 hard cooked eggs
Mustard and red pepper

Cook breasts of chicken and remove meat from bones. Shred the meat and place it on a hot platter. Cover with a sauce made as follows: Soak a small loaf of bread in milk until soft. Press dry. Grind the almonds and mix thoroughly with the soft bread and the minced egg yolks. Add mustard and red pepper to taste. Pour over chicken on platter and garnish with shredded whites of eggs, ripe olives and red peppers.

414

CHICKEN TIMBALES

2 tbsp. butter	2 tsp. lemon juice
2 tbsp. flour	1½ tsp. scraped onion
½ tsp. salt	3 eggs, well beaten
¼ tsp. celery salt	1 c. diced chicken
Few grains cayenne	¾ c. canned asparagus tips,
½ c. chicken stock	cut up
⅓ c. cream or evaporated	½ c. soft bread crumbs
milk	¼ c. blanched almonds, shredded

Blend butter, flour, salt, celery salt and cayenne. Add stock, milk or cream and cook until smooth and creamy, stirring constantly. Remove from heat, add lemon juice, onion and eggs. Add the other ingredients and mix thoroughly. Pour into molds which have been well buttered and dusted with flour. Fill molds ⅔ full. Set in pan of hot water, cover with oiled paper and bake 25–30 minutes in moderate oven (350° F.). Unmold and serve.

CHICKEN BALLS

1 lb. finely ground chicken meat	¼ c. milk
	2 eggs
2 tbsp. cracker meal or sifted crumbs	Salt and pepper

Soak crumbs in milk for half hour. Work into paste. Add other ingredients, mix thoroughly and shape into small balls. Roll in dry crumbs and fry in butter or in deep fat until golden brown.

CHICKEN CHARTREUSE

2 c. diced cooked chicken	8 tbsp. tomato juice
¾ c. diced celery	2 tbsp. fine bread crumbs
2 tbsp. chopped parsley	1 egg, well beaten
½ tsp. salt	2 tbsp. chopped pimiento
1 tsp. minced onion	1 c. rice
⅛ tsp. red pepper	

Cook rice in boiling salted water until tender. Turn out into a sieve or colander and run cold water over it. Line a buttered mold with the cooked rice to a thickness of about ¾ inch, packing it solidly. Mix the above ingredients in the order given and pack in layers into the mold, alternating a layer of the chicken mixture with a layer of rice. Cover with oiled paper and steam 45 minutes, or set in a pan of hot water and bake in moderate oven (350°–375° F.) for 45 minutes. Unmold on hot platter, garnish with strips of pimiento and slices of hard cooked egg. Serve with a hot tomato sauce. A can of mushrooms may be added to the sauce.

CHICKEN ROLL

2 c. flour	4 tsp. baking powder
½ tsp. salt	5 tbsp. shortening
¾ c. milk	1 c. minced chicken

Make biscuit dough of flour, shortening, salt, milk and baking powder and roll to ½ inch thickness. Spread with minced or diced cooked chicken, roll up jelly-roll fashion, cut into 1 inch slices. Put cut side down in buttered pan and bake 12–15 minutes in hot oven (450° F.). Serve with chicken gravy or white sauce.

MINCED CHICKEN MODERNE

1½ c. cooked chicken	¼ c. chopped green peppers
½ c. finely minced ham	½ c. mushrooms
2 hard cooked eggs	1 c. milk
2½ c. mashed potatoes	2 tbsp. flour
1 can asparagus tips	2 tbsp. butter

Blend egg yolks, potatoes and ham. Make cream sauce of milk, flour, and butter. Season. Add chicken, peppers, chopped egg whites and mushrooms. With pastry bag make border of potato mixture around edge of platter. Fill chicken mixture into center. Garnish with asparagus tips laid over all, flower fashion. Heat for a moment under broiler and serve.

CHICKEN CROQUETTES

2 c. chopped cooked chicken	1 egg yolk
	1 whole egg
¾ c. thick white sauce	1 tsp. lemon juice
½ tsp. salt	Cracker or bread crumbs
⅛ tsp. paprika	

Combine chicken, sauce, seasonings, and egg yolk. Shape into croquettes, dip into slightly beaten egg, then into crumbs, and again into egg and crumbs. Fry in deep fat (375° F.) until golden brown. At 375° F. a cube of bread browns in 40 seconds.

CHICKEN PORTOLA

1 stewing chicken, 2½–3 lbs.	1 green pepper, finely chopped
4 tbsp. olive oil	½ can tomatoes
1 onion, finely sliced	½ tsp. sugar
1 slice lean bacon, chopped	3 tbsp. shredded cocoanut
	½ can corn
	Hint of garlic

Cut the chicken into quarters. Brown the onion and bacon in the olive oil. Add the pepper, garlic, tomatoes and sugar. Blend thoroughly and cook until mixture thickens. Strain, and mix with the cocoanut and corn. Add the chicken, place in small baking dish, cover tightly and seal with a paste of flour and water. Set baking dish in a pan of water and bake in a hot oven (375°–400° F.) for an hour.

1 stewing bird
2 tbsp. chicken fat, fried
   out, or butter
½ tsp. minced onion
1 stalk celery, finely cut

¼ lb. mushrooms, finely cut
½ c. blanched almonds chopped
1 tbsp. soy sauce
½ tsp. flour
1 c. water

Stew chicken in very small amount of water until tender. Remove meat from bones and cut it into small pieces. Brown the meat lightly in the chicken fat or butter, adding the onion. Add celery, mushrooms, almonds and soy sauce. Stir thoroughly and then add the flour. Simmer for 10 minutes, add the water and simmer for 30 minutes more. Serve with bowls of steamed rice.

CHICKEN HASH I

2½ c. diced chicken
1 tbsp. minced onion
½ c. diced cooked potatoes
4 tbsp. cream

2 tbsp. butter
1 tsp. Worcestershire sauce
Salt and pepper to taste

Melt butter in skillet. Combine all the ingredients and fry lightly, stirring occasionally. Serve with toast.

CHICKEN HASH II

Use recipe for Chicken Hash 1. Add 2 beaten eggs to cream, then add other ingredients and fry in a large cake, or in small individual patties. Brown on one side and then on other. If cooked in one large cake, fold when done and serve as omelet.

CHICKEN HASH IN PEPPER CASES

Cut ends from green peppers, remove seeds and fill with well seasoned, finely minced chicken hash. Set in buttered casserole, add 2 tablespoons hot water and bake in moderate oven (350° F.) until peppers are done, about 25 minutes.

CHICKEN HASH IN TOMATOES

Remove pulp and seeds from ripe tomatoes. Fill with chicken hash and bake 25–30 minutes in moderate oven (350° F.).

CHICKEN IN BAKED CUCUMBERS

2 large yellow ripe
   cucumbers
½ sweet red pepper
Chicken stock

1¼ c. minced chicken
1 tbsp. minced onion
1 c. cream

Pare cucumbers and cut them into halves lengthwise. Scoop out the seeds and soak in cold salted water for an hour. Combine the other ingredients, except cream, using enough stock to moisten so mixture can be packed. Season. Drain the cucumbers, fill with the chicken mixture and put two halves together, fastening with toothpicks. Put into buttered baking dish, pour cream around the cucumbers and bake in moderately hot oven (375° F.) until cucumbers are tender.

417

PAPRIKA CHICKEN

3½ lb. fowl	2¼ c. flour
Salt and pepper	1½ tsp. paprika
1 onion, chopped	1½ c. chicken stock

Cut up the fowl. Season each piece and roll it in the flour mixed with the paprika. Heat the fat in a deep frying pan and cook the onion in it. Add the chicken pieces and brown well. Add boiling hot chicken stock, cover pan tightly, and simmer for about 2½ hours, or until the meat is very tender.

CHICKEN SUPREME

1½ c. cold diced chicken	¾ c. crushed pineapple, drained
½ c. pecan meats, chopped	1 c. mayonnaise
½ pt. whipping cream	

Combine the chicken, pineapple and nuts. Whip the cream, fold in the mayonnaise, and fold the chicken mixture into the cream mixture. Turn into freezing tray and freeze for 2½–3½ hours.

CHINESE CHICKEN

¾ c. crushed pineapple	2 c. diced chicken
2 tbsp. flour	3 tbsp. butter
2 tbsp. chicken stock	

Drain the pineapple and cook it for 4 minutes in 2 tablespoons butter. Add the flour which has been mixed to a paste with some of the chicken stock. Add the stock, the flour paste and cook, stirring constantly, until thickened. Season to taste and add the diced chicken. Serve with fried noodles.

CHICKEN A L'ORIENT

3 tbsp. butter	1 very small onion, chopped
½ c. tomatoes	2 c. cooked rice
1 c. diced cooked chicken	6 stalks celery, diced
½ c. gravy or broth	

Brown onion and celery in butter. Add tomatoes, rice and chicken. Pour over this the gravy or broth. Let simmer for 10 minutes.

CHICKEN GUMBO CRÉOLE WITH RICE

1 large stewing chicken	1 sprig thyme or parsley, minced
1 slice ham, diced	
2 tbsp. butter	6 fresh or 1½ c. canned tomatoes
1 small onion, minced	
1 green pepper, chopped	4 okra pods, sliced
1 bay leaf	3 qts. boiling water
	Salt and pepper to taste

Cut up the chicken as for stewing. Season with salt and pepper. Heat butter in soup kettle. Add chicken and ham, cover closely and let simmer for 10 min.

utes. Then add onion, pepper and thyme and let brown. Add the tomatoes and sliced okra pods. Now add the boiling water and let simmer on back of stove for an hour. Serve in a tureen. Accompany with a bowl of steamed rice.

CHICKEN SURPRISE

3 c. steamed rice
2 c. minced or shredded chicken
Salt and pepper

½ c. mushrooms
½ c. diced celery
2 tbsp. butter

Brown mushrooms and celery in butter, then mix thoroughly with the minced chicken. Season. Line a deep rectangular pan with wax paper. Line the pan next with a layer of the cooked rice by pressing the rice firmly about ¾ inch thick on all sides and bottom of the pan. Fill the center cavity with the chicken mixture, pressing it in firmly. Spread a layer of rice over the top, and place pan in moderate oven (350° F.) to heat all thoroughly. When done, unmold, remove the wax paper, and slice across mold of rice. Serve with chicken gravy prepared from chicken sauce or with egg sauce.

CHICKEN CHOP SUEY

1 chicken, or 2–3 c. cooked chicken meat
3 tbsp. butter or lard
1 c. shredded green pepper
2 c. shredded onion

2 c. shredded celery
2 c. bean sprouts
2 c. chicken broth
2 tbsp. cornstarch
1 c. toasted almonds
4 tbsp. soy sauce

If fresh chicken is used, barely cover the bird with hot water, add a teaspoon salt, and simmer until tender. Let cool in broth. Remove meat from bones, letting the meat remain in thin strips. Brown the onion and green pepper in the butter in a skillet. Add the meat and continue cooking until the meat is slightly browned. Add the celery and bean sprouts and the broth mixed with the cornstarch. Cook gently for 10 minutes. Stir in the almonds which have been broken into halves, and the soy sauce. Serve with hot steamed rice.

EAST INDIAN CURRIED CHICKEN

1 stewed chicken
1 c. dry rice
1 onion, sliced
½ garlic clove
½ tsp. ginger
¼ c. olive oil

1½ tbsp. curry powder
2 tbsp. flour
1 c. milk
1 c. chicken stock
½ c. fresh grated cocoanut
Milk from 1 cocoanut

Remove meat from chicken. Steam the rice. In the meantime, fry the onion, garlic and ginger in the olive oil for about 5 minutes, but do not brown. Add the curry powder and flour. Blend well. Then add gradually, while stirring, the milk and the chicken stock. Cook until slightly thickened. Add cocoanut and cocoanut milk. Keep sauce hot in double boiler until rice is done. Make a ring of the rice. Put chicken inside the ring. Pass sauce in gravy boat, followed by a bowl of ground cocoanut and another of ground nuts.

419

ARROZ Y GALLINA A LA VALENCIA (Mexican)

1 stewing bird	1 c. rice
3 tbsp. fat	1 slice onion
Water to cover chicken	1 slice garlic
1 pt. tomatoes	2 tbsp. pepper paste

Cut up the chicken, salt and dredge with flour. Brown in the hot fat. Cover with boiling water and simmer until tender and the liquid is reduced to about a pint. Heat the tomatoes and add the rice and seasonings. Cook gently, covered, until the rice has taken up all the liquid. Arrange chicken and rice on a dish and garnish with rings of red and green peppers.

CURRIED CHICKEN

1 stewing chicken	1 tsp. curry powder
1 tbsp. butter	Salt
1 c. tomato juice	1 tbsp. lemon juice
1 small onion, chopped	3/4 c. hot water

Brown the onion in butter, add the curry powder, lemon juice and the chicken cut up as for stewing. Add water, onion and tomato juice, cover and simmer gently until chicken is tender. The sauce may be thickened slightly if desired. Serve with steamed or boiled rice.

MINCED CHICKEN IN RICE RING

1 c. rice	1/2 c. milk
3 c. boiling water	Pepper
1 tsp. salt	1 tbsp. butter
3 eggs	

Boil rice briskly in water until tender. Drain. Add eggs beaten slightly, milk and pepper. Put mixture into well buttered ring mold and set mold in pan of hot water. Bake in slow oven (325° F.) until set. Unmold on platter and fill center with minced chicken, creamed chicken or chicken à la king.

CHICKEN RICE PUDDING

1 4-lb. stewing bird	2 c. uncooked rice
1 onion, sliced	6 eggs, beaten slightly
4 stalks celery	1 large can mushrooms
3 bay leaves	Rich milk or evaporated milk for
Salt and pepper	gravy

Cut up the chicken, put it into a stewpan, and just cover it with boiling water. Add the vegetables and let simmer until tender. Just before it is done add the salt and pepper. Cool. Remove chicken from broth and strain the broth. Cook the rice in the broth until tender. Strain rice. Remove the meat from the bones, cut up the pieces, but not too finely. Add the meat to the rice, season with salt and pepper, and then add the well beaten eggs. Pour into a buttered baking dish, set in pan of water and bake in a moderate oven (350° F.) about 40 minutes, or until set. Make a gravy of the remaining broth and add the mushrooms. Let the gravy stand in top of double boiler for an hour or two, if possible. When ready to serve, cut the chicken rice pudding into squares or slices, dress with mushroom gravy and serve.

FROZEN CHICKEN AND RICE

1½ c. cold cooked chicken
1 c. peas or asparagus tips
2 c. cooked rice

4 tbsp. mayonnaise
2 hard cooked eggs
Salt and pepper

Combine cold rice and mayonnaise. Add the peas and chicken and blend thoroughly. Season well. Pack in freezing tray and chill 1–1½ hours. Slice and serve on lettuce, garnished with hard cooked egg and mayonnaise.

CHICKEN AND RICE LOAF

1½ c. diced chicken
1 c. peas
2 c. cooked rice

2 eggs
½ c. milk
Salt and pepper

Combine thoroughly the rice, chicken and peas. Beat eggs, add milk and seasonings. Pour over rice mixture and blend thoroughly. Put into buttered pan, set into a pan of water and bake in a moderately hot oven (375° F.) about 40 minutes, or until egg mixture is set.

CHICKEN AND HOMINY

3 c. cooked hominy
  (1 No. 2½ can)
1 c. milk
1 tbsp. flour
2 tbsp. butter

Salt and pepper
1 egg, slightly beaten
1 tsp. minced onion
1 chicken, fried, stewed or
  fricasseed

Heat hominy thoroughly. Drain off liquor. Arrange in mound in center of platter. Around hominy arrange the portions of chicken. Make sauce of flour, butter, milk and seasonings. When thickened whip in the slightly beaten egg. Pour over hominy. Chicken gravy may be used instead of the sauce.

CHICKEN TETRAZZINI

¼ lb. spaghetti
2 tbsp. butter
1 c. mushrooms
1 c. diced celery
1 hard cooked egg
2 tbsp. minced onion
2 c. diced chicken

1 c. chicken broth
1 tbsp. flour
2 tsp. Worcestershire sauce
Slices of chicken breast
4 tbsp. chopped green pepper

Cook spaghetti briskly in boiling salted water until tender. Brown the mushrooms, celery, pepper and onion in the butter. Drain the spaghetti. Add the vegetables, diced chicken and chicken broth. Thicken with the flour which has been mixed to a paste with a little cold water or milk. Add Worcestershire sauce. Heat all thoroughly. Arrange on platter with garnish of slices chicken breast, rings of green peppers and mushroom caps.

421

CHICKEN-SPAGHETTI INTRIGUE

2 tbsp. fat
2 tbsp. flour
1/4 tsp. salt
1/8 tsp. pepper
1 1/2 c. milk

1 egg, beaten
1 1/2 c. diced cooked chicken
Cooked spaghetti
Grated cheese

Make white sauce of first 5 ingredients. Add beaten egg and blend. Add chicken. Into buttered baking dish put a layer of spaghetti, then put in the chicken and on top another layer of spaghetti. Sprinkle with grated cheese and bake in moderate oven (350° F.) until thoroughly heated and cheese is melted.

CANNELONS OF CHICKEN

1 c. cooked chicken,
  chopped fine
1 tbsp. flour
1 tbsp. butter
2 tbsp. cream

2 egg yolks
1/4 tsp. salt

1 egg yolk
Dash pepper
1/2 tsp. salt
1 tbsp. parsley
Noodle dough

Noodle Dough
1 c. flour

Beat the yolks. Add the salt and enough flour to make a stiff dough. Sprinkle flour on the bread board. Roll out the dough very thin. Dust it with flour. Cut in four inch squares. Allow to dry 2 hours.
While the noodle dough is drying mix the chicken with melted butter, well beaten egg yolk, cream, flour, salt, pepper and parsley. Make into a thick paste. Put a spoonful of this on a square of dried noodle dough, cover with another square and pinch edges together. Bake in a hot oven (425° F.) until light brown. Serve with crisp greens.

CHICKEN MACARONI AU GRATIN

1/2 lb. macaroni
2 qts. boiling water
1 1/2 tsp. salt
2 c. milk
4 tbsp. flour

2 tbsp. butter
2 c. diced cooked chicken
Salt and pepper
3/4 c. grated American cheese

Cook the macaroni in boiling salted water until tender, about 20 minutes. Drain and run cold water over the macaroni to blanche it. While the macaroni is cooking make a white sauce of the milk, flour, butter. Add the white sauce to the macaroni, and then add the chicken. Season to taste, with salt and pepper. Pour the mixture into a buttered baking dish, putting in a layer of the chicken mixture, then a thin layer of cheese, and repeating until the mixture is all in the dish. Top with grated cheese and bake in a medium oven (375° F.) until the cheese is melted.

⅔ c. cooked spaghetti
½ c. cream
½ c. milk
½ c. chicken stock
1 tbsp. butter
2 egg yolks

½ c. celery
½ c. walnut meats
½ c. peas
1 tsp. salt
1 c. chicken

Cook spaghetti in boiling, salted water until tender. Drain. Scald the cream, milk and stock, add egg yolks well beaten, butter and salt. Cook until mixture thickens, add chicken cut in cubes. Then add peas which have been drained, and celery cut in ½ inch pieces and cooked until tender. Add to spaghetti. Cook until heated through. Add nutmeats. Serve hot on toast triangles.

CHICKEN MACARONI MOUSSE

½ lb. macaroni
3 c. cooked chicken
3 tbsp. gelatin
½ c. cold water
2 c. hot chicken stock

1½ tsp. salt
½ tsp. pepper
1 c. celery, chopped fine
1 c. ripe olives
2 c. whipped cream

Cook macaroni in boiling, salted water until tender. Drain. Chop the chicken. Soak gelatin in cold water for 5 minutes, add the boiling stock and stir until gelatin is dissolved. Chill and beat until stiff. Add the rest of the ingredients. Pour into a mold. Serve on lettuce leaves with mayonnaise.

CHICKEN NOODLE PIE

½ lb. broad noodles
2 c. finely chopped cooked chicken
2 doz. large oysters
1 tsp. salt
2 tbsp. butter
1 tbsp. flour

½ c. cream
1 c. chicken stock
1 c. oyster liquid
1 tbsp. finely minced onion
1 tsp. Worcestershire sauce
⅛ tsp. pepper

Cook noodles in boiling, salted water until tender. Drain and chop slightly. Cover the bottom of a buttered baking dish with noodles, over them put one cup of the chicken; next, a thin layer of noodles, then a layer of oysters. Cover these in turn with the remainder of the noodles, and then the second cup of chopped chicken. Pour over this a thin white sauce made of the chicken stock, oyster liquid, cream, minced onion, Worcestershire sauce, butter, salt and pepper. Cover with rich biscuit dough rolled out to ⅛ inch thickness, making slits to allow the steam to escape. Bake in hot oven (410° F.) about 20 minutes, or until the crust is brown.

423

DIXIE GUMBO

¼ lb. medium noodles	1 pt. chicken stock
2 tbsp. peanut butter	1 c. water
1 chopped shallot	1 tsp. salt
2 ripe tomatoes, chopped	¼ tsp. pepper
½ lb. okra, cut thin	1 tsp. sugar
1 c. peas	½ tsp. celery salt
1 c. shredded cooked chicken	1 tbsp. browned flour

Cook noodles in boiling, salted water until tender. Drain. Melt peanut butter fry in it the chopped shallot, tomatoes, okra, peas, noodles, chicken. Add stock and water, let simmer in covered pan ¾ of an hour. If canned tomatoes and peas are used, ½ hour is sufficient. Add seasonings and moistened browned flour. Cook gently for 15 minutes. Keep hot until served. More liquid may be added if needed.

STUFFED CHICKEN TIMBALES

¼ lb. macaroni	½ tsp. paprika
3 eggs	¼ tsp. black pepper
1 c. evaporated milk	2 tbsp. melted butter
1 tsp. salt	1 tsp. Worcestershire sauce

Cook macaroni in boiling, salted water until tender. Drain. Beat eggs, add milk, seasoning, melted butter, Worcestershire sauce, and macaroni. Let stand for 1 hour so that the macaroni may absorb the liquid. Line buttered timbale cases or molds with this mixture and fill the centers with the following filling:

2 tbsp. celery, chopped	½ c. minced blanched almonds
1 tbsp. grated onion	which have been fried in butter
1 c. minced chicken	¼ c. buttered bread crumbs
	1 egg

2 tbsp. melted butter

Combine ingredients and mix thoroughly. Force firmly into the timbale cases or molds lined with macaroni, but do not disturb the position of the latter. Set into pan of hot water and bake in moderate oven (350° F.). Serve with cream sauce containing cherry flavor and French mushrooms.

BAKED NOODLES WITH PINEAPPLE CHICKEN SAUCE

1½ c. broad noodles	2 tbsp. flour
3 tbsp. butter	1 c. cream
2 eggs	1 c. pineapple liquid
12 mushrooms	1 c. canned diced pineapple
1 c. diced celery	Salt and pepper
2 c. cooked diced chicken	

Cook noodles in salted, boiling water until tender. Drain and add butter. Thoroughly beat eggs with 2 tablespoons water and add to the noodles. Place

424

in buttered baking dish and bake in a hot oven (400° F.) until top is quite brown. Cut mushrooms in quarters, pan fry carefully in butter, add celery, and chicken. Fry until light brown. Take mixture out of pan, strain fat, add flour and blend until smooth. Add the heated pineapple liquor, cream and pineapple, and let simmer slowly 20 minutes. Serve this mixture over the baked noodles.

CHICKEN AND SPAGHETTI MOLD

1 lb. spaghetti, unbroken	2 tbsp. flour
3 c. cold chopped chicken	2 tbsp. butter
1 tbsp. chopped parsley	1 egg
¾ c. milk	Salt and pepper

Cook the spaghetti in boiling water until tender, being careful not to break it. Drain thoroughly and with it line a well greased mold, twisting it around and around. Make a sauce of the milk, flour, butter and seasonings. Remove from fire and add well beaten egg. Add the chicken and parsley and pour into the center of the mold. Set mold into pan of water and bake about ¾ hour in a moderate oven (350° F.).

CHICKEN NOGALES

½ lb. long spaghetti	2 hard cooked eggs, chopped
2 c. ground cooked chicken	1 small bottle stuffed olives
8 large chili pods	1 finely minced onion
2 tbsp. butter	2½ c. (1 No. 2 can) tomatoes
1 c. grated cheese	Salt to taste

Remove seeds, wash and boil chili pods until tender. Use chicken stock with sufficient water in which chili pods were boiled to boil spaghetti until tender; drain. Add pulp from 4 chili pods, mashed. Line a baking dish with spaghetti, leaving the center as nearly open as possible. Fill this opening with alternate layers of chicken, dotted with small pieces of butter, cheese, eggs and olives. Fry the onion lightly in 2 tablespoons butter and add tomatoes and the pulp of 4 chili pods. Pour over spaghetti and bake in slow oven (325° F.) for 25 minutes.

Soups Thick and Thin

Soup stock, says an old cookbook, is "to a cook what oil is to an oil painter; it is the life and soul of all domestic cooking." Recipes from famous chefs almost invariably call for stock, and it is often precisely the cup of soup stock that gives a particular dish the indefinable flavor that sets it apart from other similar ones.

The best chicken stock jellies when it is cold, because the connective tissue has been transformed into gelatin during cooking. In stock-

To garnish the s o u p
or to serve with it.

making, therefore, the object is to get the greatest possible amount of flavor and gelatin from the poultry meat. Stewing birds and "stags" are especially desirable for soup-making. Stags are male birds that have outlived their usefulness. The meat of these mature birds is rich in extractives as well as in connective tissue.

The cords running through the drumstick down into the feet contain a high proportion of connective tissue. So thrifty cooks clean the feet carefully and use them in making stock. To clean them, dip the feet into boiling water until the tough outer skin can be pulled off. Then wash thoroughly and they are ready to use.

The same rules apply in cooking chicken for soup as for stewing it—long, slow cooking to dissolve the connective tissue. Cover the disjointed chicken with cold water. Bring the water gradually to a boil and then turn down the heat so that the water just simmers. Add two teaspoonfuls of salt and one-fourth teaspoonful of pepper, and any other seasonings desired. Simmer for three or four hours. Remove the chicken from the stock and strain the liquid through a cloth.

If the broth is to be used as stock or for bouillon, it must be entirely clear. To clarify it with egg white, use the white and the clean shell of one egg for each quart of soup. Crush the shell and mix it thoroughly with a half cup of cold water. Add gradually about one cup of the boiling soup, stirring continually. Pour the egg white mixture into the stock, stirring briskly until the soup comes to a boil. Remove from the fire, let stand ten minutes, or until the egg white settles out. Strain.

When chicken broth or stock is set aside to cool, it should be stirred occasionally so that all of it cools equally. Otherwise the outer portion nearest the outside of the container cools first and congeals, acting as a sort of insulator and preventing the soup in the center from cooling. When this happens, some of the broth cools too slowly and spoils.

When soup is to be served as the main part of a meal, it is usually thickened to give it more body and to increase its food value. It was such thickened soup to which Sir John Sinclair referred when he said, "The greatest heroes of antiquity lived on broth."

When old cookbooks refer to the thickening of soups, they speak of adding the "liaison." The favorite liaison was made with egg yolks as a base, and almost always a little sugar was added for flavor. The result was, and is, delicious.

To make the egg yolk liaison, put the yolk of one egg into a bowl, add a little sugar (about one-fourth teaspoonful), a fourth pint of warm cream, or a half pint of scalded milk. Beat thoroughly. This makes enough of the liaison to thicken a pint of soup. Add a little of the hot soup to the egg mixture, stirring constantly. Remove the hot soup from the fire, add the liaison, stirring briskly. Serve at once. Do not return the soup to the fire after the liaison has been added.

Cornstarch or tapioca may be used as thickeners, with or without egg yolk. A level tablespoonful of cornstarch or of tapioca is allowed for each cup of soup. The cornstarch is made into a smooth paste with a little cold water or milk or cream, and then it is added to the hot soup, with constant stirring, until the starch has cooked. The entire cooking of the starch requires about twenty minutes, but the soup does not need to be stirred constantly after the mixture has become somewhat clear. If pre-cooked tapioca is used, it is added to the boiling soup and cooked until done, with occasional stirring. If egg yolk is added to increase the food value and improve the color of the soup, the liaison method given above is followed, allowing one egg yolk for a quart of soup.

Because chicken soup is so delicate in flavor, bland foods combine best with it. Rice, hominy, noodles, macaroni, spaghetti and plain dumplings cooked in the broth make it more nourishing without diminishing its excellent flavor.

CHICKEN STOCK

Feet, neck and back of one 3–3½ lb. fowl
1 qt. cold water   1 sliced carrot
1 stalk celery   ½ tsp. salt
¼ tsp. peppercorns   Bit of bay leaf

Put pieces of chicken into kettle and cover with cold water. Add vegetables cut into small pieces and the spices tied in cheesecloth. Bring gradually to the boiling point. Lower the heat and let broth simmer until the meat on the neck and back is thoroughly done. Strain, chill and remove fat. To make chicken soup, dilute the stock to one quart, heat and add ½ to ¾ cup boiled rice, noodles or macaroni.

CHILLED CHICKEN BOUILLON

3 c. chicken broth   1 tbsp. gelatin
½ tsp. celery salt   ¼ c. cold water
¼ tsp. salt

Soften gelatin for 5 minutes in cold water. Add the seasonings and the boiling chicken broth. Chill. When congealed, break up into crystals by beating with fork. Serve in sherbet glasses or bouillon cups with a teaspoonful salted whipped cream on top. Garnish with slices of stuffed olives.

CHICKEN CREAM SOUP WITH NOODLES

¼ lb. noodles, fine   Salt and pepper
6 c. rich chicken stock   2 egg yolks beaten
1 tbsp. finely minced   ½ c. slightly sour cream
parsley   1 tbsp. lemon juice

Heat the stock, add noodles, parsley, salt and pepper and cook for 15 minutes. Combine beaten eggs with cream and lemon juice and add to the soup. Remove the soup from the fire and stir until slightly thickened.

HUNGARIAN SOUP WITH RAISINS

1 stewing fowl (3–4 lb.)   1 lemon, juice
2 qts. hot water   ½ tsp. grated lemon peel
Salt   ½ lb. raisins
2 tbsp. fat   1 tsp. chopped parsley
4 tbsp. flour

Disjoint the chicken and simmer it in the hot water until tender. Add the raisins. Melt the fat in a pan, add the flour and cook until slightly thickened. Add some of the chicken stock gradually, stirring so as to prevent lumping. Bring to boil and let cook 5 minutes. Add to soup, heat very hot and serve. Arrange pieces of chicken on hot platter and surround with mashed potatoes.

CHICKEN BROTH WITH CREAM

To each cup of chicken broth add 1 tablespoon thick cream. Season well.

BELGIAN CHICKEN SOUP

Cover a large whole fowl with boiling water. Add salt and let simmer for 2 hours. Add whole vegetables and cook for 45 minutes more. Serve all together in large bowl.

MARROW DUMPLINGS (Kosher)

3 tbsp. marrow	1 tbsp. minced parsley
¾ tsp. salt	3 egg yolks
¾ tsp. nutmeg	1 tbsp. matzo meal

Cream marrow, add salt, nutmeg and parsley. Mix in the yolks gradually, then the matzo meal, using just enough so that the dough can be rolled off a spoon in small balls. Put the dumplings into boiling broth and cook for 15 minutes.

CHICKEN SOUP

1 3 lb. fowl	1 small onion, sliced
2 qts. cold water	1 bay leaf
1 carrot, diced	1 stalk parsley
2 tsp. salt	A few celery leaves
½ tsp. peppercorns	

Cut up fowl as for fricassee. Cover with water, add other ingredients and let come to a boil. Reduce heat and let chicken simmer for 2½–3 hours. Remove meat. Strain soup. Chill, remove fat and reheat.

CHICKEN BOUILLON

Make chicken soup. After straining, chill and remove fat. Reheat and clarify with egg white.

CHICKEN FORCEMEAT

1 raw breast of chicken	2 egg whites
Salt and pepper	Whipping cream

Put meat through fine blade of food chopper. Pound minced meat to a pulp in a mortar, adding gradually the egg whites. Season with salt and pepper. Add cream to make a smooth paste. Enough cream has been added when a little of the mixture dropped from a spoon into boiling water will hold its shape. Drop by spoonfuls into boiling water.

CHICKEN QUENELLES

Shape chicken forcemeat into small balls and cook in boiling chicken stock or salted water. Serve as garnish in clear soup, or with white sauce as an entrée.

CHICKEN AND TAPIOCA SOUP

1—3 lb. fowl	3 egg yolks
2 qts. cold water	Salt and pepper
½ c. tapioca	1½ c. milk, scalded

Cut up fowl. Cover with water and bring gradually to boil. Simmer 2½ hours. Remove meat. Bring broth to boil, add tapioca and let cook 30 minutes. Add milk and heat. Add the beaten egg yolks, stirring, and cook 1 minute. Season with salt and pepper.

CHICKEN BISQUE

½ c. shredded chicken	2 tbsp. butter
1½ c. milk, scalded	½ tsp. salt
2 tbsp. flour	Whipped cream
1 c. chicken broth	

Heat chicken and milk together in top of double boiler. In the meantime melt butter and add flour, blending it to a smooth paste. Add chicken broth gradually, stirring to keep it smooth. Let come to boil. Add to milk and chicken in double boiler. Season with salt and pepper. Top each serving with a spoonful of whipped cream garnished with a dash of paprika.

TURKEY SOUP

Break up turkey carcass. Put into kettle with left-over bits of turkey meat. Cover with cold water, simmer for 2 hours. Celery leaves may be added during the last hour of cooking. Strain and season with salt and pepper. Rice, noodles or spaghetti may be cooked in the broth.

DAFFODIL SOUP

1 qt. milk, scalded	1 finely minced onion
4 tbsp. butter	3 tbsp. flour
4 hard cooked eggs	Salt and pepper
Parsley, minced	

Fry onion lightly in butter, add flour and blend until smooth. Add hot milk gradually, stirring constantly. Season with salt and pepper. Remove yolks from eggs, chop whites fine and add to soup. Put yolks through sieve and sprinkle over top of soup. Sprinkle with minced parsley.

GRECIAN EGG SOUP

1 c. rice	1 qt. chicken stock
Seasoning	2 lemons
2 eggs, beaten	Parsley

Cook rice in chicken stock until soft. More stock may be added as needed. Force cooked rice through sieve. Add well beaten eggs and juice of the lemons. Heat and serve in cups, garnished with parsley.

4 bouillon cubes

2 tbsp. gelatin softened in

¼ c. cold water

4 c. boiling water

4 egg yolks, beaten

Dissolve softened gelatin in boiling water, to which bouillon cubes have been added. Pour a little of the hot bouillon over the beaten yolks, stirring constantly. Add to remainder of bouillon, pour into cups and chill. Break up with a fork before serving.

CHICKEN BROTH WITH EGG

Beat egg yolks allowing 1 yolk for each cup of well seasoned chicken broth. Add eggs to hot broth, stirring constantly. Serve.

The Useful Giblets

In some markets chicken livers are sold separately, and hearts and gizzards are sold as giblets. Creamed livers or creamed giblets are delicious and economical.

In the household, however, where usually the giblets from only one or two birds are available at one time, they are cooked separately, then chopped and added either to the gravy or to the stuffing. If they are just covered with boiling water, salted slightly and allowed to simmer for three-quarters of an hour, they will be tender and juicy. Or the uncooked giblets may be ground and added to the stuffing before it is put into the chicken. The giblets of fryers may be cooked with the other pieces in the skillet. Cooked chicken liver finely mashed makes an excellent spread for appetizers and dainty sandwiches.

From the standpoint of nutritive value, the giblets are important sources of minerals. The liver particularly is rich in iron.

CREAMED GIBLETS

Giblets

1 c. milk

3 tbsp. flour

3 tbsp. butter

Salt and pepper

Simmer giblets in just enough water to cover. Season. When tender, dice and add to cream sauce which has been made from ½ cup of the stewing liquor, the milk, flour and butter. Serve in pastry shells or on toast.

431

CHICKEN LIVERS WITH SPAGHETTI

½ lb. spaghetti	1 c. soup stock
¼ lb. mushrooms	1 c. tomatoes
1 tbsp. butter	4 chicken livers
1 tbsp. flour	½ tsp. salt
1 onion, chopped fine	¼ tsp. pepper

Cook spaghetti in boiling, salted water until tender; drain. Melt butter, add onion and peeled mushrooms, cook for 5 minutes without browning. Add flour soup stock and tomatoes, cook for 15 minutes. Add seasoning. Chop chicken livers, fry in 1 tablespoon butter. Add sauce, pour over spaghetti. Cook 2 minutes.

CHICKEN LIVERS EN BROCHETTE

Chicken livers   Bacon, sliced

Cut each liver into 4 pieces. Alternate pieces of liver and squares of thinly sliced bacon on skewers, allowing 1 liver and 5 pieces of bacon for each skewer. Arrange skewers in upright position on rack in dripping pan or in a baking dish and bake in a hot oven (450° F.) until bacon is crisp. Skewers may be stuck into pieces of bread. Garnish with parsley or watercress and serve.

CHICKEN GIBLET PIE

Put chicken giblets into pan and cover with cold water. Bring gradually to a boil, season with salt and pepper. Simmer until tender. Thicken liquor with flour.

Line baking dish with rich pie crust paste. Put in giblets. Add liquor in which giblets were cooked. Cover with pie crust and bake in hot oven (425° F.) 20 minutes. Diced cooked potatoes may be added.

RECIPES FROM FAR AND NEAR

APPETIZERS

APPETIZER PLATE

3 hard cooked eggs
Chopped onion
Chopped green pepper

Pimiento, tomato or red pepper,
  chopped
Parsley

Separate the hard cooked eggs and chop whites and yolks separately. On an oval china platter arrange diagonal rows of the chopped relishes. Beginning in the center, place a row of pimiento, tomato or red pepper. At each side of this a row of egg white, then one of green pepper, then white onion, and finally at each end a mound of egg yolk. Garnish with parsley. Serve with salted or cheese wafers. This is delightful served alone as an appetizer, or as an accompaniment to caviar.

EGG CRISPS

Yolks of hard cooked eggs
Potato chips

Mayonnaise

Put egg yolks through sieve. Cream with mayonnaise to make of good spreading consistency. Season to taste. Crisp potato chips in oven and spread with egg yolk mixture. Garnish with bits of parsley and pimiento.

CAVIAR A LA RUSSE

Fill hard cooked egg whites with blue-black caviar. Garnish with minced egg yolk, finely chopped onions and slices of lemon.

ANCHOVY AND EGG ROLL

Slice off part of one end of a soft finger roll. Scoop out the soft crumb and stuff firmly with a filling of chopped egg and anchovy. Chill in the refrigerator for about an hour. Slice in very thin slices.

HOT MAYONNAISE PUFFS

1 c. mayonnaise

1 egg white, stiffly beaten
Canapé crackers

Fold mayonnaise into egg white gently but thoroughly. Pile on crackers and toast under broiler 1 minute, or until delicately browned and puffed. Arrange on platter.

433

PICKLED EGGS

2½ doz. eggs	1 qt. vinegar
2 c. water	1 oz. whole ginger
1 tsp. cloves	1 blade mace
1 tsp. black pepper	

Put the spices in a small bag, put the bag into the vinegar with the water and boil for 10 minutes. Hard cook the eggs, dash them into cold water and remove the shells. Pack the eggs into glass quart or pint jars, pour the vinegar over them and seal. These eggs may be sliced and used as a garnish, or they may be used in salads or as a relish.

CHICKEN CANAPÉ

1 c. cold chicken, finely minced	½ tsp. curry powder
4 tbsp. softened butter	¼ c. finely chopped toasted almonds
½ c. crushed, drained pineapple	3 tbsp. mayonnaise
	Toasted bread rounds

Blend the chicken, curry powder and softened butter. Spread around outer edge of toasted bread rounds and pipe inner edge thinly with mayonnaise or whipped cream dressing. In the center put a mound of pineapple and almonds which have been mixed with mayonnaise. Garnish with bits of pimiento.

CHICKEN CRISPS

Separate small leaves from head of young cabbage. Spread each leaf with finely chopped chicken salad mixture and roll. Skewer with toothpicks. Put into vegetable crisper or wrap in wet towel and put into refrigerator to become crisp.

LETTUCE ROLL

| Leaf lettuce | Roasted chicken, sliced very thin |
| Mayonnaise | Prepared mustard |

On leaves of lettuce lay slices of chicken which have been cut paper-thin. Spread thinly with mayonnaise to which a little prepared mustard has been added. Roll, skewer with toothpick and chill. Serve on appetizer plate.

CHICKEN FINGERS

Shape finely minced chicken into inch-long fingers, roll each in cracker dust and fry in hot deep fat until golden brown. Serve as appetizer with bowl of chicken bouillon. Toothpicks or small skewers stuck into each facilitate serving.

DRUMSTICK SLICES

Bone drumsticks by cutting straight slit through meat to bone on one side. Spread meat out flat, rub with salt and pepper, roll tightly and tie. Put into baking dish, add ¼ cup boiling water and cook in moderate oven (325°–350° F.) until done. Chill, remove string and slice very thin. Serve slices on appetizer platter.

Cut bread in very thin slices, pile together and wrap tightly in a damp cloth. Keep in refrigerator several hours. When ready to use, spread with minced chicken filling or very thin slices of chicken breast and roll up each slice tightly. Secure with toothpick. Toast under broiler.

Beverages

EGG NOG

4 egg whites
$\frac{1}{16}$ tsp. salt
4 tbsp. powdered sugar

4 egg yolks, beaten
2 tbsp. sherry, or wine flavoring
3 c. cold milk

Beat egg whites with salt. Add sugar, yolks and flavoring, and finally the milk. Mix thoroughly and serve.

CIDER EGG NOG

¼ c. cider
1 tsp. sugar

1 egg
Chipped ice

Shake all together and serve.

ORANGE EGG NOG

1 doz. oranges, juice
6 eggs
1 qt. milk

¼ c. sugar
6 tbsp. wine flavoring (or red or white grape juice)

Beat eggs thoroughly. Add other ingredients, then cracked ice and shake well.

COFFEE EGG NOG

4 eggs
5 tsp. sugar

2 c. strong coffee
2 c. milk

Separate yolks and whites of eggs. Beat yolks and sugar together. Then add the coffee and milk and blend thoroughly. Beat the whites and fold into the coffee mixture. Serve at once.

HOT GRAPE NOG

(From the White House Kitchen in Jefferson's Day)
1 qt. grape juice
4 tbsp. sugar

4 eggs, separated
⅛ tsp. salt

Beat the egg yolks slightly, add sugar and grape juice and heat slowly until mixture begins to thicken, stirring constantly. Add salt to egg whites and beat until stiff. Fold the beaten whites into the hot mixture and beat until whites are thoroughly blended. Serve very hot.

435

ARTISTE

1 egg yolk   Pinch cayenne
1 wineglass sweet sherry

Beat yolk, add sherry and cayenne.

MULLED EGG WINE

1 egg   Grated nutmeg
3 glasses sweet cooking sherry

Pour slowly, while stirring, ½ pt. boiling water over beaten egg. Add wine. Grate in a little nutmeg and serve.

ARCTIC FIZZ

2 egg whites   Juice of 1½ lemons
3 tbsp. sugar   Cracked ice
                 Ginger ale

Shake all ingredients except gingerale in shaker with chipped ice. Pour into glasses and fill with gingerale.

EGG COCKTAIL

1 tbsp. lemon juice   1 well beaten egg
1 tbsp. sherry   Few drops tobasco sauce

Blend ingredients thoroughly and serve in a tall glass, with spoon.

HONEY EGG MILK SHAKE

2 eggs   6 tbsp. honey
1½ c. evaporated milk   1 tbsp. orange flower water
1½ c. ice water   Chipped ice

Beat eggs and pour into mason jar or shaker. Add remaining ingredients, shake and serve. May be topped with a spoonful of whipped cream. A spoonful of ice cream may be used instead of the ice. With bread and butter and fruit this makes a pleasing meal for children. ½ teaspoonful vanilla may take the place of the orange flower water.

CHOCOLATE EGG SHAKE

2 c. milk   2 eggs
4 tsp. sugar   ¼ tsp. salt
1 tbsp. chocolate syrup   2 tbsp. cream or undiluted
                              evaporated milk

Mix all together, shake well to blend and pour over cracked ice.

MALTED MILK EGG SHAKE

6 tbsp. malted milk
1 tsp. sugar
½ tsp. vanilla

2 eggs, beaten
2 c. milk
Pinch of salt

Mix malted milk to a paste with a little of the milk. Add other ingredients and shake. A spoonful of ice cream may be added.

ROOTBEER EGG SHAKE

1 bottle carbonated rootbeer
1 egg, beaten

4 tbsp. ice cream

Shake all ingredients until thoroughly mixed.

CHOCOLATE CREAM PUFF

4 eggs
1 c. milk
½ c. chocolate syrup

½ pint vanilla ice cream
Carbonated water

Beat eggs slightly. Pour them into shaker, add other ingredients and shake.

MOCHA EGG SHAKE

2 c. strong coffee
3 tbsp. cocoa
$\frac{1}{16}$ tsp. salt
2 tbsp. cocoa

½ c. water
½ pt. vanilla ice cream
2 egg whites, beaten
Chipped ice

Combine coffee, sugar, salt, cocoa and water. Boil for one minute. Chill and add ice cream, egg whites, ice. Shake.

PINEAPPLE EGG SHAKE

1 egg, well beaten
½ c. pineapple juice
1 tbsp. lemon juice

2 tbsp. sugar
¼ c. crushed pineapple

Combine all ingredients, shake with shaved ice and serve. Garnish with candied mint leaves.

CHOCOLATE FROST

3 eggs
2 tbsp. cocoa

4 tbsp. honey
2 c. milk

Cook honey and cocoa to form a chocolate syrup. Separate eggs. Beat yolks and add to cold milk. Add crushed ice and 2 tablespoons of the honey syrup. Whip whites until stiff, and gradually add the remainder of the honey syrup. Put a spoonful of the egg white mixture into each glass, pour a cupful of the milk mixture over it and top with a spoonful of the beaten white. Dust with nutmeg or cocoa and serve. A spoonful of ice cream may take the place of crushed ice for chilling the mixture.

437

LAIT DE POULE (Hen's Milk)

1 egg

½ c. powdered sugar

2 tbsp. orange flower water

1 c. boiling milk

Beat the egg, add sugar and orange flower water. Mix thoroughly and add the hot milk, stirring as it is added.

TULIP SPECIAL

2 eggs

5 tbsp. sugar

½ c. strong coffee

3 c. rich milk

½ tsp. vanilla

Blend all ingredients thoroughly. Add crushed ice. Top with whipped cream and serve.

MAPLE FLUFF

2 eggs, separated

½ c. maple syrup

1½ c. milk

Beat yolks and one white, add 4 tablespoons syrup and the cold milk. Chill thoroughly. Heat 4 tablespoons syrup and boil for 3 minutes. Pour over stiffly beaten egg white. Beat until cool and use for topping on beverage.

EGG LEMONADE

1 egg white

2 tbsp. sugar

¾ c. water

Juice of 1 lemon

Chipped ice

Shake all ingredients together in shaker until thoroughly mixed.

EGG ORANGEADE

1 tbsp. sugar

1 egg white

Juice of 4 oranges

Chipped ice

Shake together and serve at once.

EGG LEMONADE FIZZ

1 tbsp. crushed fruit

1 beaten egg

⅔ c. gingerale

Juice of 1 lemon

Sugar to taste

Thoroughly blend all of the ingredients except the gingerale. Then add gingerale and serve at once, very cold.

EGG LIMEADE

1 lime, juice

1 egg, beaten

2 tbsp. sugar

Combine lime juice, egg and sugar. Shake until sugar is dissolved. Add chipped ice, ½ cup cold water. Shake and serve. If desired, a tablespoon of crushed fruit or a teaspoon of preserved fruit may be added.

438

ALBUMEN FRUIT BEVERAGE

⅓ c. orange or lemon juice   Honey to taste
1 egg white

Beat egg white to froth, add fruit juice and strain. Sweeten. Serve cold.

ORANGE FIZZ

2 c. orange juice   ¼ c. orange marmalade
¼ c. lemon juice   3 eggs
¾ c. sugar   Gingerale

Beat eggs, add fruit juices, sugar and marmalade. Shake until sugar is dissolved. Pour over finely cracked ice to fill tall glasses about ¾ full, and fill with gingerale.

SLEEPER

1 c. water   Juice of 1 lemon
2 tbsp. sugar   1 tbsp. sweet cooking sherry
1 clove   2 egg yolks
1 small piece stick cinnamon

Boil water, sugar and spices for 3 minutes. Add lemon juice, sherry and pour over beaten egg yolks. Strain and serve hot.

TOMATO EGG COCKTAIL

1 c. tomato juice   1 tsp. lemon juice
1 egg   ⅛ tsp. mustard
½ tsp. salt   ¼ tsp. horseradish
⅛ tsp. pepper   1 tbsp. tomato puree
¼ tsp. sugar

Separate the egg. Beat the yolk, add the tomato juice and seasonings except the horseradish. Blend with egg beater or by shaking in jar. Chill thoroughly. Whip the egg white until foamy, add the tomato puree, ¼ teaspoon salt, the horseradish and continue beating until stiff. Put 2 tablespoons of the beaten white into a glass with crushed ice and pour over it the tomato juice mixture. Top with a spoonful of the beaten white, garnish with a bit of tomato or pimiento and serve with salted wafers.

EGGS COOKED IN BEER

2 c. beer   Nutmeg
3 beaten eggs   Ginger
4 tbsp. sugar

Heat slowly 1 cup beer, sugar and beaten eggs, beating with rotary beater or egg whisk until nearly boiling. Remove from fire, add the other cup of beer, then nutmeg and ginger, and serve.

439

¼ c. matzo meal   1 tsp. salt
½ c. water   4 eggs, separated

Add the water to the matzo meal, stirring to remove lumps. Add the salt and the egg yolks which have been beaten until they are thick and light. Let stand for 5 minutes. Then fold in the stiffly beaten egg whites. Drop the mixture by spoonfuls on a hot greased skillet or griddle. Brown both sides and serve with syrup, or sugar and cinnamon, or preserves.

441

WHEY FOAM

½ c. sugar	1 tbsp. lime juice or
2½ c. whey	2 tbsp. lemon juice
2 egg whites	¼ c. crushed pineapple

Boil ½ cup whey and sugar together 5 minutes. Add sugar, fruit juice and egg whites and remaining whey. Shake with shaved ice. Put a tablespoon of

WAFFLES

3 eggs, separated	1½ c. milk
2 c. sifted flour	3 tbsp. melted fat
4 tsp. baking powder	1 tsp. salt

Sift together the dry ingredients. Beat egg yolks and add milk and fat. Stir liquids into dry ingredients. Fold in the stiffly beaten egg whites. Bake on hot waffle iron.

CHREMSEL (Jewish)

6 eggs, separated	1 c. matzo meal
½ c. sugar	6 tbsp. honey
¾ c. minced walnuts	6 tbsp. chicken fat, or goose fat
½ lemon, juice and rind	

Beat egg yolks and sugar together until light. Fold in the stiffly beaten egg whites. Fold in nuts slowly, with lemon and matzo meal. Heat the honey and fat in a skillet, and drop batter into this by spoonfuls. Fry until brown on both sides.

COCOA WAFFLES

1½ c. flour	6 tbsp. cocoa
3 tsp. baking powder	1 c. milk
½ tsp. salt	3 eggs
1 tbsp. sugar	4 tbsp. melted butter

Sift together all dry ingredients. Beat egg yolks, add the milk and butter. Combine dry and liquid ingredients. Fold in stiffly beaten egg whites. Bake in waffle iron or on griddle as for griddle cakes.

POPOVERS

1 c. flour	2 eggs
¼ tsp. salt	½ tsp. melted butter
1 c. milk	

Mix flour, salt and milk to smooth batter. Add the beaten eggs and butter. Beat the batter for 2 minutes with egg beater. Pour into muffin tins and bake in hot oven (475° F.) 30 to 35 minutes. When done make a small incision in side of popover and fill with scrambled eggs.

POTATO PANCAKES

½ c. grated potatoes	1 tbsp. melted shortening
½ c. flour	2 eggs
½ tsp. salt	

Combine all ingredients. Beat thoroughly until mixture is well blended. The batter will seem quite thin. Put the batter by spoonfuls on hot greased griddle, spread out thin and cook until one side is brown and crisp. Turn and finish cooking. The cakes should be thin, brown, and crisp on the edges.
Serve with sugar, sirup or jam.

442

SOUTHERN EGG PONE

2 c. sifted cornmeal
2 tbsp. melted butter
3 eggs

1 c. milk
2 tsp. baking powder
1½ tsp. salt

Mix all dry ingredients. Then add milk, eggs and butter. Beat until thoroughly blended. Pour into well greased pan and bake in hot oven (410° F.) about 40 minutes. Cut into squares and serve with molasses or sorghum.

NOODLE CASES

Make noodle dough of
1 egg, beaten light
1 c. flour

1 tbsp. water

Roll out dough ⅛ inch thick, cut in 4 inch squares and in center of each square put a heaping spoonful of chopped cheese, hard cooked eggs, chopped, or minced chicken. Press edges tightly together with fork. Let stand ½ hour, until dough becomes stiff. Drop into boiling salted water and boil 15 minutes, drain and fry in deep fat until golden brown. Serve hot.

FRENCH TOAST

2 eggs
1 c. milk
1½ tbsp. sugar

½ tsp. salt
8 slices stale bread

Beat eggs slightly. Add salt, sugar and milk. Dip each slice of bread into egg mixture and fry in butter on griddle. Serve with jelly or dust with powdered sugar.

FRENCH TOAST SANDWICHES

3 eggs
½ c. milk
1 pkg. cream cheese

¼ tsp. salt
1 tsp. sugar
12 thin slices stale bread

Beat eggs, add milk, salt and sugar. Spread bread with cream cheese and put 2 pieces together sandwich fashion. Dip each sandwich into egg and milk mixture and fry in butter. Brown on both sides. Serve with preserves.

GRAHAM NUT BREAD

28 graham crackers, rolled
fine
½ tsp. salt
½ c. sugar
1½ tsp. baking powder

3 eggs
½ c. milk
½ c. shortening
1 c. chopped nut meats

Mix cracker crumbs, salt, sugar and baking powder. Beat eggs and add milk and melted shortening. Add to cracker mixture and then add chopped nuts. Bake in buttered pan in moderately hot oven (375° F.) 30–35 minutes.

443

CHICKEN SURPRISE ROLLS

1½ c. pastry flour
3 tsp. baking powder
¾ tsp. salt

3 tbsp. shortening
½ c. milk
1 c. minced chicken

Sift flour, baking powder and salt together. Cut in the shortening. Add milk gradually, mixing quickly to a soft dough. Roll out ¼ inch thick on floured board and cut with biscuit cutter. Put a spoonful of seasoned minced chicken on one half of each round, fold over the other half and pinch edges together. Bake in hot oven (425° F.) 20 minutes. May be accompanied by white sauce.

BUTTERHORN ROLLS

1 c. milk, scalded
1 cake compressed yeast
1 tsp. salt
½ c. shortening

½ c. sugar
3 eggs, unbeaten
4 c. flour

Dissolve ¼ cup sugar in milk. When lukewarm, add yeast which has been softened to a thin paste with a little of the lukewarm milk. Sift in 2 cups flour and beat until smooth and full of bubbles. Set in warm place to rise until light. Cream together ¼ cup sugar, fat and salt. Add beaten eggs and add to sponge, beating in thoroughly. Add remainder of flour, kneading to make a soft smooth dough that leaves sides of pan. Cover and let rise until double in bulk. Knead down again, roll out to ¼ inch thickness. Cut into pie-shaped pieces. Roll large end to small end. Place in muffin tins or on baking sheets to rise until almost double in bulk and bake 20–25 minutes in moderately hot oven (410° F.). Makes 32 rolls.

ORANGE BREAD

Rinds of 2 large or 3 small oranges

½ c. sugar
1 c. water

Simmer rinds in hot water 10 minutes. Drain, cover with water again and cook until tender. Drain and shred. Add ½ cup water and ½ cup sugar and cook slowly until a thick syrup forms and the rinds have become semi-transparent. Cool. There should be ½ cup.

Make a batter of the following ingredients:

2½ c. flour
5 tsp. baking powder
½ c. sugar
¼ tsp. salt
3 eggs

¾ c. milk
¼ c. orange juice
1 tsp. lemon juice
2 tbsp. melted fat

Sift together all dry ingredients. Combine all liquid ingredients and marmalade. Combine dry and liquid ingredients, mixing only until the dry ones are thoroughly moistened. Bake in loaf pans in moderate oven (350° F.) 45 minutes.

444

1 c. sugar
½ c. butter
2 eggs, beaten light
1½ tbsp. sour milk
1 tsp. lemon juice
½ tsp. soda

1½ tsp. baking powder
¼ tsp. salt
3 large bananas
2 c. flour
1 c. coarsely chopped nutmeats

Cream butter and sugar. Add eggs, then bananas, put through sieve, and liquid ingredients. Add nuts and sifted dry ingredients. Blend thoroughly and bake 45 minutes in moderate oven (350° F.).

Desserts

APRICOT WHIP

1 c. apricot pulp
¾ c. sugar
1 tbsp. lemon juice

2 egg whites
Pinch of salt

Put all ingredients into bowl and beat until mixture holds its shape. Chill and serve. May be used as cake topping. Other fruit pulp may be substituted for apricot.

PRUNE WHIP

1 c. cooked stoned prunes
  (⅓ lb. uncooked
  prunes)
1 c. prune juice
3 egg yolks

2 egg whites
1 tbsp. flour
½ c. sugar
½ tbsp. lemon juice

Cook prunes until soft. Remove stones and put pulp through meat chopper. Add sugar and flour and let prunes boil again in juice. Pour this mixture over slightly beaten egg yolks. Set in a pan of hot water and stir until the mixture thickens. Cool slightly; fold in lemon juice and stiffly beaten egg whites. Serve cold.

BAKED PRUNE WHIP

2 c. prune pulp
1 tbsp. lemon juice

½ c. sugar
5 egg whites

Add the sugar to the prune pulp, which was made by rubbing cooked prunes through a sieve. Cook the pulp and sugar for 5 minutes. Cool and add the lemon juice, blending thoroughly. When cold, fold in the stiffly beaten whites. Pile into a buttered and sugared baking dish, set into a pan of hot water and bake 45 minutes in slow oven (325° F.). Serve hot or cold, with whipped cream. The whip shrinks somewhat as it cools.

445

CHOCOLATE MARSHMALLOW DAINTY

3 eggs, separated
3 tbsp. cocoa
1 tsp. vanilla

3 tbsp. powdered sugar
12 marshmallows, cut up
Pinch of salt

Beat egg yolks, add sugar, salt and cocoa mixed to a paste with a little cold water. Beat 10 minutes. Add marshmallows, nuts and then fold in stiffly beaten egg whites. Pour into mold and chill 3–4 hours. Serve with whipped cream.

EMERGENCY DESSERT

1 pt. whipping cream
1 lb. peanut brittle, crushed

3 egg whites

Whip cream and egg whites separately. Fold crushed peanut brittle into cream, and then fold in the egg white. Chill and serve.

SURPRISE EGGS

With a darning needle make a tiny hole in the small end of the shell of an egg. At the large end make a hole about 1/4 inch in diameter. Hold the egg over a bowl and blow gently into the smaller hole, forcing the egg meat through the large hole at the opposite end. Be careful not to crush the shell. When the shell is blown clear, rinse with cold water and put a bit of wax paper over the small hole. Then very carefully fill the shell through the large end with a pudding mixture, using a pastry tube or paper funnel. Chill until very cold. Serve in egg cups and chip off shell with spoon.

Pudding Mixture

1 tbsp. granulated gelatin
1/4 c. cold water
1 1/2 c. milk
3 egg yolks

1/4 c. sugar
1/8 tsp. salt
1 tsp. vanilla

Scald milk with gelatin which has been softened for 5 minutes in the cold water. Pour the hot milk mixture on the egg yolks which have been beaten with the sugar and salt. Cook in a double boiler until mixture coats spoon. Strain, add vanilla and fill into egg shells at once.

RHUBARB FLUFF

2 c. fresh rhubarb sauce
1/2 c. sugar
1 tbsp. lemon juice

1 1/2 tsp. gelatin, softened in 1 tbsp. cold water
2 egg whites, beaten with 2 tbsp. sugar

Cook rhubarb until tender. To the hot fruit add the sugar, lemon juice and softened gelatin. Stir until gelatin and sugar are completely dissolved. Cool. When mixture begins to thicken whip until it holds its shape. Fold in beaten egg whites. Chill. Serve in parfait or sherbet glasses.

446

2 egg whites
1 c. sugar
1 tbsp. lemon juice

⅛ tsp. salt
½ tsp. lemon extract
3 bananas, put through sieve

Put all ingredients into bowl and beat until mixture holds shape. Pile into individual pastry shells. Bake 20 minutes in slow oven (325° F.). Cool. Top with whipped cream and garnish with red preserves or sweetened fresh red berries, such as strawberries. If desired, nut meats, chopped, may be put into the mixture or sprinkled over the top before baking.

FIG PUDDING

½ c. figs, finely cut
3 egg whites
Whipped cream

3 tbsp. sweet cooking sherry
½ c. sugar

Pour sherry over figs and let stand 2 hours. Whip egg whites until stiff. Add sugar gradually, beating after each addition. Mash figs with fork and fold into egg whites, a little at a time. Put mixture into top of buttered double boiler and steam 1½ hours. Unmold, and serve with whipped cream. This pudding may be steamed in individual molds or custard cups.

FATTIGMAND (Norwegian)

6 eggs (omitting whites
   of 2)
6 tbsp. thick cream

Flour
6 tbsp. sugar
1 tsp. cardamon

Beat the eggs and the sugar together for half an hour. Add the cream and cardamon and flour enough to make a soft dough that can be rolled thin on a molding board. Cut into fancy shapes with a cookie cutter and fry in deep fat until a golden brown. When cold, dip in powdered sugar.

CREAM PUFFS

1 c. water
1 c. flour
½ tsp. salt

⅓ c. lard
4 eggs

Put water, salt and lard into a pan and bring to boil. Add flour and cook, stirring constantly, until paste leaves sides of pan and follows spoon around. Add unbeaten eggs, one at a time, beating in each one thoroughly before adding another. Drop by spoonfuls on baking sheet, bake 15 minutes in hot oven (450° F.), then reduce heat to moderate (350° F.) and bake 25 minutes longer. Cool and fill with sweetened whipped cream, custard filling or chocolate cream filling.

CLOVERLEAF CREAM PUFFS

Prepare Cream Puff dough. Drop by small spoonfuls on baking sheet, 3 close together to make cloverleaf. When done, fill each puff with a differently flavored filling.

447

CHEESE ÉCLAIRS

¾ c. milk	1¼ c. bread flour
6 tbsp. lard	4 eggs
¾ tsp. salt	1 c. grated cheese

Bring milk, fat and salt to a boil. Add the flour, stirring vigorously. Cook, with constant stirring, until paste does not cling to the side of the pan. Remove from fire and add eggs, one at a time, being sure each one is thoroughly blended in before another is added. When all the eggs are in add the cheese. Spread the paste in the shape of éclairs on a cookie sheet, sprinkle each with a little grated cheese and bake in a moderate oven (375° F.) 12–15 minutes. The outside should have a soft crust while the inside is creamy.

CHOCOLATE CREAM FILLING

1 c. sugar	2 c. milk
3½ tbsp. cornstarch	½ tsp. vanilla
⅛ tsp. salt	3 eggs
1 square chocolate	

Mix dry ingredients. Add milk and cook in double boiler 15 minutes, stirring until thickened. Add melted chocolate, then beaten eggs, stirring constantly. Cool and add flavoring. When thoroughly cold fill into cream puff shells or use as filling in cake or individual pies.

FRENCH FRIED CAKES (Beignets Soufflé)

1 c. water	1 c. sifted flour
⅛ tsp. salt	5 eggs
1 tsp. sugar	Deep fat for frying
¼ c. butter	

Put the water, butter, sugar and salt into a pan and bring to a boil. Add the flour, all at one time, stirring vigorously until all of the lumps are smoothed out and the mixture does not stick to the pan. Cool slightly and add the unbeaten eggs, one at a time, beating thoroughly after each addition so that each egg is entirely mixed in before another is added. Have the fat hot (380° F.) and drop in the batter by spoonfuls,—about the size of a walnut. When thoroughly brown remove from fat with wire spoon, drain on brown paper. Sprinkle with powdered sugar and serve hot.

SNOWBALLS

4 eggs, separated	Pinch of salt
¼ tsp. flavoring	1 pt. milk
½ c. sugar	

Beat egg whites until stiff, adding salt and then sugar gradually. Heat milk to boiling, and then set over hot water. Shape egg white mixture into balls and poach in the hot milk. Drain on cloth. Beat yolks slightly, add to hot milk in which whites were poached. Sweeten to taste. Cook over hot water, stirring constantly until custard coats spoon. Put a snowball into a dish, pour custard over and serve. A toasted marshmallow makes an attractive garnish.

448

Garnishing With Eggs

Slice, quarter or halve hard cooked eggs.

Put yolks of hard cooked eggs through sieve for fluffy garnish.

Put hard cooked egg yolks through seive, cream with a little mayonnaise or cream, adding a bit of horseradish. Put mixture through a pastry tube to make rosettes on salads or vegetables.

Chop separately yolks and whites of hard cooked eggs. Arrange whites at one end and yolks at other end of small platter. Separate by ridge of chopped onion. Garnish with slices of lemon. This egg platter is especially attractive and appetizing to serve with fish dishes or with caviar. It is a delightful accompaniment to a platter of cold red salmon or cheese.

Cut hard cooked eggs in half lengthwise. At large end of egg put dash of paprika on yolk only. Use as garnish on tray of appetizers.

Remove yolks from hard cooked eggs. Put through sieve and cream with mayonnaise to fluffy consistency. A little pimiento cheese may be added. With pastry tube fill creamed yolks back into whites. Top with a tiny cube of pimiento. These eggs add color, flavor and food value to a platter of raw or cooked vegetables.

Fill whites of hard cooked eggs with blue-black caviar. Arrange minced yolk, finely chopped onions and lemon garnish on platter around filled whites. This is excellent as a garnish or served alone as an appetizer.

Serve custard cubes in clear soups and as an addition to salads of greens.

Egg slices in pepper rings are a most colorful combination, either alone as a salad or as a garnish for other dishes.

EGG SLICES IN PEPPER RINGS

2 hard cooked eggs	1 tbsp. gelatin
¾ c. tomato juice	½ tsp. minced onion
⅛ tsp. salt	2 large green peppers
½ tbsp. cold water	½ tbsp. vinegar
1 bay leaf	½ tsp. sugar

Soak gelatin in cold water for 5 minutes. Boil tomato juice, onion, vinegar and seasonings. Strain. Add to gelatin and stir until gelatin is dissolved. Remove tips and seeds from peppers. Place a cold, shelled egg inside each pepper and fill space around egg with cooled tomato mixture. When thoroughly chilled, cut ¼ inch slices across pepper.

CHEESE DELIGHTS

3 egg whites	1 tbsp. flour
1½ c. grated cheese	⅓ tsp. salt
¾ c. cracker crumbs	⅛ tsp. pepper

Beat egg whites very stiff and add cheese, flour and seasonings. Form into small balls, roll in cracker crumbs and fry in deep fat, hot enough to brown a cube of bread in forty seconds (375° F.). Serve very hot with soup or salad. Season egg white with salt and pepper. Whip until light and drop by spoon-

449

fuls on hot broth just before serving. Grated cheese may be folded into egg white before cooking. Use as garnish on hot soup.

Beat the whole egg until the white and yolk are thoroughly blended but not fluffy. Season with salt and white pepper. Brush a warm skillet with melted butter. Pour the egg into the skillet in a paper thin layer. Cook only until egg is set. Remove from pan carefully, roll jelly-roll fashion, and cut into narrow strips to be used as garnish for rice, hominy and similar dishes.

Threaded eggs are delicious in clear consommé. To make them, beat 4 eggs thoroughly, add 3 tablespoons grated cheese and 1 tablespoon flour. Mix all ingredients thoroughly and put through the smallest opening of the pastry tube into boiling salted water or simmering soup.

Miscellaneous Egg Dishes

PARMESAN EGG PLATTER

4 eggs, carefully separated	4 tbsp. Parmesan or other dry
4 tbsp. flour	cheese, grated
½ tsp. salt	4 slices toast

Whip egg whites to stiff froth. Combine flour, cheese and salt and fold into the egg whites. Arrange toast on cookie sheet. Pile a mound of egg white on each slice of toast. Make a small well in each mound, place unbroken yolk carefully into well, and bake in moderate oven (300°–325° F.) until set, about 10 to 12 minutes. Garnish with parsley.

EGGS GENOA

Omit cheese from Parmesan Eggs. Spread toast with well seasoned tomato purée before putting eggs on it.

EGGS BLANDOS

Put eggs into boiling water, reduce heat and let eggs cook 5 minutes. Plunge them at once into cold water for a minute, remove shells and serve with Hollandaise Sauce. The whites of the eggs should be firm, while the yolks are still soft.

MARTHA WASHINGTON'S CORN OYSTERS

12 ears of corn	2 egg whites
2 egg yolks, unbeaten	Salt

Split the kernels of the corn with a sharp knife; scrape out the milk. Add the yolks to the corn, salt to taste and fold in the stiffly beaten egg whites. Cook on a buttered griddle.

½ c. canned salmon, flaked
¼ c. small peas
¾ tsp. salt
6 eggs

½ c. finely diced celery
1 tsp. shredded onion
¼ c. finely diced green pepper
Fat for frying

Put all the vegetables into a bowl. Break eggs over the vegetables and mix all thoroughly. Shape into small cakes like pancakes and fry in skillet until egg is cooked. The vegetables should still be crisp. Serve with any savory sauce.

EGG FOO YEUNG

6 eggs, well beaten
1 can bean sprouts or mixed vegetables, well drained

½ c. cold chicken, shredded
½ c. onion, shredded

Mix all ingredients and put by half-cupfuls into skillet in which a little cooking oil has been heated. Cook in cake form. Fry until brown on one side, then turn and brown on other. Serve with sauce made by thickening soy bean sauce with cornstarch.

SAUCE FOR EGG FOO YEUNG

1 tsp. cornstarch
1 tsp. sugar

1 tsp. soy bean sauce
½ c. water

Mix all ingredients thoroughly in a bowl and when smooth pour into the pan in which the egg foo yeung was cooked. Bring to a boil and serve.

ISBANAK TAVA (Syrian)

2 qts. or 2 cans spinach
2 tbsp. butter

5 eggs
Salt and pepper

If fresh spinach is used, wash, cut and boil it for 10 minutes. Strain. Season to taste. Spread spinach evenly in a flat buttered pan. Beat the eggs and pour them over the spinach. Pour the melted butter evenly over the spinach and eggs. Set in a pan of hot water and bake in a moderate oven (350° F.) until eggs are set, about 10–12 minutes.

HOT OYSTER RING

½ pt. oysters
3 eggs
2 c. milk

⅛ tsp. pepper
1 c. cracker crumbs
1 tsp. salt

Beat eggs and add the other ingredients. Pour into buttered ring molds, set in pan of water and bake in moderate oven (325° F.) 30 minutes. When unmolded center may be filled with creamed celery.

451

EGGS OKHOTSK

4 eggs, separated

½ c. flaked crabmeat

3 tbsp. flour

½ tsp. salt

4 slices toast

3 tbsp. butter

1 c. milk

Make white sauce of butter, flour, milk, and salt. Add crabmeat. Spread this mixture on the buttered toast. Place on baking sheet. Beat egg whites until stiff, adding ¼ teaspoon salt. Pile egg white on each slice of toast. Make a small hollow in the center and into it put the unbroken yolk. Bake in moderate oven (350° F.) until eggs are set, about 10 minutes. Garnish with parsley and paprika.

POTATO PUFFS

2 c. mashed potatoes

3 tbsp. cream

2 eggs, separated

1 tbsp. butter

Salt and pepper

Combine cream, melted butter, mashed potatoes and beaten egg yolk. Season, and beat until mixture is fluffy. Fold in the stiffly beaten egg whites. Drop by spoonfuls on greased cookie sheet. Brown in moderately hot oven (400° F.).

Sandwich Fillings

PLAIN EGG FILLING

Mash yolks of hard cooked eggs and cream them with butter. Add a little minced parsley and spread on bread.

SAVORY BUTTER AND EGG FILLING

3 hard cooked eggs

4 tbsp. savory butter

Salt

Prepare savory butter by creaming together ¼ pound butter, 1 tablespoon boiling water, 1 tablespoon lemon juice, ¼ teaspoon prepared mustard and pinch of cayenne. Add the finely chopped eggs to the butter and spread on bread. As the butter hardens it keeps the filling from falling out of the sandwiches. Savory butter is good in chicken sandwiches, too.

EGG SALAD FILLING

3 hard cooked eggs, chopped

1 tbsp. chopped pickle

4 stuffed olives, chopped

¼ c. chopped celery

1 tsp. chili sauce

1 tsp. minced green pepper

4 tbsp. mayonnaise

2 tbsp. cooked tapioca

452   Mix all ingredients thoroughly and spread on bread or rolls.

EGG SARDINE FILLING

3 hard cooked eggs
4 sardines

1 tbsp. mayonnaise
½ tsp. prepared mustard

Chop the eggs and sardines together. Add the mustard to the mayonnaise and combine all ingredients. If mustard sardines are used, omit the mustard in the recipe.

PIQUANT EGG FILLING

Hard cooked egg, chopped
French dressing
Butter, creamed

Minced watercress
A few drops lemon juice

Cream butter, add other ingredients. Add salt if necessary.

EGG AND SPINACH FILLING

2 hard cooked eggs, chopped
4 small green onions
Mayonnaise

3 c. uncooked spinach, finely minced
Salt and pepper to taste

Combine all ingredients and spread on rye bread.

EGG SANDWICH FILLING

1 hard cooked egg
1 tbsp. tomato puree

⅛ tsp. salt

Chop the egg fine, add seasoning and purée and spread on bread. Other puréed vegetables or mashed left-over vegetables may be used in place of the tomato.

Chicken Sandwiches

CHICKEN GIBLET SANDWICHES

Giblets from 1 chicken
1 tbsp. cream or evaporated milk
½ tsp. salt

½ tsp. Worcestershire sauce
1 tsp. tomato catsup or chili sauce
1 hard cooked egg

Cook giblets in salted water until tender. Put giblets and hard cooked egg through food chopper. Add seasoning and spread on sandwiches.

MINCED CHICKEN FILLING

1 c. finely ground chicken
1 tbsp. mayonnaise

½ tsp. prepared mustard
½ tsp. horseradish

Cream all together until of proper consistency to spread.

453

BATTER CHICKEN SANDWICHES

Butter slices of bread. Add a layer of seasoned minced chicken, another slice of bread, then a layer of chicken, and so on until there are three layers of filling. Press down firmly and slice. Dip in egg and milk batter and brown in butter. Serve hot.

CHICKEN AND PEANUT SANDWICHES

Thoroughly mix equal parts of finely minced chicken and finely chopped peanuts. Season. Moisten with whipping cream or mayonnaise to spreading consistency. Spread on whole wheat or raisin bread and trim.

CHICKEN AND MANGO SANDWICHES

Spread thin slices of bread with butter which has been creamed with a little dry mustard. On this place thin slices of preserved mango or chutney. Next spread on finely ground chicken which has been thoroughly mixed with an equal quantity of pâté de foi gras. Cover with another slice of bread, trim and serve.

FOR CHICKEN SALAD SANDWICH FILLING

To prevent chicken salad sandwich filling from falling out, add a little cooked minute tapioca to the filling. This acts as a binding agent and helps make the sandwiches easier to serve.

Salads

EGG GELATIN SALAD

4 hard cooked eggs, diced	1 tbsp. lemon juice
½ c. chopped celery	½ tsp. salt
1 tbsp. chopped green pepper	¾ c. mayonnaise
	1 tbsp. gelatin
1 tbsp. chopped pimiento	4 tbsp. cold water

Soak gelatin in cold water 5 minutes. Set over hot water until gelatin has melted completely. Cool. Add to mayonnaise and blend this with the other ingredients which have been thoroughly mixed. Rinse mold with cold water and put salad into it. Chill. Serve on salad greens. Garnish with tomatoes, cucumbers and radishes.

DEVILED EGG SALAD

6 hard cooked eggs	Pinch of salt
2 tbsp. grated cheese	Pepper to taste
1 tbsp. cream	Endive or watercress
¼ c. mayonnaise	

Remove yolks from eggs and mash. Add cream, grated cheese, 1 tablespoon mayonnaise, and beat until fluffy. Arrange 3 egg halves on a bed of curly endive so that points of eggs are in. With pastry tube fill yolk mixture back into whites. Garnish with pickled midget onions and radish roses.

454

TOMATO EGG SALAD

Hard cook as many eggs as needed. Chill, remove shells and cut into halves crosswise. Mash yolks, season and blend with a little mayonnaise. Fill back into whites, put halves together and set aside. Heat 3 cups tomatoes with a minced onion, a few celery leaves, 1½ tablespoons sugar, salt and pepper to taste. Cook 15 minutes. Strain and add 2 tablespoons gelatin which has been softened in ¼ cup cold water. Stir until gelatin is dissolved. Add 3 tablespoons lemon juice. Cool. Pour a little of the tomato mixture into mold, chill and when thick arrange the stuffed eggs. Pour remaining tomato-gelatin mixture over them and let congeal. When jellied, serve on shredded cabbage. Garnish with green peppers. Serve with mayonnaise or boiled dressing.

EGG AND LETTUCE SALAD

3 hard cooked eggs, sliced   ½ tsp. salt
1 head lettuce, shredded   1 tsp. minced onion
                                 French dressing

Sprinkle salt over lettuce, add onion and egg and toss lightly together. Marinate in French dressing and chill, or blend with a rather tart cooked dressing.

HAM AND EGG SALAD

3 hard cooked eggs,   10 stuffed olives, chopped
   chopped   Mayonnaise
2 c. diced cooked ham   Salad greens
6 sweet pickles, sliced thinly

Combine all the ingredients lightly, add mayonnaise as desired, and serve on salad greens.

EGGS IN GRASS

3 hard cooked eggs, sliced   French dressing
Watercress or curly endive   Radish roses

Chop salad greens fine. Marinate with French dressing. Arrange on salad dish and in center put slices of egg. Garnish with radish roses.

EGG AND PEPPER RING SALAD

6 eggs, hard cooked   Lettuce
2 green peppers

Arrange alternate slices of hard cooked egg and green pepper on bed of lettuce on large platter. Arrange in form of ring. Pour over a little French dressing and garnish with mayonnaise and pimiento rings.

455

EGG AND SHRIMP SALAD

4 hard cooked eggs	¼ c. chopped olives
1 c. or 1 small can shrimp	½ c. mayonnaise
½ c. diced celery	Salad greens
½ c. peas	

Cut eggs into quarters lengthwise. Place on bed of salad greens, with points toward center. Combine shrimp, celery, peas, olives and mayonnaise. Put a mound of the shrimp mixture into center of each plate. Garnish with mayonnaise.

TOMATOES STUFFED WITH EGG AND CABBAGE SALAD

3 hard cooked eggs, chopped	¼ c. boiled dressing
	¼ c. whipping cream
¾ c. chopped cabbage	4 medium tomatoes
½ tsp. salt	Salad greens

Cut tops from tomatoes, scoop out centers and sprinkle lightly with salt. Invert on tray in refrigerator while remainder of salad is prepared. Cabbage may be shredded finely, but coarsely chopped cabbage is much easier to eat. Combine eggs and cabbage. Whip the cream and salad dressing together. Fold the whipped mixture into the salad, reserving a small amount for garnishing. Fill the salad into the tomatoes. Place tomato on salad greens and serve

EGG SALAD IN CUCUMBER BOATS

2 cucumbers	3 hard cooked eggs, chopped
½ c. Thousand Island dressing	½ c. celery, chopped
	Salad greens
¼ c. radishes, sliced thinly	

Select short, plump cucumbers. They may be pared or not, or they may be made decorative by running a fork the length of the vegetable. This leaves green ridges with white showing through. Cut cucumbers in halves, lengthwise. Scoop out the seeds and a little of the pulp. Put into ice water or wrap in damp cloth in refrigerator to crisp. Prepare egg salad by combining eggs, celery, radishes and dressing. Put cucumber boats on bed of greens and fill with the egg mixture. Garnish with ripe olives and radish roses. The cucumber boats will be easier to eat if they are cut almost through at inch intervals before the salad is filled into them.

JELLIED EGG SALAD IN PEPPERS

3 hard cooked eggs, shelled	3 large green peppers
	1 tbsp. cold water
1 tbsp. gelatin	2 tsp. vinegar
¾ c. tomato juice	1 bay leaf
½ tsp. minced onion	½ tsp. sugar
⅛ tsp. salt	

Remove stem ends and seeds from peppers. Soak gelatin in cold water for 5 minutes. Boil tomato juice, vinegar and seasonings. Add to gelatin and stir until gelatin is dissolved. Strain and cool. Place an egg into each pepper. When tomato jelly is cool pour into pepper around egg. Place in cup to hold upright and set in refrigerator to congeal. When congealed, slice 1/4 inch slices across each pepper and arrange 3 slices on a lettuce leaf or other salad green. Garnish with mayonnaise.

HUMPTY DUMPTY EGGS

4 stuffed eggs
3/4 c. mayonnaise

1 1/2 tbsp. gelatin
4 tbsp. cold water

Soak gelatin in cold water 5 minutes. Melt gelatin over hot water. Cool and add to mayonnaise. Dip the stuffed eggs into the mayonnaise. Decorate with bits of pickle, olive or pimiento to form amusing faces. Serve on lettuce.

EGG CUCUMBER SALAD

6 hard cooked eggs, diced
2 c. diced cucumbers
1 c. diced celery
4 tbsp. chopped pimiento

2 tbsp. chopped onion
1/2 tsp. salt
1/4 tsp. paprika
3/4 c. salad dressing

Combine all ingredients and chill. Serve in large bowl lined with lettuce.

EGG AND TUNA SALAD

4 hard cooked eggs
1 bunch radishes, diced
1 No. 1 can tuna fish
1 small bottle olives

2 tbsp. cream cheese
Mayonnaise to moisten
Salt and pepper to taste

Shell the hard cooked eggs. Cut them in half lengthwise and remove the yolks, leaving the whites intact. Put yolks through a sieve, add cream cheese and 1 tablespoon of mayonnaise. Season with salt and pepper. Add diced radishes. Put mixture into egg whites. Arrange eggs around a platter on a bed of crisp lettuce. Mix the tuna fish with chopped olives and moisten with mayonnaise. Pile lightly in the center.

EGG AND SPINACH SALAD

2 hard cooked eggs put
through a coarse sieve
1 pt. cooked chopped
spinach
1 tbsp. onion, minced

1 green pepper or pimiento
minced
Salt and paprika to taste
Mayonnaise to moisten
1/2 c. celery, chopped

Mix the ingredients well and press into a mold. When ready to serve, remove from mold and garnish the top with hard cooked egg white cut to represent the leaves of a daisy. Place sections of the egg white and salad dressing around the base. If preferred the salad may be molded in individual molds. Chill before serving.

457

JELLIED STUFFED EGGS

4 hard cooked eggs
2½ c. chicken stock or
canned chicken soup
1½ tbsp. gelatin
1 tbsp. finely chopped pickle

1 tbsp. finely chopped stuffed
olives
½ tsp. finely minced onion
1 tbsp. mayonnaise

Cut the eggs into halves lengthwise, remove yolks carefully and put them through a sieve. Add pickle, olives, onion and mayonnaise and blend thoroughly. Fill back into the whites and put halves together. Put each stuffed egg into an individual mold, such as a custard cup, and over it pour a gelatin mixture that has been prepared as follows:

Heat clarified chicken stock to boiling. Season with salt and pepper. Canned chicken soup or a bouillon made with bouillon cubes may be used instead of the stock. Dissolve in the hot stock 1½ tablespoons gelatin which has been softened in 3 tablespoons water. Cool the stock and when cold pour over the eggs.

Unmold the jellied eggs on a bed of salad greens, garnish with stuffed olives and celery curls.

EGG SALAD PIQUANT

4 hard cooked eggs
1 c. pecans
6 stuffed olives, sliced

1 tbsp. pimiento, chopped
Whipped cream dressing

Combine all ingredients and serve in lettuce cups.

VACATION SALAD

4 hard cooked eggs
1 c. diced beets
1 c. diced celery

French dressing
Salad greens

Cut eggs in halves. Remove yolks and put through sieve. Chop whites and combine with beets and celery. Marinate lightly with French dressing. Arrange on beds of shredded lettuce and cover with sieved yolks. Chill.

Chicken Salads

CHICKEN WALNUT SALAD

½ c. walnut meats, broken
1½ c. diced cooked chicken
½ tsp. salt

¾ tbsp. butter
¾ c. diced celery

Melt butter in pan, add walnuts and heat in oven until crisp, stirring often. Combine nuts with other ingredients and chill. Mask with salad dressing or mayonnaise and serve on salad greens.

458

CHICKEN SALAD SUPREME

2 c. cooked chicken	2 tbsp. capers
2 tbsp. chopped stuffed olives	2 tbsp. chopped ripe olives
1 c. diced celery	2 tbsp. chopped mixed pickle
½ c. toasted almonds	2 hard cooked eggs, sliced
	¾ c. mayonnaise

Combine all ingredients lightly. Serve on lettuce or water cress.

CHICKEN SALAD HAWAIIAN

1 c. diced chicken	½ c. nut meats
¾ c. crushed pineapple, drained	2 c. diced celery
	¾ c. mayonnaise

Combine all ingredients and then blend the mayonnaise with them. If desired, ½ cup whipping cream may be whipped and folded into ½ cup mayonnaise and the combination may be used instead of mayonnaise.

FROZEN CHICKEN SALAD

¾ c. cold diced chicken	½ c. whipping cream
¼ c. pecan meats, chopped	½ c. crushed pineapple
	½ c. mayonnaise

Combine the chicken, pineapple and nuts, blending thoroughly. Whip the cream and fold in the mayonnaise. Fold in the chicken mixture. Put into freezing tray and freeze 3–4 hours.

CHICKEN SALAD GELÉE

4 tbsp. gelatin	1 c. cold water or chicken broth
1 c. boiling water or chicken stock	¾ c. mayonnaise
1 tsp. salt	1 c. diced chicken
1 tsp. grated onion	1 tbsp. chopped pimiento
¼ c. lemon juice	2 tbsp. chopped green pepper
¼ tsp. paprika	½ c. chopped celery

Soften the gelatin in ¼ cup cold water, then dissolve in the boiling water or broth. Add the salt, paprika, onion, lemon juice and remaining cold water or cold broth. Cool until the mixture begins to thicken. Beat in the mayonnaise. Fold in the chicken, celery, pimiento and pepper. Chill in loaf pan which has been rinsed with cold water. When firm, unmold and garnish with olives, pimiento strips and mayonnaise.

CHICKEN SALAD PIE

1½ c. diced cooked chicken	½ c. shredded almonds, toasted
½ c. crushed pineapple, drained	½ c. diced celery
	Mayonnaise or cream dressing

Blend all ingredients, chill and fill into individual baked pastry shells.   459

CHICKEN SALAD PIQUANT

6 ripe tomatoes	1/4 c. chopped green pepper
1 c. diced celery	Mayonnaise
1 c. diced chicken	

Peel tomatoes, remove top and scoop out center. Combine all other ingredients, fill into tomato. Top with mayonnaise and garnish with parsley.

CHICKEN AND ORANGE SALAD

2 c. cold diced chicken	1/2 c. salad oil
4 seedless oranges	1/2 tsp. salt
1 tbsp. vinegar	1/8 tsp. pepper
Lettuce	1/4 tsp. paprika

Peel oranges and slice very thin. Blend oil, seasonings and vinegar thoroughly. Mix chicken and oranges lightly, so as not to break up orange slices. Pour salad oil mixture over chicken and let stand in cold place 15–30 minutes.

COLONIAL BOUQUET SALAD

1 c. diced cooked chicken	6 hard cooked eggs
2 c. diced celery	Parsley
1/2 c. mayonnaise	Shredded lettuce

On servings of lettuce arrange a mound of chicken and celery, which has been moistened with mayonnaise. Surround mound with half slices of hard cooked egg to represent lace scallops of colonial bouquet. Insert tiny sprigs of parsley for foliage.

CHICKEN AND NOODLE SALAD

1 c. cold diced chicken	1 tsp. lemon juice
1 c. cold cooked noodles	1/2 tsp. Worcestershire sauce
1/2 c. chopped celery	1/2 c. mayonnaise
1/2 tsp. salt	2 hard cooked eggs, sliced

Mix together all ingredients except hard cooked eggs. Put salad into lettuce cups and garnish with slices of hard cooked eggs.

CHICKEN AND RICE SALAD

1 1/2 c. cold cooked rice	1/8 tsp. pepper
1 c. cooked chicken	3/4 c. salad dressing
1/4 tsp. paprika	Salad greens
1 tsp. salt	

460 Combine all ingredients except lettuce. Blend thoroughly. Chill. Serve in lettuce cups. Garnish with slices of tomatoes.

1 tbsp. butter
1 tbsp. flour
1 c. chicken stock
2 tbsp. gelatin
2 tbsp. cold water
1 tsp. lemon juice
1 c. diced cooked chicken

½ c. Malaga grapes
¼ c. diced celery
¼ c. chopped nuts
4 tbsp. mayonnaise
⅓ c. whipping cream
4 individual pastry shells

Melt butter, add flour and blend. Add chicken stock gradually, stirring until thick. Add gelatin which has been softened in the cold water. Add chicken and season well with salt, pepper and paprika. When cold and somewhat thick, fold in whipped cream, mayonnaise and lemon juice. Pile into pastry shells and chill. Garnish with mayonnaise.

CHICKEN SALAD ROLLS

Slice top from fresh rolls, remove most of crumb from inside of roll, fill with chicken salad, put top back. This is a good way to prepare chicken or egg salad for a picnic. Wrap each roll in wax paper.

CHICKEN SALAD KEOLIAN

1 c. cold diced chicken
3 hard cooked eggs
1 tsp. dry mustard
½ tsp. salt
½ tsp. paprika

½ c. grated cheese
3 tbsp. salad oil
2 tsp. prepared mustard
2 tbsp. vinegar

Separate yolks from whites of eggs. Combine chicken, cheese and chopped white of 1 egg. Put yolks through sieve, add salad oil, mustard, salt, vinegar and paprika and cream until smooth. Add to chicken mixture. Serve on lettuce. Garnish with rings of the egg white.

CHICKEN SALAD LOAF

1 c. cold boiled rice
⅓ c. mayonnaise
1 c. diced cooked chicken

2 tbsp. chopped nut meats
Salt and pepper to taste
1 small can asparagus tips

Mix thoroughly the rice, chicken, asparagus and mayonnaise. Add nuts and seasoning. Pack firmly into mold and chill for 3 hours. Unmold, garnish with salad greens. Serve in slices, with mayonnaise.

461

TOMATO AND CHICKEN SALAD

¾ c. diced cooked chicken	⅔ c. mayonnaise
½ c. string beans, cut	⅔ c. whipping cream
½ c. cold boiled rice	½ tbsp. gelatin
2 tbsp. chopped green	2 tbsp. cold water
pepper	½ tsp. salt
½ c. diced celery	Tomato ice
½ tbsp. minced parsley	

Combine chicken, beans, rice, pepper, celery and parsley. Combine mayonnaise and whipped cream. Soften gelatin in cold water 5 minutes. Then melt it over hot water. Cool. Add salt and combine all ingredients except tomato ice. Pour a layer of tomato ice, previously frozen to mushy stage, into freezing tray. Then arrange layer of chicken salad and cover with another layer of tomato ice. Freeze. Serve in slices on lettuce.

TOMATO ICE

Season tomato juice and add 1 tablespoon gelatin for each 2 cups of juice. Melt gelatin in 1 cup of the tomato juice, add remaining juice and freeze.

OTHER CHICKEN SALAD COMBINATIONS

2 cups diced chicken, ½ teaspoon salt, ⅛ teaspoon pepper, 1½ cup diced celery, 2 hard cooked eggs, sliced or quartered, mayonnaise, lettuce.

Chicken, green peas, celery, pimiento.

Chicken, cucumbers and watercress.

Chicken, stuffed olives, salted almonds and salad greens.

Sauces

HOLLANDAISE SAUCE

½ c. butter	¼ tsp. salt
2 egg yolks	1½ tbsp. lemon juice or
⅓ c. hot water	1 tbsp. vinegar
⅛ tsp. paprika	

Beat egg yolks, adding gradually the softened butter, hot water, and seasonings. Cook in double boiler until mixture coats spoon. Remove from fire and add gradually lemon juice or vinegar, stirring constantly. The trick in making Hollandaise lies in beating the egg yolks thoroughly at first, and in adding the lemon juice after the sauce has been removed from fire.

BÉRNAISE SAUCE

To Hollandaise Sauce add 1 teaspoon minced parsley, 1 teaspoon minced chives and 2 teaspoons spiced or tarragon vinegar.

462

MOCK HOLLANDAISE SAUCE

2 egg yolks
1 c. thick white sauce

3 tbsp. lemon juice
Few grains cayenne

Add the hot white sauce to the beaten eggs, while stirring constantly. Remove from fire, add lemon juice and cayenne.

VINAIGRETTE SAUCE

2 yolks of hard cooked
   eggs
2 tbsp. minced white
   onion

1 tsp. white pepper
3 tbsp. cooking oil
1 tsp. salt
3 tbsp. tarragon vinegar

Press yolks through sieve, add gradually the oil, stirring constantly. When thoroughly mixed, add seasonings and vinegar.

YELLOW SAUCE FOR VEGETABLES

1 c. milk
2 tbsp. flour
2 egg yolks

3 tbsp. butter
½ tsp. salt

Mix the flour to a paste with a little of the milk. Heat the remainder of the milk and add the flour paste, cooking and stirring until thick. Remove from fire and add butter, salt and egg yolks and beat thoroughly. Return to fire for a minute, stirring constantly. This sauce is good over asparagus, peas, cauliflower, or blended with spinach purée.

EGG CREAM FOR VEGETABLES

4 eggs
4 tbsp. grated cheese

4 tbsp. cream or top milk
½ tsp. salt

Beat eggs, add salt and cream and cook in top of double boiler until thickened, stirring constantly. Add cheese. Toss the vegetables in the egg sauce and serve.

YELLOW FOAMY SAUCE FOR VEGETABLES

1 c. milk
1 tbsp. flour
2 tbsp. butter

½ tsp. salt
2 egg yolks and 1 white

Make a paste of the flour and a little of the milk. Heat the remainder of the milk, add the flour paste and cook, stirring constantly, until thickened. Add butter and the slightly beaten egg yolks. Return to low flame for 1 minute. Remove from fire and add the stiffly beaten egg white, beating lightly to make sauce smooth. This is excellent on green or white vegetables.

463

CUSTARD SAUCE

1 c. top milk or thin cream
½ tsp. salt

3 egg yolks, slightly beaten
2 tsp. sugar

Scald the milk, add the sugar and salt, stirring until dissolved. Pour over the beaten yolks and cook in double boiler until mixture coats spoon. Serve hot or cold.

YELLOW SAUCE

3 egg yolks
¾ c. sugar

1 whole egg
1 tsp. vanilla

Beat the yolks and the egg in the top of a double boiler until thick and light. Add the sugar, stirring constantly. Cook until sugar is dissolved and mixture coats spoon. Remove from fire, cool and add flavoring.

SHERRY EGG SAUCE

½ c. sugar
1 egg, separated
2 tbsp. boiling water

4 tbsp. butter
2 tbsp. sweet sherry

Cream butter and sugar. Add egg yolk, sherry and mix thoroughly. Last fold in the beaten egg white. Set bowl containing sauce into hot water, add the boiling water and stir 2 minutes.

SAUCE SUPREME

2 eggs
1 c. whipping cream

1 c. sugar
1 tsp. rum flavoring

Beat the eggs until thick and light. Add sugar gradually, continuing beating. Fold in the stiffly whipped cream and add flavoring. This sauce is excellent on puddings, ice creams and slices of plain cake.

COFFEE SAUCE

¾ c. pulverized coffee
⅓ c. sugar
Pinch salt

3 egg yolks, beaten
2 c. sweet cream

Heat 1 cup cream, add coffee, and let stand, covered, over hot water for 10 minutes. Strain through cloth. Add sugar, salt and remainder of cream and egg yolks. Cook in top of double boiler, stirring constantly, until mixture coats spoon.

464

FRESH MINT FOAMY SAUCE

¼ c. butter
¼ c. strawberry juice (or other fruit juice)

2 tbsp. chopped fresh mint
1 c. powdered sugar
1 egg, well beaten

Cream butter and sugar until fluffy. Add beaten egg, then fruit juice and beat with Dover beater until light. Add mint about 10 minutes before serving. This sauce is good on fruit short cakes.

CHICKEN SAUCE

2 tbsp. butter
2 tbsp. flour
1 c. chicken stock

1 egg yolk
¼ tsp. salt
¼ tsp. pepper

Melt butter in a sauce pan. Add flour and stir to a smooth paste. Add stock gradually, stirring constantly and continue stirring and cooking until slightly thickened. Add slightly beaten egg yolk. Stir until thick.

SAVORY CHICKEN SAUCE

1 c. chicken stock
½ bay leaf
2 tbsp. butter
½ c. milk
1 slice onion
Dash pepper

1 sprig parsley
1 small carrot
2 tbsp. flour
6 peppercorns
¼ tsp. salt

Cook stock 20 minutes with onion, carrot, bay leaf, parsley and peppercorns. Strain and measure. If necessary add water to make ½ cup. Melt butter in sauce pan. Add flour and stir to a smooth paste. Add chicken stock and milk gradually, stirring constantly until thickened. Add salt and pepper. Serve with fried chicken, croquettes, chicken loaf, or patties.

SUPREME SAUCE FOR CHICKEN

6 tbsp. butter
1 pt. fresh mushrooms, sliced
Livers of the chickens, chopped

1 tsp. minced onion
¼ c. boiled lean ham, chopped
1 tsp. parsley, chopped
Salt and pepper
4 slices pineapple

Fry the minced onion lightly in the butter. Add the fresh mushrooms. Smother until the mushrooms are nearly dry. Add the chopped liver, ham and parsley. Cook 2–3 minutes. Season to taste. Cover and set in a warm place. Broil the chicken. When almost done broil the slices of pineapple lightly. Arrange chickens on hot platter. Add drippings to the sauce and pour over chickens. Garnish with the slices of pineapple.

465

YELLOW BECHAMEL SAUCE

1½ c. chicken stock
1 tbsp. minced onion
1 tbsp. minced carrot
½ bay leaf
Sprig of parsley
6 peppercorns

4 tbsp. butter
4 tbsp. flour
1 c. milk, scalded
½ tsp. salt
3 egg yolks, beaten

Cook onion, carrot, bay leaf, parsley and peppercorns in stock 20 minutes. Strain. Melt butter in pan, blend in the flour and then add gradually the hot stock, stirring constantly. Add the scalded milk and let come to boil. Pour a little of the sauce over the beaten egg yolks, stirring constantly. Add yolks to remainder of the sauce and serve.

HOW'S AND WHY'S
IN COOKING EGGS

To Boil or Not to Boil

EGGS cooked in the shell, commonly known as boiled eggs, are not literally boiled when they are at their best. Egg white coagulates at 140°–149° F., egg yolk at 149°–158° F., and whole egg at 149°–158° F. So it is hardly necessary to use such strenuous measures as heating eggs to the boiling temperature (212° F.) in order to cook them.

As a matter of fact, when gently cooked the egg rewards the cook by being delicately tender. But when boiled it literally turns tough, for high temperatures toughen every kind of protein. The white, being almost pure protein, suffers more from extremely high cooking temperatures than does the yolk with its high fat content.

Manufacturers of much of the new egg cookery equipment have taken these facts into account and have designed egg cookers which cook the egg without overheating it. Some of them use steam. Others heat the egg just to the boiling temperature, and as soon as this temperature is reached the heat goes off. The time during which the water around the egg is at a high temperature is so short that the egg does not become tough.

Convenient as it is to use special equipment, such equipment is not essential. The common household method of cooking eggs gives excellent results. Any metal container, from cup to saucepan, answers the purpose.

One way to cook eggs is to pour boiling water over them in the pan, turn the flame *very* low, so low that the water just simmers, and leave the eggs in the hot water the required time. For soft-cooking,   467 this means about three minutes; for medium, about five; for hard, fifteen to twenty minutes. If the eggs are cold, as when they have just been taken from the refrigerator, it is better to have the water merely warm rather than boiling, for boiling water causes the eggshells to crack. The exact time for cooking eggs to a certain stage varies with the size of the egg, the temperature of the egg at the beginning of the cooking period, the proportion of water to eggs, and the temperature of the water. One or two trials with the equipment at hand will serve as a guide for future timing.

Another way to get satisfactory results is to cover the eggs with cold water, bring it just to a boil, and then turn the flame down so that the water just simmers. The eggs are soft-cooked or coddled when the water reaches the boiling stage. For medium cooking they are left in the water two to five minutes, depending on how firm they are desired. For hard-cooking they are left in for fifteen to twenty minutes.

When eggs in the shell are cooked for more than fifteen or twenty minutes, a dark ring forms where the white and the yolk touch. This is due to the natural combination of the iron in the yolk with the sulfur in the white to form ferrous sulfide, which is dark in color. It is entirely harmless, but it detracts from the attractive appearance of the cooked egg. In general, the higher the cooking temperature and the longer the time of cooking, the more darkening takes place.

Much, and often all, of this color change can be avoided if the egg is plunged into cold water as soon as it is cooked. This lowers the temperature and reduces the pressure and thus prevents the formation of ferrous sulfide. Cooling the eggs quickly immediately after cooking also makes it easier to remove the shell smoothly.

An eggshell cracks when a cold egg is suddenly put into boiling water. The air in the air cell at the large end of the egg expands so quickly under these conditions that it cannot escape rapidly enough through the pores of the shell and the egg bursts. Eggs which have been stored in waterglass or which have been shell-protected with oil sometimes crack because the pores have been sealed and the air cannot escape. The cracking can be avoided if the shell is punctured with a needle or pin before the egg is put into the cooking water. The little hole simply gives the air in the egg an avenue of escape when it begins to expand with the heat.

Hard-cooked eggs, stuffed, sliced, halved, quartered or whole, form the basis for many delicious, nutritious dishes. The delicate flavor of eggs blends perfectly with that of almost any other food, and stuffed eggs have a peculiarly tempting attractiveness.

Some stuffings that are especially good in hard-cooked eggs are mashed yolk seasoned with mayonnaise; soft cheese; minced sardines; mashed yolk with mustard; anchovies with parsley and cream sauce; minced onions and mushrooms browned in butter; green and red peppers, cheese and egg yolk; finely ground chicken or other meat; finely ground, seasoned fish; mashed vegetables (asparagus, peas, spinach); caviar with lemon juice; savory bread with dressing; chopped nuts and cheese.

Entrées

CREAMED EGGS

(Basic Recipe)

4 hard cooked eggs, halved, quartered or sliced	½ tsp. salt
	1½ c. milk, scalded
	3 tbsp. flour
3 tbsp. butter	⅛ tsp. white pepper

Melt butter, add flour and stir. Gradually add the hot milk, stirring to prevent lumping. Season. Add eggs to sauce or pour sauce over eggs on deep platter.

VARIATIONS OF CREAMED EGGS

To above recipe add one of the following

½ tin sardines	½ c. diced cooked meat
½ c. shredded chipped beef	¼ c. diced cheese
	¼ c. flaked fish (salmon, cod, etc.)
2 tbsp. chopped green pepper and 1 tbsp. chopped pimiento	½ c. peas
	6 ripe olives, pitted and chopped

EGGS GOLDENROD

4 hard cooked eggs	1½ c. milk, scalded
3 tbsp. butter or bacon fat	3 tbsp. flour
½ tsp. salt	⅛ tsp. pepper
4 slices toast	

Remove yolks from eggs and put them through sieve. Chop the whites. Make white sauce of milk, flour, butter, salt and pepper. Add chopped whites to sauce. Pour over toast. Put a mound of sieved yolks over each serving. Serve hot, garnished with parsley.

CREAMED MUSHROOMS AND EGGS

2 tbsp. butter	3 hard cooked eggs
½ tsp. salt	2 c. milk
¼ tsp. paprika	⅛ tsp. pepper
4 tbsp. flour	2 c. mushrooms

Melt butter, add flour, salt, pepper and paprika and stir until smooth. Add milk and cook until thick and smooth, stirring constantly. Add mushrooms and eggs, cut in slices. If fresh mushrooms are used, wash, peel caps, slice and fry in butter for 10 minutes. Canned mushrooms need only be drained of their liquor before being added to sauce.

CREAMED EGGS AND CELERY ON TOAST

1½ c. milk	¾ c. diced celery
3 tbsp. butter	4 hard cooked eggs
4 tbsp. flour	4 slices toast
½ tsp. salt	

Melt butter, add flour and then milk, stirring constantly. Cook until thick. Season and add celery. Quarter eggs, place on toast points, and pour celery mixture over. Garnish with parsley and serve.

EGGS A LA KING

6 hard cooked eggs, sliced	½ tsp. salt
3 tbsp. butter	3 tbsp. chopped pimiento
3 tbsp. flour	6 tbsp. chopped green peppers
1½ c. milk	½ c. mushrooms, sliced

Make white sauce of flour, butter, milk, and seasonings. Add other ingredients, heat, and serve on toast or in noodle ring.

EGGS HUNTINGTON

6 hard cooked eggs, sliced	½ c. buttered crumbs
2 c. thick white sauce	½ tsp. salt
1 c. diced American cheese	⅛ tsp. white pepper

In buttered baking dish arrange layers of sliced eggs, cheese, seasonings and white sauce. Sprinkle top generously with crumbs and cheese and bake in moderate oven (350° F.) until brown.

NOODLE OYSTER LOAF WITH CREAMED EGGS

¼ lb. noodles	3 eggs, beaten
¾ c. milk	½ pt. oysters
¼ tsp. salt	

Cook the noodles in boiling salted water 15 minutes. Drain. Combine with milk, beaten eggs and oysters and mix thoroughly. Season and pour into buttered pan which has been dusted with flour or sifted crumbs. Set in pan of hot water and bake in moderate oven (350° F.) for 45 minutes. Unmold on platter and slice. On each slice place a hard cooked egg cut into halves lengthwise, mask with white sauce and garnish with parsley and paprika.

4 hard cooked eggs, sliced
1/4 lb. spaghetti
2 tbsp. flour
1 small onion, chopped

2 tbsp. cooking oil or fat
1 c. tomatoes
1/2 tsp. salt
1/4 tsp. pepper

Cook spaghetti in boiling salted water until tender. Drain. Fry the onion in the fat for a few minutes. Add flour to make a paste, stirring to keep it smooth. Add the tomatoes, heat thoroughly, stirring until thickened. Pour over the spaghetti. Add the hard cooked eggs, reserving some of the slices for garnishing.

SCALLOPED EGGS AND SHRIMP

1 c. milk
2 tbsp. flour
2 tbsp. butter
1/2 tsp. salt

1 small can, or 1 c. shrimp
4 eggs, hard cooked
1/2 c. bread crumbs

Make white sauce of milk, flour, butter and salt. In buttered casserole alternate thin layers of white sauce, shrimp, sliced eggs and crumbs. Brown in moderate oven. Garnish top with a few whole shrimp and slices of egg.

SCALLOPED EGGS, SALMON AND MACARONI

1 No. 1 can salmon
4 hard cooked eggs, sliced
1/2 c. bread crumbs
1 c. milk

2 tbsp. flour
2 tbsp. butter
1/2 tsp. salt
1/4 lb. macaroni

Cook macaroni in boiling salted water until tender. Drain. Make a sauce of the milk, flour butter and salt. Into a greased baking dish put a thin layer of the sauce, then a layer of macaroni, and then salmon. On top of the salmon put a layer of sliced eggs, and then a few crumbs. Repeat until all ingredients have been put into the dish. Cover top lightly with cream sauce, then sprinkle with crumbs. Bake in a moderately hot oven (400° F.) until thoroughly heated and crumbs are browned.

SCALLOPED EGGS AND OYSTERS

3 tbsp. flour
3 tbsp. butter
1 1/2 c. milk
4 hard cooked eggs, sliced

1/2 pt. oysters
1/2 c. buttered crumbs
1 tbsp. minced parsley
3/4 tsp. salt

Make white sauce of flour, butter and milk. Add the parsley and salt. Cover the bottom of a buttered baking dish with a thin layer of the sauce. Arrange a layer of sliced eggs, then a layer of oysters and another of eggs. Pour the remainder of the sauce over all, sprinkle the top with the crumbs and bake in hot oven (425° F.) until crumbs are brown, about 15 minutes.

471

EGGS IN TOMATO SAUCE

5 hard cooked eggs, cut
into halves or quarters
2 c. canned tomatoes

1 tsp. salt
4 tbsp. flour
3 tbsp. butter or bacon fat

Melt the butter or bacon fat. Add flour and salt, stirring to make smooth paste. Add the tomatoes gradually, stirring. Cook until thickened. Pour over the eggs, or add eggs to the sauce, and serve.

EGGS ITALIENNE

¼ lb. spaghetti
2 tbsp. fat
3 tbsp. chopped green
pepper
1 small onion, chopped

½ tsp. salt
2 c. medium white sauce
4 hard cooked eggs
½ c. grated cheese

Cook spaghetti in boiling salted water until tender. Drain. Cook the fat, pepper, and onion and salt together in skillet for 10 minutes. Add to hot white sauce. Put spaghetti on hot platter, arrange sliced eggs on spaghetti, pour sauce over all and sprinkle with cheese. Put under low broiler flame a few moments to melt cheese.

EGGS TETRAZZINI

4 hard cooked eggs
½ c. mushrooms
¼ c. blanched almonds
¼ lb. spaghetti
1 tbsp. minced onion
4 tbsp. butter

½ c. milk
½ c. diced celery
1 tsp. Worcestershire sauce
1 tbsp. flour
1 tbsp. chopped green pepper
Salt to taste

Cook spaghetti in boiling salted water until tender. Brown almonds in butter. Remove almonds from pan and brown vegetables. Add flour and stir until slightly thickened, then add milk. Chop 3 eggs and add to vegetables. To serve, pile spaghetti in center of hot platter, surround with vegetable-egg mixture, and garnish with browned almonds and slices of eggs.

BAKED PEAS AND EGGS

2 tbsp. butter
4 tbsp. flour
½ tsp. salt
2 c. milk

3 hard cooked eggs
1 tbsp. prepared mustard
1 can peas, drained
Buttered bread crumbs

Melt the butter and add the flour. Stir until smooth. Add the salt, mustard and milk and cook, stirring constantly, until the sauce thickens. Add the peas and the eggs which have been cut up coarsely. Turn into a buttered baking dish and top with bread crumbs. Bake in a moderate oven (375° F.) until lightly browned.

472

Cut hard cooked eggs in half lengthwise. Remove yolks, mash and season them. For variety, some may be seasoned with Roquefort cheese, some with anchovy paste or caviar, horseradish, mustard or plain mayonnaise. Arrange on bed of curly endive, watercress, or lettuce. Garnish platter with pie-shaped pieces of cheese, cold ham and radish roses. This platter is excellent served with potato salad.

STUFFED EGGS ALLEMANDE

4 eggs, hard cooked	2 c. bread crumbs, soaked in ½
1 egg	c. milk
⅛ tsp. pepper	1 tsp. salt
1 tbsp. minced green	1 tsp. minced onion
pepper	

Remove yolks from hard cooked eggs, mash and add to the stuffing for eggs which has been prepared as follows: Soak bread crumbs in milk until they have absorbed all the liquid. Add the salt, pepper, onion, green pepper and the egg. Mix thoroughly, fill the egg whites with this mixture. Spread the remaining stuffing in a thin layer on the bottom of buttered baking dish. Place the stuffed egg halves on top and bake in moderate oven (350° F.) for 20 minutes. Garnish with parsley.

ROYAL EGG FRITTERS

4 hard cooked eggs	½ c. ground chicken, seasoned
½ c. mayonnaise	2 tbsp. minced parsley

Cut eggs lengthwise, remove yolks and stuff whites with ground chicken. Allow a tablespoon of meat for each half egg. Dip each egg in batter and fry in deep fat (375° F.) until golden brown. Cream the yolks with mayonnaise, add parsley and serve as an accompaniment. Flaked fish, ground veal, pork or beef may be substituted for the chicken.

EGG ROLL

1 c. flour	½ c. milk
2 tbsp. grated cheese	¼ tsp. salt
2 tsp. baking powder	2 tbsp. shortening

Make biscuit dough of above ingredients, cutting in cheese with shortening. Roll out to about ¼ inch thickness and spread with the following mixture:

EGG FILLING

1 c. milk	3 tbsp. butter
½ tsp. salt	3 tbsp. flour
	4 hard cooked eggs

Make a thick white sauce of the flour, milk, salt and butter. Add the chopped hard cooked eggs. When cool, spread on the biscuit dough. Roll the dough jelly-roll fashion and cut into half-inch slices. Place slices cut side up in greased pan and bake in hot oven 15 minutes. Serve with cheese sauce.

473

CHEESE SAUCE

1½ c. milk	1 tbsp. butter
½ tsp. salt	1½ tbsp. flour
4 tbsp. grated cheese	

Make white sauce, adding cheese last. Pour over egg rolls and garnish with chopped parsley and paprika.

RAGOUT OF EGGS

6 hard cooked eggs	½ c. milk
2 c. mushrooms, sliced	Salt
3 tbsp. butter	Paprika
1 tbsp. flour	1 tsp. minced onion

Melt the butter and add the mushrooms and onion and fry lightly. Moisten the flour in a little of the cold milk, add to the mushrooms and stir well. When well mixed, add the remaining milk, salt and paprika. Simmer until the mixture thickens. Cut the eggs in halves lengthwise, removing the yolks. Place the whites hollow side up on a hot platter. Fill the centers with the mushroom mixture. Place a few mushrooms around the eggs for garnish. Put yolks through a sieve and sprinkle them lightly over the mixture. Garnish with parsley and serve at once.

DEVILED EGGS WITH RICE

2 c. boiled rice	1 tsp. chopped pimiento
6 hard cooked eggs	1 tsp. chopped parsley
½ tsp. mustard	Vinegar or mayonnaise
1 tsp. salt	Pimiento or tomato sauce
1 tsp. chopped pickle	

Press the rice into a greased round mold and set over hot water until ready to use. Cut the eggs in half lengthwise and remove yolks. Mash the yolks with seasonings and add enough vinegar or mayonnaise to moisten. Fill egg cavities with this mixture. Turn the rice out on a hot plate, arrange the eggs around it, garnish with strips of pimiento and green pepper and serve hot with pimiento or tomato sauce.

STUFFED EGGS A LA KING

6 hard cooked eggs	3 tbsp. flour
2 tbsp. grated cheese	2 tbsp. minced pepper
1 tsp. vinegar	2 c. milk
¼ tsp. mustard	2 tbsp. chopped pimiento
Salt and cayenne	⅛ tsp. paprika
4 tbsp. butter	Toast

Cut eggs into halves. Remove the yolks and mash them with the cheese, vinegar, mustard, salt and cayenne. Stuff the whites with the mixture and place in a hot dish. Melt the fat, add pepper and pimiento and cook slowly for 5 minutes. Stir in the flour which has been mixed to a paste with a little cold milk. Then add the milk. Cook until thickened, season to taste, pour over the eggs and garnish with toast points.

474

EGG AND FISH LOAF

3 hard cooked eggs
1 c. cooked fish, flaked
1 c. cold boiled rice
1 tsp. minced onion

3 thin slices bacon cut into bits
Salt and paprika to taste
½ c. milk
1 egg, slightly beaten

Butter a baking mold. Fry bacon lightly. Add onion and then fish and rice. Combine milk and egg and add to first mixture. Season to taste. Slice one of the eggs in thin rings and place around the side of the mold for a garnish. Press the fish mixture into the mold and bake for 30 minutes in moderate oven (350° F.). Turn out on a hot platter and serve with tomato sauce.

BAKED STUFFED EGGS

6 hard cooked eggs
1 tbsp. butter
3 uncooked egg yolks
Salt and pepper

1 tsp. minced parsley
1 c. sour cream

Cut eggs into halves crosswise. Remove yolks. To the yolks add melted butter, 1 uncooked egg yolk, parsley, salt and pepper to taste and 2 tablespoons sour cream. Mix thoroughly and fill into egg whites. Put halves together and place eggs into buttered baking dish. Beat remaining uncooked egg yolks with sour cream, add a pinch of salt and pour over stuffed egg. Set into pan of hot water. Bake in moderate oven (350° F.) 30 minutes.

EGG CUTLETS

2 hard cooked eggs
1 c. milk
3 tbsp. flour
1 tbsp. butter
3 tbsp. grated cheese

Minced onion
Parsley or celery to taste
Salt
Pepper

Make a white sauce of the butter, flour and milk. Put the eggs through a coarse sieve. Combine the eggs and other ingredients with the white sauce and let the mixture stand until cold. Shape into small cutlets. Beat an egg and add 3 tablespoons of milk. Dip the cutlet into the egg mixture, roll in bread crumbs and fry in deep fat. Drain on soft paper. Serve on hot platter with a mound of peas in the center.

SCALLOPED HAM AND EGGS

4 hard cooked eggs, sliced
¾ c. buttered bread
    crumbs
3 tbsp. butter

3 tbsp. flour
1½ c. milk, scalded
½ tsp. salt
1 c. cooked diced ham

Melt butter and add flour, stirring until thickened. Gradually add the hot milk, stirring to keep from lumping. Add salt. Into a buttered baking dish put a thin layer of crumbs, then a layer of ham, then one of egg slices, and then one of cream sauce. Repeat until all of the ingredients are used, topping with a thin layer of crumbs. Brown in moderate oven (375° F.).

475

EGGS AND ANCHOVIES IN MUSTARD SAUCE (Swedish)

½ c. milk, scalded   ½ c. cream, scalded
2 tbsp. butter   2 tbsp. flour
½ tsp. salt   1 tsp. dry mustard
4–5 anchovies   3–4 hard cooked eggs

Melt butter in top of double boiler, add flour and seasoning. Stir until well blended. Add scalded cream gradually, stirring constantly until thick and creamy. Pour out on deep platter and put the halves of eggs on top of the sauce. Garnish with anchovies.

EGGS AND ASPARAGUS AU GRATIN

1½ c. milk   6 hard cooked eggs
4 tbsp. flour   2 bunches asparagus tips
¾ tsp. salt   ¼ tsp. celery salt
3 tbsp. butter   ½ c. buttered bread crumbs
½ c. grated cheese

Make white sauce of milk, flour, butter and salt. Add the cheese. Sprinkle bottom of buttered baking dish with crumbs. Arrange alternate layers of asparagus, cut into inch lengths, and sliced eggs. Pour cheese sauce over all. Sprinkle top lightly with crumbs and set into a hot oven (400° F.) until crumbs are browned and mixture is heated through.

CRÉOLE EGGS

4 hard cooked eggs, sliced   Salt
  or quartered   2 tbsp. butter
3 tbsp. flour   ¾ c. tomatoes
4 tbsp. chopped green   2 tbsp. chopped onion
  pepper

Cook pepper and onion in butter for 5 minutes. Add flour, blending smoothly and stirring constantly. Add tomatoes and salt and cook until well thickened. Pour over eggs.

CURRIED EGGS I

3 hard cooked eggs cut   ¼ tsp. curry powder
  into quarters   2 tbsp. butter
¼ tsp. salt   2 tbsp. flour
⅛ tsp. pepper   1 c. hot milk

476 Make sauce of butter, flour and hot milk. Add seasonings. Put eggs into sauce, heat and serve on toast.

4 hard cooked eggs
2 tbsp. butter
2 tbsp. flour
1 tbsp. minced onion

1 c. stock
1 tsp. curry powder
½ tsp. salt
¾ c. cooked rice

Separate yolks from whites. Chop whites. Put yolks through a sieve. Make sauce of butter, onion, flour and stock. Add seasonings and rice and then chopped egg whites. Fill into noodle nests or pastry shells and top with sieved yolk.

EGG CASSEROLE

6 hard cooked eggs, sliced
¾ tsp. salt
1 can clear chicken soup, heated
2 tbsp. butter

3 tomatoes, sliced
¼ tsp. pepper
12 large soda crackers, rolled fine
½ c. grated cheese

Arrange eggs and tomatoes in alternate layers in buttered baking dish. Pour hot chicken soup over ⅔ of the cracker crumbs. Add 1 teaspoon butter and beat until smooth. Add cheese and mix well. Pour over eggs and tomatoes. Sprinkle with remaining cracker crumbs, dot with butter and bake 20 minutes in hot oven (425° F.).

BAKED EGGS AU GRATIN

6 eggs, hard cooked
2 tbsp. butter
2 tbsp. flour
1 c. milk
¼ c. bread crumbs

½ c. American cheese
¼ tsp. salt
¼ c. chopped cooked ham or fish
½ tbsp. chopped parsley

Shell eggs and cut into halves or quarters. Make cream sauce of butter, flour, milk and salt. Grind cheese and add ¼ cup to the cream sauce with the ham or fish and parsley. Put a tablespoonful of the sauce mixture into each ramekin if individual ones are used, or a thin layer in a buttered shallow baking dish. Arrange the eggs in the dish and cover with the remainder of sauce. Sprinkle with crumbs and the remainder of the grated cheese. Bake in moderate oven (350° F.) until cheese is melted (15–20 minutes).

HOT STUFFED EGGS

4 hard cooked eggs
1 tbsp. cream

1 c. tomato sauce
Salt and pepper

Shell hard cooked eggs, cut them lengthwise and remove yolks. Put yolks through sieve, season with cream, salt and pepper and fill back into whites. Arrange 3 halves on buttered toast points, and pour hot tomato sauce over them.

477

Hard cooked eggs may be the beginning of high adventure for the imaginative cook.

STUFFED EGGS

Remove yolks from hard cooked eggs, mash yolks and add seasonings or various minced stuffings, and fill into whites. Stuffed eggs may be served hot or cold. Fillings for them may be made of

    Anchovies, parsley and cream sauce
    Chopped onions and mushrooms browned in butter
    Green and red peppers, cheese and egg yolk
    Finely ground chicken or other meat
    Finely ground seasoned fish
    Mashed vegetables (asparagus, peas, spinach)
    Caviar with lemon juice
    Savory bread dressing
    Chopped nuts and cheese

CREAM NOODLE RING

3 eggs, slightly beaten   ¾ c. cream
¼ lb. noodles   1 tsp. salt

Cook noodles in boiling salted water. Drain and add cream. Add eggs. Butter a ring mold and dust it with fine dry crumbs. Put noodle mixture into ring, set into pan of hot water and bake 45 minutes in moderate oven (350° F.). Unmold on hot platter and fill center with chicken or eggs à la king.

478

EGGS AND ASPARAGUS IN SPAGHETTI RING

½ lb. spaghetti
1 c. liver, ground
1 clove garlic, chopped fine
½ c. thick cream

1 pimiento, chopped fine
½ tsp. salt
¼ tsp. pepper
2 eggs, beaten light

Filling

1 bunch asparagus, cooked
2 tbsp. butter
2 tbsp. flour
3 hard cooked eggs

1½ c. milk
½ tsp. salt
¼ tsp. pepper

Cook spaghetti in boiling, salted water until tender; drain. Soak liver in cold water, then place in boiling, salted water, cook gently 15 minutes. Put through meat grinder. Add to the spaghetti; also the garlic, pimiento, salt, pepper, beaten eggs, and cream. Mix and place in a ring mold. Place in a shallow pan of hot water and bake 1 hour. Turn out on platter. Melt the butter for the filling, add the flour, pour on the milk. Cook until thickened, stirring constantly. Season with salt and pepper and stir in the cooked asparagus. Fill center of spaghetti ring with creamed asparagus and top with slices of hard cooked eggs.

Poached or Pocketed Eggs

Many a romantic figure was so fond of poached eggs as to have a way of preparing them named after him (or her)—eggs à la So-and-So. Cookbooks of famous chefs are full of such glamorous names as those of the great Italian actress Duse, the French dramatist Dumas, the English statesman Gladstone, the French composer Gounod, the English general Marlborough and the admiral Nelson, the banker Rothschild, the explorer Stanley, the novelists Scott and Sand, to say nothing of many royal personages.

Poaching is really cooking the egg, without a shell, in water or steam. It corresponds to "boiling" the egg except that the shell has been removed. In a well poached egg the yolk should be covered with white, although the covering over the yolk may be merely a thin veil. The word *poach* comes from the French word *pocher* which means "to place in a pocket." In real poaching the yolk is pocketed or pouched in the white.

As in all egg cookery, the most important rule to remember in poaching eggs is to cook them just under the boiling temperature so as to keep them delicately tender.

There are at least three distinct methods for poaching eggs directly in water. For the first two methods, use a rather shallow pan holding 479

a generous amount of water. Each egg is first carefully broken into a cup or small dish and then slipped into the poaching water.

For one method, add one tablespoonful of salt for each quart of water. Let the water come to a boil, drop in three or four eggs, and then set the pan off the flame where the water will remain hot but will not boil. Cover the pan and let the eggs remain in the hot water three minutes or more, depending on how firm the eggs are to be cooked. Lift the eggs out with a skimmer, trim and serve.

The second method is similar to the first, except that instead of a tablespoonful of salt, one teaspoonful of salt and one tablespoonful of vinegar are added to each quart of water. The eggs are then cooked as in the first method. Shape the eggs gently with a skimmer while they are cooking so that the poached egg has an elongated shape. The vinegar hastens the coagulation of the egg and helps to keep the white snowy and tender.

A third method of poaching is sometimes spoken of as the French method, though there is no reason to believe that it is peculiar to France. Instead of a shallow pan use a rather deep large one. Add a teaspoonful of salt and a tablespoonful of vinegar to each quart of water. When the water has reached the boiling point, stir it around and around until a cone-shaped hollow, or a vortex, forms in the water. Into this hollow drop the egg. Continue stirring so as to keep the water in circular motion. The movement of the water gives the egg its attractive shape. The disadvantage of this method is that only one egg can be poached at a time.

Eggs may be poached in milk, meat or vegetable stock or sauces. When this is done the liquid is thickened and used as a sauce over the eggs. A poached egg in clear broth is a popular luncheon dish. Among chefs such eggs are generally known as "dropped eggs."

The easiest way to be sure that each poached egg will be attractive in shape is to use a poacher, many types of which are available. In most cases the cover of the poacher is so designed that the steam which condenses on the lid drips back into the lower part of the pan instead of on the eggs. Many poachers are excellent for steaming custards and other dishes for which the directions say, "Set in a pan of water and bake."

Poached Eggs

POACHED EGGS CAROL

¼ lb. fine-cut noodles   4 poached eggs
1 c. paprika sauce

Cook noodles in boiling salted water until tender. Drain and blanch them. Arrange on hot platter, pour over the hot paprika sauce and place poached eggs on top. (See Sauces)

POACHED EGGS MARLBOROUGH

Cut thick slices of green tomato. Dip each slice in beaten egg, then into sifted bread crumbs. Fry in butter. When nicely browned place a poached egg on each slice.

POACHED EGGS NANTUA

Arrange poached eggs on buttered toast. Over them pour a cream sauce to which shrimp and mushrooms have been added. Allow ½ cup shrimp and ¼ cup mushrooms for each cup of cream sauce.

POACHED EGGS DUMAS

Arrange poached eggs on toast, cover with horseradish sauce, sprinkle with grated Parmesan cheese and dot with butter. Brown quickly under broiler flame and serve. (See Sauces)

JAPANESE POACHED EGGS

1 c. rice   1 tbsp. chopped celery
1 c. cream sauce   6 eggs
1 tsp. grated onion

Cook the rice in boiling salted water. Drain. Add the cream sauce which has been made from 1 cup milk, 2 tablespoons flour and 2 tablespoons butter. Season to taste. Add the grated onion and the chopped celery. Arrange on hot platter and put poached eggs on top.

481

POACHED EGGS WALSH

Spread slices of smoked beef tongue lightly with prepared mustard. Sprinkle with bread crumbs and brown under broiler. Place a poached egg on top of each slice, put a tablespoonful of tomato catsup on each egg, sprinkle with grated cheese and bread crumbs and brown quickly.

POACHED EGGS DUSE

4 patty shells	¼ c. grated cheese
4 poached eggs	½ c. mushrooms
¼ lb. spaghetti	¼ c. onions
1 c. tomato sauce	2 tbsp. butter
¼ c. shredded ham	

Cook the spaghetti in boiling salted water until tender. Drain and blanch. Brown the mushrooms and onions in the butter. Add to the spaghetti, and then add tomato sauce, ham and grated cheese. Blend thoroughly and heat. Fill into hot patty shells and place a poached egg on top of each.

POACHED EGGS ALICE

Place poached eggs on buttered toast, cover with Hollandaise sauce, decorate with small sardines. Garnish with flowerlets of cooked cauliflower.

POACHED EGGS ARGENTINE

Fry thick slices of eggplant in butter. Place on each slice a tablespoon of highly seasoned tomato sauce, and top with poached egg.

POACHED EGGS ARCHDUKE

Cook ¼ pound finely cut noodles in boiling salted water until tender. Drain and blanch. Toss lightly in skillet with 3 tablespoons butter and add ¾ to 1 cup shredded cooked ham. Arrange noodles on platter, put eggs on top of noodles and cover with paprika sauce. (See Sauces)

POACHED EGGS BUCKINGHAM

Arrange poached eggs on buttered toast. Pour over cream sauce to which has been added Swiss cheese cut into cubes. Place under broiler for a few moments to melt cheese.

POACHED EGGS FLORIDA

Form round cakes of mashed sweet potato and fry in butter. On each cake place a poached egg. Cover with tomato sauce and serve.

POACHED EGGS FRENEUSE

Cook white turnips in boiling salted water until tender. Mash and season with salt and butter. Arrange in serving dish. Place poached eggs on turnips, cover with white sauce and serve.

Poaching eggs in the modern manner.

FLORENTINE POACHED EGGS

2 c. spinach, cooked
2 tbsp. butter
½ c. cream sauce

¼ c. grated cheese
4 eggs

Toss the spinach in butter, arrange on hot dish. Put eggs on spinach and pour cream sauce over. Sprinkle with grated cheese and melted butter. Place for a moment under broiler flame to brown.

POACHED EGGS NOVA SCOTIA

Place poached eggs on codfish cakes which have been fried. Serve with tomato sauce.

POACHED EGGS VIRGINIA

2 c. corn (1 No. 2 can)
½ c. flour
½ c. milk
2 eggs, beaten

½ tsp. salt
Dash of pepper
Fat for frying
Poached eggs

Combine all ingredients, except poached eggs, shape into cakes, drop into hot fat to fry. Drain and arrange on hot platter. Put poached egg on top of each cake and cover with cream sauce. Buttered green peas are a good accompaniment for this dish.

POACHED EGGS ROMAINE

On a hot platter arrange a bed of cooked spinach. Cover with tomato sauce. Arrange poached eggs on spinach and over them sprinkle grated cheese and melted butter. Put under broiler flame to melt cheese and brown slightly.

POACHED EGGS STANLEY

Arrange poached eggs on buttered toast. Pour horseradish sauce over the eggs. Garnish with fried bananas.

POACHED EGGS SOUTHERN

Drain liquid from a can of hominy. Brown the hominy in butter. Season. Arrange on a hot platter. Make small depressions in the layer of hominy. Fill depressions with shredded chicken, ham or other meat. Over the meat place poached eggs. Serve with cream sauce to which green peas have been added.

EGGS BENEDICTINE I

4 eggs	4 English muffins toasted, or
1 small can flaked codfish	pastry shells
or salmon	1½ c. milk
3 tbsp. flour	3 tbsp. butter
½ tsp. salt	

Make white sauce of milk, flour, butter and salt. Add the flaked fish. Fill this into the toasted muffins or pastry shells and on top place a poached egg. If desired, garnish with mushroom caps that have been browned in butter.

EGGS BENEDICTINE II

On a toasted English muffin put a thin slice of broiled ham, then a poached egg and pour Hollandaise sauce over all.

POACHED EGGS SUZETTE

Cut baked potatoes in halves, scoop out the potato, mash with some cream, butter and seasonings and refill potato shells, leaving a small depression into which put a poached egg. Cover with white sauce to which ½ cup grated cheese has been added, sprinkle lightly with cheese and put under broiler flame to brown.

POACHED EGGS CHANTILLY

Fill patty shells with purée of peas. Place a poached egg on top of each and cover with white sauce, a dash of paprika and a sprig of parsley. Toast may be used instead of pastry shells.

POACHED EGGS GRAND DUO

Arrange 6 slices of toast in a circle on platter. On each put a poached egg. Cover with a thick white sauce to which have been added the yolks of 2 eggs and ½ cup grated cheese. Brown for a moment under the broiler flame. Garnish with sprigs of parsley. Browned mushrooms may also be added as garnish.

POACHED EGGS DOREMUS

1½ c. milk
2 tbsp. butter
½ tsp. salt
1 c. minced chicken
4 mushroom caps

2 tbsp. flour
1 tsp. Worcestershire sauce
4 tartlet crusts
4 eggs, poached

Make white sauce of milk, butter, flour and Worcestershire sauce. Brown mushroom caps in one tablespoon butter. Fill tartlet shells with hot minced chicken. Place a poached egg on each, top with a mushroom cap and serve with cream sauce.

POACHED EGGS PACIFIC

½ c. rice
1½ c. milk
½ tsp. minced onion
4 green pepper rings
3 tbsp. melted butter
4 eggs

½ c. or 1 small can shrimp
½ tsp. salt
⅛ tsp. celery salt
2 tbsp. flour
1 c. sliced mushrooms
4 slices tomato

Cook rice in boiling salted water until tender. While rice is cooking, make white sauce of milk, flour and 1 tablespoon butter. Brown mushrooms and onion in remaining butter, and add to white sauce. Add shrimp and seasonings. When rice is done, drain, form into molds by pressing it into measuring cup up to ¼ cup mark. Unmold on hot platter, place a slice of tomato on each mold. Poach eggs, place a poached egg on each mold, pour hot sauce around, garnish with pepper rings and serve.

POACHED EGGS HOLLANDAISE

6 slices toast
½ c. mayonnaise

6 eggs
1 c. hot medium white sauce

Place one poached egg on each slice of toast. Fold mayonnaise into the hot white sauce and pour over all. Serve at once.

POACHED EGGS WITH CORNED BEEF HASH

Put corned beef hash into buttered baking dish, put eggs on top and bake in moderate oven (350° F.) until eggs are set.

POACHED EGGS À LA PORTUGAISE

Fill round buttered molds with rice which has been steamed in tomato sauce. Unmold in a circle on a pie dish of oven proof glass, place a poached egg on each rice cake, cover with cheese sauce. In the center of platter arrange grilled tomato slices or half tomatoes. Brown quickly in a hot oven and serve.

POACHED EGG DAISY

On a slice of grilled ham put a thick slice of ripe tomato. Season with salt and pepper and cook for 5 minutes under broiler flame. Put a poached egg on top and cover with Hollandaise sauce. Garnish with strips of green pepper.

485

CHICKEN RAREBIT WITH POACHED EGGS

1 tbsp. shortening	1 tsp. finely minced parsley
1 tbsp. flour	Salt and pepper to taste
1 c. milk	1 c. chopped chicken
1 tbsp. finely chopped cheese	4 poached eggs
	4 toasted rolls or rounds of toast

Make cream sauce of shortening, flour and milk. Add the cheese and stir until melted and smooth. Add the parsley and season with salt and pepper. When ready to serve add the chicken and heat. To make the toasted rolls, cut away a slice from the top and cull out some of the center. The softer roll is more suitable. Brush with melted butter. Place a poached egg in the roll and cover with chicken rarebit.

POACHED EGG SALAD

Put poached eggs on cooked spinach and over each put 1 tablespoon cream with which has been blended ½ teaspoon prepared mustard and 1 teaspoon vinegar.

EGGS COMMODORE

With doughnut cutter, cut rounds of bread. Fry these lightly in butter. Fill the hole with pâté de foie gras. On top put a poached egg and pour rich Bechamel sauce over all. A drop of vinegar may be added to the sauce.

POACHED EGGS A LA RHINE

4 slices toast, buttered	1 c. mushrooms, sliced
2 tbsp. butter	4 poached eggs
1 c. medium white sauce	½ c. grated Parmesan cheese
Pimiento for garnish	

Brown mushrooms in butter and put on hot toast. Top with poached egg. Over all pour hot white sauce to which ½ cup Parmesan cheese has been added. Sprinkle with a little grated cheese and brown quickly in a hot oven. Garnish with a bit of pimiento.

Sauces to Serve With Poached Eggs

ITALIAN SAUCE

1 tsp. grated carrot	½ c. stock or water
2 tbsp. chopped onion	½ c. strained tomatoes
3 tbsp. butter	½ tsp. salt
1 bay leaf	Dash of pepper
2 tbsp. flour	

Put the butter into a pan and to it add the carrot, onion and bay leaf. Brown slightly. Add the flour, stirring to make a smooth paste. Then add the stock or water and stir until thickened. Add salt and pepper to taste.

486

CREAM SAUCE

1 c. milk
2 tbsp. flour

2 tbsp. butter
½ tsp. salt

With a little of the cold milk make a smooth paste of the flour. Heat the remainder of the milk and add to it the flour paste, stirring continually. When thickened, add the butter and salt and blend.

PAPRIKA SAUCE

2 tbsp. flour
2 tbsp. butter
1 tbsp. paprika

½ tsp. salt
1 c. chicken stock or milk

Blend the flour, paprika and salt. Make a paste of the flour mixture and a little of the stock or milk. Heat the remainder of the liquid, add to it the flour paste, stirring until thickened.

HORSERADISH SAUCE

3 tbsp. butter
1 c. water or stock
2 tbsp. flour

½ tsp. salt
Dash of white pepper
½ c. well-drained horseradish

Make a paste of the flour, salt and a little water or stock. Heat the remainder of the water to boiling and to it add the flour paste, stirring constantly. When thickened remove from fire and add the butter and stir until well blended. Just before serving add the horseradish, which has been pressed as dry as possible. Blend thoroughly.

CURRY SAUCE

4 tbsp. onion, minced
2 tbsp. butter
2 tbsp. flour
1 tsp. curry powder

½ tsp. salt
1 c. boiling water or chicken stock

Melt the butter in a saucepan. Add the onion and cook for a few moments, but do not brown the onion. Blend flour, curry powder and salt and add to the onion. Add water or stock. Stir until well cooked. Standing covered over hot water for a few minutes before serving develops the flavor of this sauce.

Baked or Shirred Eggs

Shirred eggs, also called baked eggs, are prepared by breaking the eggs into buttered ramekins, custard cups or casseroles, and baking in a moderate oven until the eggs are set. Grated cheese or other seasoning may be lightly sprinkled over the top of the egg, or a tablespoon of cream may be put into the dish before the egg is broken into it.

487

Shirred eggs with chicken livers make any breakfast an event.

SHIRRED EGGS EN CRÊME

4 eggs   Salt and pepper
4 tbsp. cream

Into each of 4 buttered custard cups or ramekins put 1 tablespoon cream. Break an egg into each, sprinkle with salt and pepper, and bake in moderate oven (350° F.) until eggs are set.

SHIRRED EGGS AU GRATIN

Shirred eggs, plus
3 tbsp. grated cheese
Sprinkle cheese over eggs before baking.

SHIRRED EGGS DIJON

4 eggs   3 tbsp. butter
2 c. mashed potatoes   ⅛ tsp. pepper
½ c. midget onions   ½ tsp. salt
½ c. mushrooms

On ovenproof platter prepare a border of mashed potatoes and brown lightly in oven. In the meantime brown the onions and mushrooms in butter. Put browned mushrooms and onions into cavity in center of platter, break eggs on top, season, dot with butter and cook in moderate oven until egg yolk looks as if it were covered with a thin veil.

488

6 turnips or 4 rutabagas   ½ tsp. salt
2 tbsp. butter   6 eggs

Cook turnips in boiling salted water until tender. Drain and mash. Add salt, pepper and butter. Put mashed turnips into buttered baking dish and make 6 small hollows in the top of the turnips. Into each hollow break an egg, sprinkle lightly with salt and bake in moderate oven (350° F.) for 10 minutes, or until eggs are set. Mashed potatoes or other vegetables may be used instead of turnips.

ALSATIAN EGGS

3 thin slices boiled salt   5 eggs
   pork   4 tbsp. thick cream
¼ c. grated cheese   Salt and pepper, if desired

Arrange slices of salt pork in baking dish and over it sprinkle grated cheese. Break eggs over this, cover with cream and cook in slow oven (300°–325° F.) for 12–15 minutes.

JAPANESE PLATTER

2 c. cooked rice (¼ c.   6 tbsp. butter, melted
   uncooked)   1 c. cooked peas, or 1 No. 1 can
5 eggs   of peas, drained
½ c. grated cheese   Parsley
¾ tsp. salt

Mix the melted butter, salt, peas and half the grated cheese thoroughly with the rice. Spread on buttered ovenproof platter. Make 5 small wells in the rice, drop an egg into each, sprinkle the remainder of the cheese over the rice and bake in a moderate oven (350° F.) until eggs are set and cheese is melted (about 12–15 minutes). Or set the platter under a moderate broiler flame to cook the eggs and melt the cheese.

EGGS WITH SPINACH

Put chopped cooked spinach, well seasoned, into flat buttered baking dish. With the bowl of a large spoon make small hollows. Drop an egg into each, sprinkle with salt, dot with butter and bake 12–15 minutes in moderate oven (350° F.), or until eggs are set. Grated cheese may be sprinkled over before baking.

SHIRRED EGGS ALEXANDRA

1 c. minced chicken   4 eggs
4 tbsp. cream   Salt and pepper

Put layer of chicken into buttered individual baking dishes or into baked pastry shells. Break an egg over each, sprinkle with salt and pepper, and add a tablespoon of cream to each. Bake 10–15 minutes in moderate oven (350° F.), or until eggs are set.

EGG VALENCIENNES

4 eggs	1 tsp. salt
1 c. strained tomatoes	1/8 tsp. white pepper
1 c. boiled rice	1/4 tsp. grated nutmeg
4 tbsp. grated cheese	Dash paprika

Put the tomatoes into a saucepan, add the rice and when hot add the grated cheese, stirring until heated through. Add the salt, pepper and nutmeg. Brush an earthenware dish with a little melted butter and make a border of the rice, tomatoes and cheese; into the center break the eggs. Season, place in hot oven for 4–5 minutes or until done. Sprinkle with chopped parsley.

EGGS SHIRRED ON TOMATOES

4 thick slices of tomatoes	1/4 tsp. pepper
1 tsp. salt	Butter
	4 eggs

Broil slices of tomatoes slightly. Put each slice into a buttered individual baking dish, break an egg over the tomato, season with salt and pepper, and bake in moderate oven (350° F.) 10–12 minutes.

EGG HIDEAWAYS

3 potatoes, for baking	3/4 tsp. salt
3 tbsp. butter	6 eggs
3/4 c. hot milk	

Bake potatoes. When done, cut into halves, remove inner portion and mash with the salt, butter and hot milk. Beat until fluffy. Put back into shells, leaving a depression. Break egg into depression, dot with butter, cover with a little of the mashed potato and return to hot oven (450° F.) for 7–10 minutes.

EGGS IN BACON RINGS

4 slices bacon	Salt and pepper
4 eggs	

Broil or fry bacon until done but not crisp. Put into a muffin pan, forming each slice into ring and setting it on edge in muffin cup. Break egg into each ring and bake in slow oven (325° F.) for 5–10 minutes, or until set as firmly as desired.

EGGS IN TOMATO CUPS

4 eggs	2 tbsp. butter
4 large ripe tomatoes	Salt and pepper

Peel tomatoes, cut off tops and scoop out centers. Sprinkle lightly with salt. Break an egg into each tomato, add a little salt and 1 teaspoon butter. Set tomatoes on ovenproof platter and bake in moderate oven (350° F.) until tomatoes are thoroughly hot and eggs are set.

The decorative character of shirred eggs put them in a preferred class.

SHIRRED EGGS IN GREEN PEPPERS

Cut green peppers into halves lengthwise. Remove seeds. Put into each a bit of butter and put into buttered baking dish. Break an egg into each pepper case, sprinkle with salt, add 2 tablespoons boiling water. Cover and bake in moderate oven (350° F.) 15–20 minutes.

SHIRRED EGGS WITH CHICKEN LIVERS

Cut cleaned chicken livers into small pieces. Fry lightly in butter for 4 or 5 minutes. Season with salt. Into buttered ramekins or custard cups put a spoonful of liver, then break an egg carefully into each. Sprinkle with salt and pepper, dot with butter and bake in moderate oven (325° F.) until eggs are set.

LYONNAISE EGGS

2 c. onions	$\frac{1}{4}$ c. cream
3 tbsp. butter	1 tsp. salt
4 eggs	$\frac{1}{8}$ tsp. pepper

Smother onions in buttered skillet. Place on hot buttered ovenproof platter, place eggs on top, pour cream over eggs, season with salt and pepper and bake in a moderate oven (350° F.) until eggs are set.

EGGS BUENAVENTURA

$\frac{1}{4}$ lb. noodles	1 pimiento, chopped
8 eggs	$\frac{1}{2}$ c. grated cheese
2 tbsp. butter	$\frac{1}{2}$ tsp. Worcestershire sauce
2 tbsp. flour	1 hard cooked egg, chopped
1 c. milk	

Cook noodles in boiling, salted water until tender. Drain. Butter 4 individual shirred egg dishes and line with noodles, shaping 2 nests in each dish. Break an egg into each nest and set under the broiler flame until eggs are set.

491

Make cream sauce of butter, flour, milk. Add cheese, pimiento, Worcestershire sauce, chopped egg, salt, pepper, celery salt, or other desired seasonings. When the cheese has melted, pour over the eggs and return to the broiler for 3 minutes. Serve with hot toast.

EGGS IN MACARONI

½ lb. macaroni	2¼ c. strained tomatoes
6 eggs	1¼ tsp. salt
¾ c. grated cheese	Pepper to taste

Cook the macaroni in boiling, salted water until tender. Drain. Mix macaroni, tomatoes, salt and pepper. Pour into shallow baking dish. Drop six eggs in carefully, season with salt and pepper. Sprinkle with the grated cheese and dot with butter. Bake in slow oven (325° F.) until egg whites are set.

DAFFODOWNDILLIES

¼ lb. fine noodles	¼ tsp. dry mustard
¼ c. sweet milk	¼ tsp. salt
½ c. evaporated milk	½ c. grated American cheese
¼ c. lima stock	½ c. cooked baby lima beans
2 tbsp. flour	4 or 5 eggs
2 tbsp. butter	

Cook noodles in boiling, salted water until tender; drain. Make mustard-cheese white sauce by melting butter, then adding slowly the flour, salt, mustard, lima stock, sweet milk and evaporated milk. With a fork fold into the hot sauce first the cheese, then the noodles and last the lima beans. Butter individual ramekins and fill ¾ full with the prepared mixture. Break a whole egg into the top of each dish. Sprinkle with buttered bread crumbs and bake in slow oven (325° F.) until the eggs are set. Once or twice during baking baste each Daffodowndilly with a teaspoon of butter and lima stock.

EGGS IN NOODLE-MUSHROOM NESTS

½ lb. noodles	1½ c. milk
2 tbsp. butter	½ tsp. salt
¼ lb. fresh mushrooms	¼ tsp. pepper
(or 1 small can)	4 eggs
2 tbsp. flour	

Cook noodles in boiling, salted water until tender. Melt butter in sauce pan. Fry for 5 minutes the mushrooms, which have been peeled, washed and cut in quarters. Add flour, salt, pepper and mix well. Add milk and stir constantly till creamy and smooth. Drain noodles and arrange in round baking dish, leaving four slight depressions in center. Pour mushroom sauce over noodles. Break one egg into each depression made in the noodle nest. Sprinkle with salt and pepper and add a dot of butter to each egg. Set in moderate oven till eggs are just set.

Line individual baking dishes with minced, seasoned chicken, break in an egg and bake. Cover with hot spinach purée.

The 'Twice-Cooked Egg Mollet

Eggs *mollet* are half-cousins to poached eggs, yet they are cooked in the shell. They might almost be called twice-cooked eggs. They are first soft-cooked in the shell and then plunged into cold water. The shell is carefully removed and at serving time the egg is lowered into hot water or broth to be heated through. Or the shelled egg may be dipped into slightly beaten uncooked egg, then into sifted crumbs and fried in deep fat to a golden brown. The frying requires only a few moments—just time enough to heat the eggs. Eggs *mollet* prepared in deep fat are attractive served with tartar sauce instead of the fish course at a dinner, or as the main dish at luncheon.

The Favorite Fried Egg

Eggs properly fried are one of the world's most delectable foods. Accompanied by crisp slices of bacon or a slice of juicy ham, fried egg is without doubt the favorite American breakfast dish, at least for the male portion of the population. Whether the eggs are cooked "sunny side up," or turned over, or whether they have the yolk whole or broken, they are still fried eggs.

But there are at least two main types of fried eggs: American fried and French fried. Eggs fried by the American method should perhaps be called sautéd eggs, but the term fried eggs has come to mean eggs that have been broken into a skillet containing a little fat and cooked over an open flame, either covered or uncovered. When cooked uncovered, the fat is dipped up over the eggs to help cook the top. If the skillet is covered the top of the eggs is steam-cooked.

Putting two or three tablespoonfuls of water into the skillet when the eggs have begun to set gives them a glossy, tempting appearance.

Frying eggs on a griddle that has been rubbed lightly with a bit of bacon or ham trimming avoids enveloping them with the thin fatty film which is the basis of most objections to fried foods. This film, however, gives the eggs a pleasing flavor, and if the fat has not been scorched, it is not objectionable.

French-fried eggs are cooked in deep fat. In order to do this satisfactorily, the eggs are first cooked in the shell or poached and then dipped in crumbs or batter and fried in deep fat. In this respect French-fried eggs are the same as eggs *mollet*.

493

Ham and eggs, America's favorite.

BACON AND EGGS

Put slices of bacon into cold skillet. Heat gradually, cooking bacon at moderate temperature. When crisp, drain excess fat from skillet, break in the eggs and cook slowly. If sunny, bright yolks are preferred, leave skillet uncovered. Baste the eggs occasionally with a little of the fat. For shiny eggs, cover skillet and through pouring spout add 2 teaspoons boiling water as soon as the eggs have begun to set.

HAM AND EGGS WITH PINEAPPLE

Broil or fry a thick slice of ham. Remove from skillet to hot platter. In the ham drippings brown slightly as many slices of pineapple as required. Arrange as border around ham. Fry eggs and put an egg on top of each slice of pineapple. Garnish with parsley.

FRIED EGGS WITH HAM AND VEGETABLES

⅔ c. cooked string beans   1 slice ham
⅓ c. cooked spinach   4 eggs

Chop beans and spinach very fine. Mix and season. Fry ham lightly and transfer to hot platter. Heat vegetables in the ham dripping, season and put on top of ham. Fry eggs and place on vegetables. Garnish with parsley and serve.

494

Hard cooked eggs	Mayonnaise
Sifted crumbs, salted	1 uncooked egg, beaten with
Deep fat for frying	1 tbsp. cold water

Shell hard cooked eggs. Cut into halves lengthwise. Remove yolks, mash and season with mayonnaise. Fill back into whites. Dip each piece into the beaten egg, then into crumbs, into egg and into crumbs again. Fry golden brown in deep fat at 375° F. At this temperature a cube of bread browns in 40 seconds. Serve with tartar sauce.

FRIED EGGS AU BEURRE-NOIRE

Fry 2 eggs as preferred. Remove from skillet and melt and brown 4 teaspoons butter. When brown add 1 teaspoon vinegar and pour over eggs.

The Art of Scrambling

Scrambled eggs are eggs which have been broken out of the shell, whipped lightly so as to mix the yolks and the whites thoroughly, and then cooked in a skillet containing a little butter or bacon fat. Cream, fruit juice, vegetable juice or meat stock may be added, a tablespoonful of the liquid for each two eggs, before the eggs are beaten. Meats or vegetables, diced, minced or shredded, added to the eggs before cooking, make possible many delightful flavor variations.

In order to maintain the low cooking temperature that is essential if scrambled eggs are to be a fluffy mass of soft yellow rolls, the top of the double boiler may be substituted for the skillet in cooking. The butter is melted in the top of the boiler, the beaten eggs are poured in, and then they are stirred occasionally during the cooking to make the light fluffs or "scrambles" that are the mark of well scrambled eggs.

When a skillet is used, the fat is melted and the eggs are poured into it when it is quite hot. The heat is lowered to complete the cooking. Occasional stirring forms the rolls of scrambled egg by removing the cooked portion from the bottom and sides of the pan, letting the uncooked part touch the pan. Some cooks prefer a fork for stirring. Care must be used not to overcook the eggs. It is better to have them somewhat underdone when they are removed from the skillet, for the heat in the eggs completes the cooking.

495

SCRAMBLED EGGS

4 eggs	½ tsp. salt
3 tbsp cream	⅛ tsp. pepper
2 tbsp. butter	

Beat all ingredients except butter until blended. Melt butter in top of double boiler or in skillet, pour in egg mixture and let cook, stirring occasionally with a fork. When eggs are still somewhat shiny but not wet remove to hot platter and garnish.

SCRAMBLED EGGS IN SAUSAGE CUPS

8 slices soft summer sausage, 1¼ inch thick	3 tbsp. butter
	2 tbsp. cream
4 eggs	⅛ tsp. pepper
½ tsp. salt	

Leave skins on slices of sausage. Fry quickly in butter. The skins cause the sausage slices to curl and form little cups. Beat eggs slightly, add cream and seasonings, scramble and fill into sausage cups. Arrange on hot platter. Garnish with parsley.

SCRAMBLED EGGS WITH OYSTERS

4 eggs	⅛ tsp. white pepper
½ pt. oysters	2 tbsp. cream
¾ tsp. salt	2 tbsp. butter

Beat eggs and add cream, seasoning and oysters. Melt butter in skillet and pour in the egg mixture. Cook slowly until done, stirring occasionally to form eggs into soft, fluffy rolls.

SCRAMBLED EGGS WITH HOMINY AND CHEESE SAUCE

Pile hot hominy in center of platter. Surround with scrambled eggs. Over the hominy pour cheese sauce which has been made as follows:

1 c. milk	2 tbsp. butter
½ tsp. salt	1 tbsp. flour
4 tbsp. grated cheese	

Make white sauce, adding cheese last.

SCRAMBLED EGGS EN MUFFINS

4 muffins or buns	4 eggs
2 tbsp. cream	¾ tsp. salt
¼ tsp. pepper	2 tbsp. butter

Scoop centers from left-over muffins or day-old buns. Toast lightly. Beat eggs and other ingredients to blend them. Cook in butter, stirring occasionally. Fill eggs into the muffin cases and serve.

496

SCRAMBLED EGGS ORIENTAL

3 fresh tomatoes
3 tbsp. cream or milk
Salt and pepper

6 eggs
4 tbsp. butter

Cut tomatoes in halves, brush cut surface with melted butter and broil under flame until tomatoes are thoroughly heated through. While tomatoes are broiling scramble the eggs in butter. When tomatoes are done, arrange on plates and partially cover with the scrambled eggs. The eggs may be seasoned with anchovy paste or minced sardines.

SCRAMBLED EGGS WITH MACARONI

6 eggs
1/4 c. milk
1/2 c. cooked macaroni (or cooked rice, or diced bread, or diced boiled potatoes)

1/2 tsp. salt
2 tbsp. cooking fat

Beat the eggs, add milk, salt and macaroni. Melt the fat in a skillet, add the egg mixture and cook slowly, stirring occasionally. When done arrange on platter. If desired, garnish with sardines. Or the sardines may be added and cooked with the eggs.

SPANISH EGGS

6 eggs
2 tbsp. butter

1 can tomato soup
1 can pepper pot soup

Beat eggs thoroughly and add soups, undiluted. Scramble in melted butter. Serve on toast or crackers.

SCRAMBLED EGGS WITH RICE AND CHEESE SAUCE

1 c. rice, uncooked
1 c. milk
1/2 tsp. salt
4 tbsp. grated cheese

3 tbsp. butter
6 eggs
1 tbsp. flour

Cook the rice in boiling salted water until done. Drain. While the rice is cooking prepare the cheese sauce. Melt 2 tablespoons of the fat in a pan, add the flour and salt and stir until smooth. Add the milk gradually, stirring continually. When thickened, add the cheese. Scramble the eggs in the remaining tablespoon of fat. Arrange the rice on a hot platter, the scrambled eggs around it and pour cheese sauce over the rice.

OYAKODOMBORI (Mother and Child) (Japanese)

Scramble eggs with small pieces of left over chicken, season to taste with soy sauce and sugar. Serve on hot rice.

SCRAMBLED EGGS WITH EGG PLANT

4 tsp. butter	½ c. flour
1 tsp. salt	4 eggs
¼ tsp. paprika	4 tsp. milk
½ egg plant	

Peel and dice egg plant. Mix flour, salt and paprika and roll egg plant in this mixture. Melt butter in skillet and fry egg plant until tender and brown. Add eggs which have been slightly beaten with milk and seasoning. Cook, stirring occasionally, until set and serve on buttered toast. Garnish with parsley.

BREAKFAST SALAD

Scrambled eggs	Lettuce
Boiled ham	Tomato

On bed of lettuce put a thick slice of tomato which has been slightly broiled. Put thin slice of ham on tomato and top with scrambled eggs. Serve with French dressing.

SCRAMBLED EGGS TARTRUFFE

4 eggs, slightly beaten	¼ tsp. pepper
1 c. canned tomatoes	3 tbsp. butter
1 tsp. sugar	1 tbsp. minced onion
¾ tsp. salt	

Fry onion in butter for 3 minutes. Add tomatoes, salt and sugar and let simmer for 5 minutes. Add eggs and stir with fork until light and creamy. Garnish with parsley.

Other combinations with scrambled eggs:

Sausages	Flaked codfish
Green peppers	Onions
Minced ham	Sardines
Mushrooms	Asparagus tips
Shrimp	Chipped beef

How to Make Perfect Omelets

An omelet is a sort of happy combination of French gaiety and French practicality. There is about this delightfully versatile dish much of lightness and delicacy, as well as much of nourishment and deliciousness.

Its nourishing qualities were probably responsible for the title given an omelet recipe in Rabisha's "Cookery," published in 1661. This old cookbook gives directions as to "How to make a fryed meat, called an Amlett." Contrasted with a modern recipe the proportions are amazing, and the directions leave much to the judgment of the cook, as all old recipes did. This is the recipe as Rabisha quaintly wrote it:

"Beat in according to your pan, sixteen eggs (more or less), with a grated Nutmeg, and a Lemmon cut out in the likeness and quantity of dice, beat them together well, put butter in your pan, set it over the fire, let it be indifferent hot (but not to burn) then put in your eggs, keep them stirring that they grow not to the pan, put in butter by the sides, to make them shift up and down, and when they begin to harden and congeal, shake them round; by constant putting in of butter, they will move around, then turn them in your plate, put butter into your pan, and turn the other side downward; fry it of a pure yellow brown, so take it out of the pan on your plate, and dish it up, scruise on a Lemmon or two, garnish it about with oranges, and scrape on Sugar."

There was another dish known in England as tansy that was a sort of omelet made chiefly with eggs and chopped herbs. When strips of bacon were added it was called froise. Still another dish, described as early as the fifteenth century, was omelet-like, but it contained grated bread and was seasoned with sage and colored with saffron. It was known as jussell.

During the cooking school that was held in London at the time of the International Exhibition of 1873, Buckmaster, who was in charge of the school, chose the omelet as the dish to be demonstrated the day Queen Victoria attended his lecture. In his introductory remarks Buckmaster gave the reasons for his choice: "The specimen of cooking which is now to be presented takes only five minutes, and is within the reach of almost the poorest of your Majesty's subjects. The materials cost only four pence, and they furnish a savory and nourishing dish." The five essentials to be observed in omelet making, he said, were a clean pan, not beating the eggs too much, not too many eggs in one omelet (he preferred three or four), quick cooking, immediate serving and eating.

The omelet as we know it today might almost be called the national dish of France. Scarcely a meal, from the simplest luncheon to the most gorgeous dinner, is complete without an omelet in some course.

Delicate, tender French omelets have brought fame to many a cook, but to none in such great measure as to the late Madame Poulard, to whom the world's food connoisseurs give the title of Omelet Queen of the World. From her little hotel perched high on top of rocky Mont Saint-Michel in France the fame of her charm and her omelets spread to the corners of the earth.

As might be expected, many people claim to have the recipe for Madame Poulard's famous omelet. Never would she tell the secret

An omelet that speaks French.

of what made her omelets just a little better than any other omelets in the world. Some said it was the sea air, but sea air can be had in many a place. Some said it was the famous long-handled pan she kept sacred for making her omelets. Some said it was not the omelet so much as it was the Madame's friendly smile. Still others were sure it was the method she used. Doubtless it was a combination of all of these.

It was inevitable that there should grow up a number of ways to make this popular dish. And since the method of making determines the qualities of the finished product, different names were given to the various kinds of omelets. Most cooks differentiate between two types, though some insist there is a third. The two best known kinds are the French and the puffy omelets. The French omelet is also called the plain omelet, while the puffy one is sometimes known as omelet *soufflé*.

The French Omelet

One man who was a guest for several months at the Poulard hotel believed he acquired during that time not only the recipe but also the art of making omelets like Madame Poulard's. At any rate, his results are strictly comparable with hers, and that would seem to be all that is necessary. This is the way he makes his.

Beat the eggs, unseparated, with a fork, adding one tablespoonful each of cream and of water for each egg. Into a heavy frying pan with a large surface put plenty of butter and let it get sizzling hot. Then pour in the eggs and turn down the flame a little so as to have it "medium high." Immediately start shaking the pan back and forth, and roll the omelet as soon as the edge is firm and while it is still wet. The inside of the omelet cooks while it is being removed from the pan. Part of the secret of Madame Poulard's delicious omelets is the fact that they were never overcooked. In fact, one guest says when they were at their best they were what she describes as "loose."

The type of frying pan used is important. It must have a large surface so that the layer of egg will not be too deep. And it must be very hot when the egg is put in. This results in almost instantaneous cooking of the edge and a thin layer on the bottom so that the omelet can be rolled or folded almost at once.

Rolling an omelet is the art of transforming a sort of flat egg pan-cake into a golden roll whose inner portion is just nicely jellied, while its outer portion is delicately crisp and brown. To accomplish the rolling, lift one edge of the omelet and fold it over. Tilt the skillet in the direction the omelet is to be rolled, and with a little push here and there from a helpful spatula or knife, the omelet rolls itself, jelly-roll fashion. Slip it from the skillet to a hot platter and garnish.

Although some people insist that no liquid must ever be added to a French omelet, others find it much creamier and more to their liking if a little cream is added to the eggs before they are beaten—perhaps one tablespoonful of thick cream for each two eggs used. Meat stock, vegetables or fruit juices and even liquors have been used instead of cream by many a famous cook to give an omelet individuality and delicious flavor. The kind of liquid to be used is determined by the filling. Fruit juices are especially good for fruit-filled omelets, meat stock for meat-filled ones, and so forth.

Madame Poulard's method is adaptable to the modern kitchen with its gas or electric range and its shorter-handled skillets. The important thing is to have the flame right, and the skillet heavy enough to prevent easy scorching and of a size suitable to the number of eggs used in the omelet.

The Puffy Omelets

As contrasted with the French omelet the puffy or foamy omelet is just what its name implies. The egg whites and yolks are beaten separately. The white is beaten quite stiff, a little stiffer than for

501

angel food cakes and meringues. Then the yolks are beaten with the seasonings and folded gently into the whites. The mixture is quickly poured into a hot skillet which contains a little melted butter. But the skillet must be hot so that the egg starts cooking at once and the yolk will not settle out at the bottom of the pan and thus make the finished omelet unattractive.

This kind of omelet may either be cooked on top of the range or baked, or it may even be started on top of the range and then finished in the oven. When it is cooked on top of the range, the pan is covered, and after the first few minutes the flame is turned down quite low so that the omelet will not become tough. When it is done (in 10 to 12 minutes, depending on the size of the omelet and the height of the flame) it is uncovered and run under the broiler flame for a few moments to brown the top.

For baking, the egg mixture is put directly into a hot skillet and then into a hot oven (425° F.) for five minutes. Then the temperature is reduced to 350° F. for twenty minutes. The hot initial temperature prevents the yolk from settling out.

When the omelet is started on top of the stove, the pan is covered until the omelet puffs up. It is cooked for about five minutes over the direct flame, which is turned fairly low, and then the pan is uncovered and transferred to a slow oven (325°–350° F.) for about twenty minutes.

When the omelet is done it is folded over and served. Puffy omelets always shrink a little when they are taken from the pan.

If the whites of the eggs for making a foamy omelet are thick and viscous, the finished omelet will be larger and lighter if a tablespoonful of cold water is added for each two egg whites when they have been whipped until they are just frothy. Then the whipping is continued until the whites are stiff. The water acts as a sort of extender of the whites.

If the whites are not beaten stiff enough, the yolk tends to separate out during cooking. Sometimes, especially when an omelet is cooked in an iron pan, a greenish color develops where the egg touches the pan. This is due to the combination of the sulfur of the egg white with the iron of the pan. The color is entirely harmless, but it is unattractive. Sometimes this discoloration takes place when an aluminum pan is used. It happens when the yolk settles to the bottom. Here, as when eggs are cooked in the shell, the iron of the yolk combines with the sulfur of the white. If the omelet is cooked quickly at first, before the yolk can separate out, very little of this discoloration takes place.

How to Fold An Omelet

The easiest way to fold an omelet is to cut short incisions, about a half to three-quarters of an inch long, at opposite sides of the cooked omelet. Then, with a case knife, the omelet is creased down the center, from cut to cut, the pan is tipped and the omelet folds over the edge of the knife. To remove the omelet from the pan, place a hot platter over the pan and invert them together. If a filling is used, spread it on half the omelet before folding.

PLAIN OMELET

4 eggs   3 tbsp. cream or top milk
½ tsp. salt   ⅛ tsp. pepper
2 tbsp. butter

Beat eggs with cream and seasonings until thoroughly mixed. Heat butter very hot in skillet, pour in eggs and cook quite quickly, shaking the skillet so that the egg cooks evenly. With a knife lift the edge of the omelet, tipping the skillet to let some of the uncooked mixture run under the cooked portion. When the egg is almost cooked but still somewhat shiny, roll the omelet, slip out of skillet to hot platter and serve immediately.

PARSLEY OMELET

Plain omelet recipe, plus   Sprigs of parsley
½ c. minced parsley   2 tbsp. butter

Combine ¼ cup minced parsley with omelet mixture before cooking. Cream the butter and add the remaining ¼ minced parsley. When omelet is cooked, spread it with the parsley-butter mixture, roll, transfer to platter and garnish with sprigs of parsley.

FLUFFY OMELET

4 eggs   2 tbsp. cold water
½ tsp. salt   1 tbsp. butter

Separate yolks from whites. Beat whites until frothy. Add the salt and water and continue beating until stiff. Beat the yolks until light and thick and fold into the whites. Pour the mixture into a hot pan in which the butter has been melted. Cover the pan and let omelet cook on top of burner, with flame turned quite low, until mixture has puffed up. Then uncover the omelet, transfer pan to a slow oven (325°–350° F.) to finish cooking, about 20 minutes. The omelet should spring back when touched with the finger. Fold over and serve.

OMELET WITH SPINACH

6 eggs	3 tbsp. butter
1 tsp. salt	3 c. cooked, chopped spinach
1/8 tsp. pepper	1/2 c. white sauce
1/4 c. milk	

Beat the eggs slightly, add the salt, pepper, and milk. Melt the fat in a hot frying pan, pour in the egg mixture and cook slowly until firm. Fold over and turn out on a bed of finely chopped, creamed spinach. Mix the spinach with the white sauce and season with salt, pepper, and a hint of garlic or onion.

SWEDISH OMELET WITH CHEESE (Omelett med Ost)

1 tbsp. flour	4 eggs
1 c. milk	1 tbsp. fat
1 tsp. salt	6 tbsp. finely shredded cheese
1/8 tsp. pepper	

Mix flour, milk and seasonings. Add eggs beaten very light. Melt fat in frying pan, and when hot turn in the egg mixture. Put into lower part of hot oven until brown and well puffed up. Then put on top shelf of oven to brown slightly. Spread cheese over the omelet, fold omelet, turn out on hot platter and serve at once.

CREAMED CHICKEN OMELET

Plain omelet	1 1/2 c. milk or 3/4 c. milk and
1 c. diced cooked chicken	3/4 c. chicken stock
3 tbsp. flour	3 tbsp. butter, bacon fat, or
1/2 tsp. salt	chicken fat

Make cream sauce of butter, flour, milk and salt. Add chicken meat, heat thoroughly and put between layers of omelet, reserving a small amount to put at the open side. Dust with paprika for garnish.

CHICKEN TAPIOCA OMELET

4 eggs	2 tbsp. granulated tapioca
1/2 tsp. salt	1 tbsp. butter
1/8 tsp. pepper	1 c. diced chicken
3/4 c. milk	

Scald the milk and to it add the tapioca and seasonings and cook 20 minutes in double boiler, stirring frequently. Separate the eggs, beat the yolks until thick and the whites until stiff. Add the butter to the tapioca and pour over the egg yolks. Add the chicken and fold in the egg whites. Turn into a hot buttered skillet and cook in a moderate oven (350°–375° F.) for 20 minutes.

FLUFFY CHEESE OMELET

4 eggs
8 soda crackers, rolled fine
½ c. grated American cheese

¾ c. hot milk
½ tsp. salt
2 tbsp. butter

Separate eggs and beat yolks until lemon colored. Pour hot milk over finely rolled crackers and beat until creamy. Season, add ¼ cup cheese and combine with beaten egg yolks. Fold in stiffly beaten egg whites. Heat butter in heavy frying pan. Pour in omelet and cook, covered, over very low flame until barely set. Fold, sprinkle with remaining cheese and slip on to a hot platter. Serve at once.

TOMATO OMELET

Plain or fluffy omelet
Sliced ripe tomatoes

Fat for frying
Sifted crumbs, salted

Dip tomato slices into crumbs and fry in fat to golden brown. Put a few slices between folds of omelet and place remainder around omelet on platter.

PEANUT BUTTER OMELET

Warm peanut butter in top of double boiler, add a tablespoon of cream or undiluted evaporated milk and spread in omelet. A tablespoonful of peanut butter may be blended with the omelet mixture before cooking. Serve with warm honey.

ENDIVE OMELET

Braise curly endive slightly by tossing it for a few minutes in hot butter or bacon fat. Put the braised endive between the layers of omelet and garnish with crisp, uncooked endive.

HAM OMELET

Add ½ teaspoon prepared mustard to plain omelet mixture before cooking. Between layers of cooked omelet spread diced chopped ham.

MUSHROOM OMELET

Brown a cupful of mushrooms in 2 tablespoons butter, season with salt and pepper and spread in omelet. If canned mushrooms are used, use some of the liquor instead of the cream in the omelet mixture.

ASPARAGUS OMELET

Heat asparagus, either stalks or cut pieces, in a little butter and put between layers of omelet.

CHICKEN LIVER OMELET

Chop chicken livers, add a little minced onion, seasonings, and heat in butter. Spread on omelet.

CORN OMELET

Season corn, either fresh or canned, with cream, salt and pepper and add to omelet mixture before cooking.

505

ORIENTAL OMELET

To recipe for plain omelet add ½ cup cooked rice. Fill cooked omelet with shrimp and season with cocktail sauce.

TOMATO AND CHEESE OMELET

5 eggs	2 tbsp. butter
2 tbsp. milk	⅛ tsp. pepper
2 tsp. salt	1 tsp. sugar
¼ tsp. pepper	¾ c. grated American cheese
2 c. canned tomatoes	

Stew together the tomatoes, butter, sugar, and 1 teaspoon salt and pepper, until the tomatoes are thick. This takes about 20 minutes of quite rapid cooking. Separate the eggs, beating the whites until stiff and the yolks until lemon colored, add the milk, the teaspoon of salt and the ¼ teaspoon pepper to the egg yolks, stirring. Fold in the whites and turn the whole into a medium-size frying pan, in which 1 tablespoon butter has been melted. Cook the omelet slowly, lifting it occasionally from the bottom with a spatula or broad-bladed knife. When golden brown on the bottom, spread over half the amount of tomato and sprinkle on the cheese. Set in the oven until the cheese has melted, fold over and cut at right angles to the handle. Slide onto a hot platter and garnish with the remaining tomato and some parsley.

OATMEAL OMELET

4 eggs	½ tsp. salt
½ c. cooked oatmeal	1 tbsp. fat
¼ c. milk	

Beat the eggs slightly, add the oatmeal, salt and milk. Mix thoroughly. Melt the fat in a hot skillet and turn in the mixture. Lower the heat so egg will not cook too fast. With a knife loosen the edge of the omelet and tilt the skillet so the uncooked portion may run underneath the cooked part. When done, crease through the center with a knife, fold over on a hot platter and serve. Flaked fish, left-over vegetables or ground cheese may be put between the layers of the cooked omelet.

EASTER OMELET

½ lb. elbow macaroni	1 c. rich milk
6 eggs, separated	1 tbsp. chopped parsley
1 c. boiled ham cut in cubes or squares	1 tsp. chopped onion
	Salt and pepper to taste

Cook macaroni until tender in boiling salted water and drain. Beat egg yolks, milk, salt and pepper until light. Add macaroni, ham, onion, and parsley and last fold in the beaten egg whites. Pour into hot buttered baking dish, set in pan of hot water and bake 45 minutes in moderate oven (350° F.). Unmold and garnish with parsley and boiled cauliflower sprigs.

506

Sweet Omelet

OMELET WITH PRESERVES

Just before serving spread a plain or fluffy omelet with preserves and fold. A spoonful of preserves may be used as garnish. A tablespoon of the preserves beaten into the omelet mixture before cooking gives a delightful flavor.

PINEAPPLE OMELET

4 eggs, separated
2 tbsp. shortening

4 tbsp. pineapple juice
½ tsp. salt
1 tsp. sugar

Beat the whites stiff, adding the salt. Beat the yolks, sugar, fruit juice and fold into the whites. Before folding over the omelet spread half of it with crushed pineapple.

ORANGE FLOWER OMELET

4 eggs
Pinch salt
Orange marmalade

3 tbsp. orange flower water
1 tsp. sugar
Candied orange peel

Beat together all ingredients except marmalade. When done, spread with marmalade and garnish with strips of candied orange peel.

STRAWBERRY OMELET

6 eggs
4 tbsp. milk or cream
½ tsp. salt

2 tbsp. butter
1 pt. strawberries
¼ c. sugar

Hull and wash strawberries. Cut the larger ones in halves, using a sharp knife. Do not crush the berries. Sprinkle the sugar over them, cover and let stand for several hours. Beat the eggs, milk, 1 tablespoon sugar and salt until thoroughly blended. Melt the butter in a hot skillet and pour in the egg mixture. Turn the flame down to medium. With a spatula raise the edges of the omelet and tip the skillet so some of the uncooked mixture will run under the cooked layer. Continue doing this until all of the mixture is cooked. Then spread the berries over one half of the omelet, fold over the other half, and remove to hot platter. Garnish with a few whole berries.

APPLE SAUCE OMELET

Heat apple sauce, add 1 tablespoon sugar with which has been blended a little cinnamon and cloves. Spread between layers of omelet, reserving a spoonful or two to use as garnish.

ORANGE OMELET

4 eggs
Pinch salt
3 tbsp. orange juice

1 tsp. sugar
Orange sections or slices

Beat all together, omitting orange sections. Cook in usual way. When done fill with sections of fresh orange. Garnish with orange sections or slices. Dust with powdered sugar.

507

OMELET MELBA

Fill puffy omelet with sweetened sliced peaches. Garnish with slice dpeaches.

HOLIDAY OMELET

Heat ½–¾ cup mince meat over hot water while omelet is being made. Spread between layers of omelet.

CHOCOLATE OMELET

Sprinkle chipped sweet chocolate over top of hot omelet before rolling it.

BANANA OMELET

In plain omelet mixture substitute 4 tablespoons mashed banana for the cream. Between the layers of the omelet put glazed banana halves.

To glaze the bananas, melt ½ cup brown sugar and 4 tablespoons butter with 2 tablespoons hot water. When smooth put in bananas which have been cut into halves lengthwise. Let cook 3 minutes on one side, turn and cook 3 minutes longer. Remove from skillet and put into omelet.

HAWAIIAN OMELET

4 eggs, separated	½ c. milk
12 soda crackers, rolled fine	2 tbsp. butter
1½ c. crushed pineapple	3 tbsp. grated cheese

Beat egg yolks, add milk and cracker crumbs. Fold in stiffly beaten whites. Pour into skillet or omelet pan in which butter has been melted. Cover and cook until bottom is browned. Finish cooking in moderate oven (350° F.) for 5 minutes. While omelet is cooking let pineapple simmer to thicken juice. Pour hot pineapple on half of cooked omelet, fold over and transfer to hot platter. Sprinkle with grated cheese and put under broiler for a minute to melt cheese. Serve at once.

Other Fillings for Omelets

Creamed oysters	Chopped green peppers in
Creamed codfish	tomato sauce
Peas	Buttered spinach
Chopped nuts and olives	String beans
Pork sausage	Chipped beef
Flaked crabmeat	Green herbs, minced (parsley,
Tomatoes and sardines	chives, spinach, sorrel)
Buttered calves' brains	Fried onions
Cooked rice mixed with green	Fried egg plant cubes
peppers and onions	Diced avocado
Minced stewed giblets	Braised endive
Grated cheese	Bacon strips
Chicken livers and minced onion	

Other Sweet Omelet Fillings

Stewed dried fruits	Any sweetened fresh fruits
Cream fillings	Jellies
Crushed macaroons	

The delicate fluff called soufflé.

The Simple Secret of the Soufflé

The word *soufflé* means puffed or spongy. And that expresses exactly the texture of these delicate combinations that have a base of milk and flour with eggs or with some other puffing agent. Egg soufflés are, of course, the most popular because eggs add flavor and extra nutrients to their puffy quality.

Many a cook hesitates the moment soufflé is mentioned. Yet making one is not at all a difficult process and requires no special skill. The thing that makes most for success is not so much the actual mixing and cooking, although they do play a part, as the organization of the procedure. The baking dish should be buttered and the oven heated. Then the white sauce should be prepared. Only after these steps have been completed should the eggs be beaten and the actual soufflé mixture be put together.

Most soufflés have as their foundation a thick white sauce, made with at least three, and sometimes four, tablespoonfuls of flour to each cup of milk. The white sauce is first made, seasoned with butter and salt, and to it are added whatever ingredients are desired—diced chicken, chopped ham, vegetables, cheese, fruit. Then the beaten yolks are folded in and finally the stiffly beaten whites. The whites are carefully folded in so that they are thoroughly distributed throughout the mixture, but they need not have disappeared from sight.

The soufflé mixture is then poured into the buttered baking dish, which is set into a pan of hot water, custard fashion, and baked in a slow oven (325°–350° F.) until it springs back when touched. This

509

requires about thirty minutes, but the precise time depends on the size and depth of the dish, the quantity of soufflé, and the oven temperature.

There are two types of soufflés: those that contain vegetables, meats, fish or cheese and are served as entrées, and those that are sweetened or contain fruits and are served as desserts. For the latter type the baking dish is often buttered and then sugared, just as a cake pan is floured.

PLAIN SOUFFLÉ

2 tbsp. butter	1 tsp. salt
2 tbsp. flour	1/8 tsp. white pepper
2 c. milk, scalded	4 eggs, separated

Melt butter, add flour, stirring to blend smoothly. Add hot milk, stirring constantly. Add seasonings. Cook in top of double boiler 10 minutes. Remove from heat and add the beaten yolks. Fold in stiffly beaten egg whites and pour into buttered baking dish. Set into pan of hot water and bake in slow oven (325° F.) until firm, about 35–45 minutes.

HOT CHICKEN SOUFFLÉ

1½ c. minced chicken	2 egg whites
1¾ c. milk	2 egg yolks
1 tbsp. flour	1 tsp. salt
1 tbsp. butter	¼ tsp. pepper

Make white sauce of milk, flour, salt, pepper. Cook in double boiler until the mixture coats the spoon. Add egg yolks. Add chicken, then fold in stiffly beaten egg whites. Pour into casserole, set into pan of hot water and bake about 25–30 minutes, or until egg is set.

MACARONI CHICKEN SOUFFLÉ

¼ lb. macaroni	2 eggs
2 tbsp. butter	½ tsp. salt
1 c. milk	⅛ tsp. pepper
2 tbsp. flour	½ c. chicken, shredded

Cook macaroni in boiling salted water until tender. Drain and measure. There should be 2 cups. Make a white sauce of butter, flour and milk. Pour this over the beaten egg yolks, add seasoning, shredded chicken and macaroni. Fold in the beaten egg whites. Pour into a buttered baking dish, place in a pan of hot water and bake 45 minutes in a slow oven (325° F.). Serve hot.

1 c. milk	3 egg yolks
½ tsp. salt	1 c. shredded chicken
¼ c. cold water	1 tbsp. gelatin
¼ c. boiling water or chicken stock	3 egg whites

Make custard of egg yolks, milk and salt. Cool. Soak gelatin in cold water and dissolve in hot water or stock. When cool, beat until light. Combine chicken with cooled custard, fold into beaten gelatin and pour into wet mold. Chill. Garnish with stuffed olives and pickle fans and serve.

CHICKEN SOUFFLÉ

6 tbsp. flour	2 tbsp. minced carrot
¾ tsp. salt	1 tbsp. minced parsley
Pepper	3 tbsp. butter
1 c. milk	3 eggs, separated
1 c. chicken broth	1½ c. minced chicken meat
½ bay leaf	2 or 3 minced mushrooms
1 tsp. minced onion	

Make a paste of the flour, salt, pepper, and a little of the milk. Combine the remaining milk, broth, bay leaf, onion, carrot, parsley and bring to a boil. Let simmer for 10 minutes. Strain and add the flour paste, stirring constantly. Cook until the mixture thickens. Add the butter, and then the egg yolks which have been thoroughly beaten. Blend thoroughly. Cool. Add chicken and mushrooms, and last fold in the stiffly beaten egg whites. Pour mixture into a buttered baking dish, set into a pan of hot water and bake in a slow oven (325° F.) about 40 minutes. Serve at once.

CHICKEN NOODLE SOUFFLÉ

3 c. noodles	3 c. shredded cooked chicken
4 c. chicken stock	3 eggs
1 tbsp. flour	Salt and pepper to taste

Cook noodles in just enough boiling water to make them tender and swell to natural size. Heat stock and thicken it with flour. Cool and add beaten egg yolks. Beat egg whites until stiff. Combine noodles, chicken, and sauce and fold in egg whites. Bake in moderate oven (340° F.) until center is firm.

Baked cheese fondue, delight of the epicure.

MACARONI SHRIMP SOUFFLÉ

¼ lb. macaroni	4 eggs
4 tbsp. butter	1 tsp. salt
4 tbsp. flour	¼ tsp. pepper
2 c. milk	1 c. shrimp

Cook macaroni in boiling salted water until tender. Drain immediately, chill in cold water, then drain and measure 2 cups. Make a white sauce of butter, flour and milk. Pour this over the beaten egg yolks, add seasoning, shredded shrimp and macaroni. Fold in the beaten whites. Pour into buttered baking dish, place in a pan of hot water and bake 45 minutes in a slow oven (325° F.). Serve hot.

CHEESE SOUFFLÉ

3 eggs, separated	3 tbsp. butter
½ tsp. salt	3 tbsp. flour
1 c. grated cheese	1 c. milk, scalded

Melt butter, add flour and stir until thickened. Add hot milk gradually, stirring constantly. Pour over beaten yolks, add cheese and salt. Fold in the stiffly beaten egg whites. Pour into buttered casserole, set in pan of hot water and bake in slow oven (275°–300° F.) for 35 minutes, or until firm.

JELLIED CHEESE SOUFFLÉ

1 c. milk	¼ c. cold water
3 eggs	¼ c. boiling water
½ tsp. salt	1 tbsp. gelatin
1 c. grated American cheese	

Soak gelatin in cold water. Dissolve it in boiling water and cool. In the meantime, heat the milk in a double boiler and pour it over the beaten egg yolks, stirring constantly. Add the grated cheese and salt. Return to fire and cook, stirring until mixture coats spoon. Cool. As soon as the gelatin begins to thicken, beat it until it holds its shape. Beat the egg whites until stiff and fold into the cooled custard. Add the beaten gelatin and chill until firm.

512

SPINACH SOUFFLÉ

3 eggs
1 c. spinach purée
1 c. milk

3 tbsp. flour
4 tbsp. butter
1/8 tsp. pepper

Make a white sauce of the butter, flour and milk and add the seasonings.
Beat the yolks of the eggs until thick. Cool the white sauce slightly and stir
them in. Add the spinach and last fold in the egg whites beaten stiff. Set in
pan of hot water. Bake in greased baking dish for 30 minutes in moderate
oven (325°–350° F.).

SPINACH FONDUE

2 c. cooked spinach, well
  drained
1 c. grated American
  cheese

3/4 tsp. salt
1 tsp. minced onion
3 eggs, separated

Chop spinach. Add onion, cheese, salt and beaten egg yolks. Fold in stiffly
beaten egg whites. Bake in buttered casserole set in pan of hot water in moderate oven (350° F.) 30 minutes. Serve at once.

SALMON SOUFFLÉ

2 c. (1 No. 1 can) salmon
1/2 c. milk
Salt and pepper

1/2 c. bread crumbs
3 eggs, separated
Paprika

Flake salmon and remove bones. Heat bread crumbs in milk for 5 minutes.
Add salmon, and the well beaten egg yolks. Fold in stiffly beaten whites.
Pour into buttered mold, set into pan of hot water and bake in moderate oven
(350° F.) for 45 minutes, or until firm.

CRABMEAT SOUFFLÉ

3 tbsp. butter
3 tbsp. flour
1/2 tsp. salt
1 c. flaked crabmeat

4 tbsp. chopped ripe olives
3 eggs, separated
1 1/2 c. milk

Make white sauce of butter, flour, milk and salt. Cool, and add crabmeat,
olives and well beaten yolks. Fold in stiffly beaten egg whites. Pour into
buttered baking dish, set in pan of hot water and bake in moderate oven
(350° F.) until firm, about 35–45 minutes.

CORNMEAL SOUFFLÉ

⅓ c. cornmeal
3 eggs, separated
3 tbsp. butter or bacon fat

1 c. boiling water
1 tsp. salt
½ c. milk

Bring water to boil, sift in cornmeal, stirring constantly. Add salt and put into top of double boiler to cook until cornmeal is done, about an hour. Cool slightly, add fat, milk, and beaten egg yolks. Fold in stiffly beaten egg whites and pour into buttered baking dish. Set in pan of hot water and bake in moderate oven (350° F.) until firm to touch. Serve with cheese or tomato sauce.

NOODLE SOUFFLÉ

1¼ c. cooked noodles
6 tbsp. butter, melted
1 tbsp. chopped pimiento
1 c. grated cheese
3 eggs, separated

1 c. bread crumbs
1 tbsp. chopped onion
1 tbsp. chopped green pepper
1 c. milk, scalded
Salt and pepper

Combine all dry ingredients. Add melted butter, cheese, beaten egg yolks and hot milk. Season. Fold in beaten egg whites, pour into buttered baking dish, set into pan of hot water and bake 40 minutes in moderate oven (350° F.). Serve with mushroom sauce.

SWEET POTATO SOUFFLÉ

4 c. mashed sweet
    potatoes
¾ c. cream
¼ tsp. pepper

4 tbsp. melted butter
½ tsp. salt
3 eggs, separated

Add melted butter, cream, beaten yolks and seasonings to hot mashed sweet potatoes. Fold in stiffly beaten whites. Pour into buttered baking dish. Set into pan of hot water, bake in moderate oven (350° F.) about 25 minutes.

EGG AND CHEESE TIMBALES

3 eggs, beaten
1 c. milk, scalded
1 tbsp. flour
1 tbsp. butter

1 c. grated cheese
1 chopped green pepper
½ tsp. salt

Melt butter, stir in the flour and gradually add the milk, stirring constantly. Pour over the beaten eggs, add cheese, pepper and seasonings. Pour into buttered custard cups, set in pan of hot water, and bake in moderate oven (350° F.) about 45 minutes or until egg is set. Unmold on hot platter, garnish with parsley and serve with tomato or chili sauce.

VANILLA SOUFFLÉ

4 tbsp. flour	4 tbsp. sugar
3 tbsp. butter	4 eggs
1 c. milk, scalded	½ tsp. vanilla
½ tsp. salt	

Melt butter, add flour and then gradually the hot milk, stirring constantly. Bring to boil. Pour over well beaten egg yolks to which the sugar and salt have been added. Cool. Fold in the stiffly beaten egg whites. Pour into baking dish which has been buttered and sugared. Set into pan of hot water and bake in moderate oven (350° F.) 30–35 minutes. Serve at once.

PINEAPPLE CHEESE SOUFFLÉ

1 c. crushed pineapple	3 eggs, separated
2 tbsp. butter	½ tsp. salt
2 tbsp. flour	½ c. grated cheese

Melt the butter in the top of a double boiler, add the flour and salt and blend thoroughly. Add slowly the juice from the pineapple brought to a boil, and mix until very smooth. Remove from the fire, add the grated cheese and mix only slightly. Add the yolks of eggs beaten until lemon colored. Let the mixture cool for a few minutes, add the pineapple pulp, about ½ cup. Fold in the beaten egg whites. Turn into a buttered baking dish and set in pan of hot water. Bake 30–40 minutes in slow oven (325° F.). Serve at once.

MOCHA SOUFFLÉ

1 c. cold strong coffee	1 c. cold milk
1 tbsp. cocoa	¼ c. sugar
⅛ tsp. salt	⅝ c. flour
½ tsp. vanilla	¼ c. butter
4 eggs, separated	

Mix coffee and milk. Mix flour, cocoa, sugar and salt. Add flavoring and enough of the cold milk-coffee mixture to make a smooth paste. Bring the rest of milk and coffee to a boil with the butter, and while hot stir into the flour-cocoa paste. Stir until smooth and let cool. Then add gradually the egg yolks which have been beaten until they are light and thick. Beat the egg whites stiff and beat into them ¼ cup sugar. Fold the whites into the first mixture. Bake in custard cups which have been buttered and then sugared. Set in pan of hot water and bake in moderate oven (350° F.) 15–20 minutes. Serve at once.

APPLE SOUFFLÉ

3 c. quartered apples	6 egg whites
2 tbsp. butter	Nutmeg
¾ c. sugar	1 tbsp. lemon juice
2 egg yolks, beaten	

Steam apples. Add butter, sugar, egg yolks, flavoring and lemon juice. Cool. Fold in stiffly beaten egg whites. Pour into buttered and sugared baking dish, set in pan of hot water and bake in moderate oven (350° F.) 45–50 minutes. 515

Cakes Made With Eggs

Such an important part do eggs play in some kinds of cakes that a discussion of them naturally belongs to a discussion of egg cookery. Delicate, snowy angel food cakes, golden sunshine cakes, tender sponge cakes, sweet, melt-in-your-mouth meringues, all owe their very existence to eggs. Thus it is that the rules for egg cookery are the rules which apply in the making of these popular desserts.

Kind of Eggs to Use in Cakes

Many good cake-makers are agreed that eggs which are too fresh are not the most desirable ones for cake-making. The eggs should preferably be at least two or three days old. The most scientific cooks of all do as the commercial baker does—insist that they must use "April eggs" the year around. By April eggs is meant early spring eggs. Why spring eggs whip more satisfactorily and why they make the largest, most pleasing cakes are questions that have not yet been answered. But that these things are so has been demonstrated over and over again.

The commercial baker assures himself of a year-around supply of spring eggs by having them frozen. When these fine eggs are broken out of the shell, put into sterile cans and then frozen and kept frozen until time to use them, eggs that were spring eggs when they went into the can are still spring eggs when they come out. But eggs are frozen only in large containers, in quantities for bakers to use, because they require constant refrigeration. So frozen eggs are not yet available to the homemaker.

She, too, can usually get spring eggs if she wants them and really appreciates their worth. Most of the eggs that go into storage are spring eggs, so all that the housewife needs to do is to use storage eggs. Using storage eggs is not only good for the cake—it is good for the food budget, too. For when eggs are put into storage in spring they are plentiful and therefore cheap. So when they come out of storage in fall they are usually cheaper than the fresh eggs that are scarce in fall and winter, and that for all their vaunted freshness and scarcity make no better cakes than the storage eggs. Perhaps not so good—at least so says many an experienced cook.

Separating Whites and Yolks

Many recipes call for the separation of the white and the yolk. The reason for this has been explained elsewhere. In separating, however, it is most important that none of the yolk be allowed to get into the white. For the yolk contains fat, and if even a tiny bit of it gets into the white, the white will not whip to the stiff froth that is necessary if the egg white is to do the greatest possible amount of leavening.

Important as it is to keep the yolk out of the white, it is equally so to get every bit of the white, not forgetting the stringy white chalazae or cords at each side of the yolk. These are almost pure albumen and add to the whipping quality of egg white.

It is usually desirable to separate each egg into a cup before putting it into the measuring container. Should a particle of yolk get into the white, or should the yolk break before the parts are separated, the egg can be put aside for another use.

Eggs separate most easly when they are cold. The low temperature seems to cause the yolk to be somewhat stiffer than when it is warm.

There are any number of egg openers and separators available. Most cooks, however, still use the method their mothers taught them: striking the egg a sharp blow with a knife or on the edge of a dish. In commercial egg-breaking plants a fixed knife is used for opening eggs.

How to Whip Eggs

Although eggs separate best when they are cold, they whip best when they are at least at room temperature. This is especially true of the yolks. Very often chefs warm the bowl slightly before they put the egg yolks into it for making sponge cakes. Great care must be used not to heat the bowl too much, else the egg yolks will cook. The simplest method for household practice is to use a heavy glass, china or crockery bowl and to warm it by pouring in some hot water, letting it stand a moment, and then pouring it out. The bowl should feel just pleasantly warm to the hand. Chefs say that this slight warming of the yolks makes them more elastic so that they can entangle more air. It may also enable the eggs to dissolve the sugar more easily. Some recipes for sponge cakes call for boiling or hot water. The temperature of the water warms the eggs and has the same effect as warming the bowl.

Egg whites usually whip well when they are at room temperature. It is better not to have them extremely cold. For making angel food cakes and meringues, letting the egg whites stand, covered, on the kitchen table for an hour or two before using brings them to a good temperature.

Captured air, imprisoned in the delicate meshes of egg white, is the secret of many a delectable dish.

Kinds of Egg Beaters

There is a great variety of egg beaters on the market, varying from the simple wire spoon to quite elaborate mechanical beaters. All of them give satisfactory results, and a good rule to follow is to use the type of beater which best suits the individual using it. Whips with very fine wires or blades tend to get results a little more quickly than those with coarser blades. Mechanical whips operate so quickly that care must be used lest they overbeat a mixture.

When Are Egg Whites "Stiff"?

Most recipes direct the cook to beat the egg whites until stiff.

On the interpretation of the word *stiff* depends the success or failure of many a cake.

If egg white is overbeaten, it becomes dry and shows tiny flecks of a solid whitish substance. Those white specks are egg white that is in the same condition as cooked egg white. The beating has coagulated it. When it has reached this stage it has lost its elasticity and therefore its leavening power. A cake made from such overbeaten egg white is small and quite compact instead of large, fluffy and tender.

The exact stage at which egg white is at its best is somewhat difficult

Beaten egg white is the
principal ingredient of
meringue kisses.

to describe. The light, fluffy foam holds its shape in peaks when the beater is drawn out of it, and when the bowl is tipped the egg white just moves—so slowly that it almost seems not to move at all. At this stage the egg white still looks slightly shiny.

Effect of Other Ingredients on Egg White

A little salt added to egg white improves its whipping quality. That is why most recipes which call for whipped egg white suggest adding the salt to the egg white.

Acids tend to make egg tender. This may be the chief purpose of the acid cream of tartar in angel food cake. Cream of tartar also makes the cake snowy white. Without it, angel cakes are creamy in color. The vinegar in meringues serves a similar purpose. Sometimes fruit juices, such as lemon, orange, grapefruit, lime or pineapple juice, are used. These juices not only supply the acid but they add flavor and a delightful fruity fragrance as well.

When some substances containing fat are added to beaten egg white, the foam usually decreases in volume. It gets smaller and smaller, depending on the amount of fat added and the amount of handling. Milk added to beaten egg white makes the foam break down as if by magic. Whipped cream, on the other hand, can be successfully folded into beaten egg white. In fact, egg white is sometimes used in this manner to make whipped cream go farther and to make it taste somewhat less rich.

Folding in the Foam

The real leavening, when beaten egg white is used, is air. The egg white simply acts as the container for the air—each little air cell being a separate container full of the elusive substance which gives some cakes lightness. Naturally, after every effort has been made to entangle as much air as possible, it is important to continue to use care so that as little air as possible is lost during the process of combining the beaten egg white with the other ingredients.

The gentlest way to do this is to fold either the foam into a batter or the dry ingredients into the foam. Folding is simply a gentle process of running a spoon or a spatula down one side of the container, up the other side, bringing some of the mixture with it, and then starting all over again. With each "fold" the bowl is turned a little, so that every part of the mixture is included in the folding process.

If the egg white foam is being folded into a batter, usually all of the white is added at one time and folded in with the least possible amount of handling. If dry ingredients, such as sugar or flour, are folded into the egg white, results are best if only a little of the dry substance, perhaps four tablespoonfuls, is sifted over the top of the foam, then folded in, and the process repeated until all of the dry ingredients have been added.

In such cakes as angel food, when flour is folded into egg white, the flour goes in without lumping if it is first sifted four times with a little of the sugar—four tablespoonfuls of sugar to the cup of flour being a good proportion to allow. Some cooks prefer to sift half of the sugar with the flour. The remainder of the sugar may be beaten into the egg white or folded into it. If beaten in, the sugar is very much more likely to be thoroughly dissolved than if folded in. When the sugar is not dissolved, it shows up in the finished cake as sugar spots on the crust of the cake.

Why an Ungreased Pan?

Egg cakes of every kind are baked in ungreased pans.

As the air in the batter expands and the cake rises, the batter clings to the sides and the tube of the pan, and thus the cake literally lifts itself up to its fluffy height. If the pan is greased the batter cannot cling to the metal; it slips back and the cake falls. The tube in the center of an angel food cake pan provides another surface to which the rising cake batter can cling.

Baking Temperature

Most batters which consist chiefly of egg are baked at a low or moderate temperature. There are several reasons for this. One is that the egg cooks and thus becomes more or less rigid during cooking. The higher the cookery temperature, the more rapidly this happens. If this happens to the egg in the cake before the air has expanded, the cells break and the cake falls.

Another reason is that since high temperatures toughen egg proteins, a cake cooked at a high temperature would lack the delicate tenderness that, next to flavor, is the most desirable quality of egg cakes.

Cooling the Cake in the Pan

When egg cakes are removed from the oven they are inverted on a cake cooler and allowed to remain in the pan until they have cooled. If the cake is taken from the pan while hot, the thin cell walls are so soft that they cannot support the weight of the cake, and it collapses. But if the cake cools while it is still held in shape by the sides of the pan, the cell walls become somewhat more rigid, so that when the cold cake is cut from the pan it will hold its attractive shape.

Cakes Containing Fats

When eggs are used in cakes which contain fat of some kind, they may serve as a leavening, or they may help to keep the particles of fat small and separated, or they may simply add flavor and food value. While eggless cakes are perhaps economical so far as the purse is concerned, they lack the nutritive elements furnished by eggs.

The usual procedure in making cakes containing fat is to cream the fat and the sugar until the mixture is light and fluffy. Then the beaten egg yolks are added. The yolks tend to emulsify the fat—to keep it separated into tiny fluffy bits. Then the dry ingredients and the liquid are added, and finally the stiffly beaten whites are folded in. The beaten whites help to leaven, though in this type of cake the chief leavener is the baking powder or soda. The egg helps to build up a pleasing cake structure which is often described as velvety.

521

STANDARD ANGEL FOOD CAKE

1 c. egg whites	1¼ c. sugar
1 tsp. cream of tartar	1 c. pastry flour
½ tsp. salt	1 tsp. flavoring

Sift ¼ cup sugar with the flour. Beat egg whites until frothy, add cream of tartar and salt and continue beating until egg whites are stiff but not dry. Sift a little of the sugar over the whites and fold it in, and continue until all the sugar has been added. Thne fold in the flour-sugar mixture, about 3 or 4 tablespoons at a time, until it has all been added. Fold in flavoring. Bake in ungreased angel food pan in slow oven (300°–325° F.) for 1¼ hours. Cool in pan.

PRIZE ANGEL FOOD CAKE

1 c. pastry flour	¾ tsp. salt
1½ c. sugar	2 tsp. cream of tartar
1¾ c. egg white	1 tsp. vanilla

Sift sugar once. Add ½ cup of it to the flour and sift together three times. Beat egg whites with Dover beater until frothy. Add cream of tartar and salt and continue beating until eggs are stiff enough to hold their shape. Add the sugar gradually, beating thoroughly after each addition. When sugar is in, fold in the flour, folding in about ¼ at a time. When all flour is in, fold a few additional times. Bake in large ungreased angel food pan. Bake in moderate oven (325° F.) for 60–75 minutes. Let cool in pan.

SMALL ANGEL FOOD CAKE

6 egg whites	¼ tsp. salt
¾ tsp. cream of tartar	¾ c. pastry flour
¾ c. sugar	½ tsp. flavoring

Beat egg whites, salt and cream of tartar until stiff. Sift sugar over whites, beating it in with beater. Fold in sugar gradually, sifting a little at a time over the whites. Add flavoring last. Bake in small ungreased angel cake pan, loaf pan or one-pound coffee cans. This quantity fills two of the 1-pound cans. Bake in slow oven (325° F.) for an hour.

MAPLE ANGEL FOOD CAKE

1 c. sifted pastry flour	1 c. egg whites
½ c. powdered sugar	¼ tsp. salt
1 c. maple syrup	1 tsp. cream of tartar

Sift flour and sugar together 4 times. Boil the syrup until it forms a soft ball in cold water (232° F.). Beat the egg whites until frothy, add the salt and cream of tartar and beat until the whites are stiff. When the syrup has cooled to about 180° F., pour it gradually over the beaten whites, beating constantly. Sift a little of the flour-sugar mixture over the whites and fold it in carefully. Repeat until all of it has been added. Bake in an angel food cake pan, in a slow oven (300° F.) for an hour. Let cool in pan.

CHOCOLATE ANGEL FOOD CAKE

1¼ c. egg whites   1 tsp. cream of tartar
¼ c. cocoa   1 tsp. vanilla
1½ c. sugar   ⅛ tsp. salt
¾ c. pastry flour

Sift together 6 times the sugar, cocoa and flour. Beat egg whites until frothy, add cream of tartar and salt and continue beating until stiff. Sift a little of the flour-cocoa-sugar mixture over the egg whites, about 2 or 3 tablespoons at a time, and fold in carefully. Bake in ungreased angel food cake pan in slow oven (325° F.) for an hour.

DARK CHOCOLATE ANGEL FOOD CAKE

12 egg whites   ½ c. cocoa
½ tsp. salt   1 c. pastry flour
1 tsp. cream of tartar   1 tsp. vanilla
2 c. sugar

Add salt to egg whites and beat until foamy. Add cream of tartar and beat until stiff. Sift flour with 1 cup sugar 5 times. Sift cocoa 5 times with other cup of sugar. Fold cocoa and sugar mixture into the beaten whites, not more than 2 tablespoons at a time, using a wire whip. Then fold in the flour and sugar. Finally fold in vanilla. Bake 1½ hours at 300° F.

SUN TAN ANGEL FOOD CAKE

1½ c. egg whites   ¾ c. general purpose flour
½ tsp. cream of tartar   3 tbsp. cocoa
¼ tsp. salt   1 tsp. vanilla
1½ c. sugar

Sift flour 3 times. Sift sugar 3 times. Add cocoa to 1 cup sugar and sift twice. Add remaining sugar to flour and sift twice. Beat egg whites until frothy. Add cream of tartar and salt and beat until stiff. Fold in sugar and cocoa gradually, a few tablespoonfuls at a time. Add flavoring. Fold in flour and sugar mixture, a little at a time. Bake in ungreased angel food cake pan in slow oven (325° F.) an hour.

HONEY ANGEL FOOD CAKE

½ c. sugar   6 egg whites
½ c. cake flour   ⅛ tsp. salt
1 tsp. cream of tartar   ½ tsp. flavoring
¼ c. honey

Sift the sugar and flour together 5 times. Beat the egg whites until frothy and add the salt and cream of tartar. Continue beating until stiff. Add the honey slowly, beating in each addition. Fold in the flour and sugar mixture, adding about ¼ of it at a time. Add the flavoring and bake in ungreased angel food cake pan in a slow oven (325° F.) for about 50 minutes.

FILLED ANGEL FOOD CAKE

Make a large angel food cake. When cold, fill the center and spread the surface of the cake with the following filling:

1½ tbsp. gelatin	¾ tsp. vanilla
1½ c. milk	Pinch of salt
3 egg yolks, beaten	1½ c. whipping cream
¾ c. sugar	

Soak the gelatin in a little of the cold milk for 10 minutes. Heat the remainder of the milk in the top of a double boiler. Add the gelatin, stirring until completely dissolved. Dissolve the sugar and salt in the milk. When somewhat cooled, add the egg yolks and vanilla. Let cool until the mixture thickens. Add to it the whipping cream and beat thoroughly until the mixture holds its shape. Candied fruits may be folded in, and nuts or cocoanut sprinkled over the top.

ANGEL FOOD ROLL

Bake angel cake in loaf pan, split and fill with marshmallow icing and roll. Serve in slices.

MARBLED ANGEL FOOD CAKE

Part I

1 c. egg whites	1¼ c. sugar
¼ tsp. salt	1 c. pastry flour
¾ tsp. cream of tartar	1 tsp. vanilla

Use method for making angel food batter.

Part II

⅔ c. egg whites	½ c. pastry flour
⅛ tsp. salt	2 tbsp. cocoa
½ tsp. cream of tartar	1 tsp. vanilla
⅔ c. sugar	

Use method for chocolate angel food.
Put batter into ungreased angel food pan by tablespoonfuls, alternating light and dark. Bake in slow oven (325° F.) for 1¼ hours. Cool in pan.

SNOWBALLS

524 Put angel cake batter to a depth of about one inch into custard cups and bake 35–40 minutes in slow oven (325° F.). Ice all over with 7-minute icing and roll in shredded cocoanut.

4 eggs, separated
1 c. sugar
1 c. pastry flour

⅛ tsp. salt
Grated rind of ½ lemon
1 tbsp. lemon juice

Beat the egg yolks until thick and light, adding gradually the sugar, lemon juice and rind. Beat egg whites, adding salt when they are frothy. Fold flour, which has been sifted 4 times, into the yolks, and then fold whites into the batter. Bake in ungreased pan in slow oven (325° F.) 45 minutes. Let cool in pan.

RUTH HEATON'S SPONGE CAKE

6 eggs
1 c. sugar
½ tsp. salt
1 tsp. cream of tartar

½ c. + 2 tbsp. general purpose flour
½ tsp. each vanilla and lemon flavor

Beat whites and yolks separately. Into whites beat ½ sugar and add salt and cream of tartar. Into yolks beat ½ cup sugar. Fold the whites into yolks and fold in the flour and add the flavoring. Bake in slow oven (320° F.) 45 minutes.

LEMON SPONGE CAKE

6 eggs
1½ c. powdered sugar
Juice of 1½ lemons
Rind of 1 lemon

½ c. cold water
1½ c. pastry flour
¼ tsp. salt

Beat whites of eggs until frothy. Add the salt, lemon juice, rind and 2 tablespoons water and continue beating until whites are stiff. Beat for at least 5 minutes, gradually adding the remainder of the cold water. Beat the yolks until very light, gradually adding ¾ cup sugar and beat until sugar is dissolved. Fold the whites into the yolks. Fold in the flour. Bake in ungreased loaf or round pan, in a slow oven (300°–325° F.) 50–60 minutes. When done, invert on cooler and let cake cool in pan.

HOT WATER SPONGE

1½ c. pastry flour
1½ tsp. baking powder
½ tsp. salt
1 c. sugar

6 egg yolks
½ c. boiling water
1 tsp. flavoring

Sift the flour and baking powder together 4 times. Beat the yolks until light and thick, adding gradually the sugar and salt. Beat until the sugar appears to be dissolved. Add the hot water, a little at a time, beating it in thoroughly so as not to break down the foam. Fold in the flour, about ¼ of it at a time. Bake in an ungreased pan in slow oven (325° F.) 45 minutes. Cool in pan.

ROYAL SPONGE CAKE

1½ c. sugar
6 eggs, separated
1 c. pastry flour

½ c. water
½ tsp. cream of tartar
1 tsp. flavoring

Sift flour 6 times with cream of tartar. Boil sugar and water together until the syrup spins a thread. Pour over stiffly beaten egg whites and beat until cool. Beat yolks until light and thick, add flavoring and fold into whites. Fold in flour, a little at a time. Bake in an ungreased pan in slow oven (325° F.) for an hour.

SYRUP SPONGE CAKE

3 eggs, separated
½ c. light corn syrup
½ c. sugar
1¼ c. pastry flour

1 tsp. baking powder
7 tsp. hot milk
½ tsp. salt
½ tsp. flavoring

Beat egg whites until stiff, then beat in gradually the sugar and then the corn syrup. Beat yolks until light and thick. Fold yolks into whites. Add flavoring. Sift flour, baking powder and salt together 3 times. Sift a little of the flour mixture over the eggs, fold in and repeat until all of the flour has been added, adding hot milk gradually. Bake in ungreased pan in slow oven (325° F.) 45 minutes.

SPONGE CAKE SPECIAL

1 c. pastry flour
3 whole eggs
2 egg yolks

1 c. sugar
Rind of 1 lemon

Put eggs, egg whites, sugar and rind into a bowl and beat for 15–20 minutes. Fold in flour which has been sifted 4 times. Bake in ungreased pan for 45 minutes in slow oven (325° F.).

PINEAPPLE FEATHER CAKE

6 eggs, separated
½ c. pineapple juice
1 tbsp. lemon juice
1½ c. sugar

1½ c. pastry flour
1 tsp. baking powder
¼ tsp. salt

Sift flour and baking powder together 4 times. Beat together until light and thick, the yolks, fruit juice and ¾ cup sugar. Beat whites and salt until stiff. Then beat in ¾ cup sugar. Fold the whites into the yolks. Fold in the flour, adding ¼ or ⅓ of it at a time, folding only enough to be sure all the flour is mixed in. Bake in an ungreased angel food tube pan 60 minutes at 300°–325° F. If baked in a large spring pan, bake 75 minutes.
If desired, bake in a large flat pan about 2 inches deep for 45–50 minutes. When cool split in halves lengthwise. Spread each half with icing, roll jelly roll fashion, wrap in a damp towel and put into refrigerator for an hour or two. When ready to serve slice into ¾ inch slices.

526

6 eggs, separated   1½ c. pastry flour
½ c. orange juice   1 tsp. baking powder
1 tbsp. lemon juice   ¼ tsp. salt
1½ c. sugar

Method the same as for Pineapple Feather Cake.

BANANA SPONGE CAKE

6 eggs, separated   1½ c. sugar
½ c. banana pulp   1½ c. pastry flour
   (3 medium bananas)   1 tsp. baking powder
2 tbsp. lemon juice   ¼ tsp. salt

Method the same as for Pineapple Feather Cake.

MAPLE SPONGE

1½ c. maple syrup   ½ tsp. cream of tartar
6 eggs, separated   ¼ tsp. salt
1 c. pastry flour

Sift flour 6 times with cream of tartar and salt. Boil maple syrup until it spins a thread. Pour over stiffly beaten egg whites, beating constantly. Beat until cool. Beat yolks until light and thick. Fold in flour, a little at a time. Fold in the whites. Bake in ungreased pan in slow oven (325° F.) for an hour.

HOT MILK SPONGE

3 eggs   ¾ tsp. salt
1½ c. sugar   1½ tsp. baking powder
1½ c. flour   ¾ c. hot milk

Beat the eggs without separating, adding the sugar and salt gradually. Add flavoring. Sift the flour and baking powder 3 times. Fold into the eggs. Add the hot milk gradually, stirring constantly. Bake in ungreased loaf pan in slow oven (300°–325° F.) an hour.

CHOCOLATE SPONGE CAKE

4 eggs, separated   ½ tsp. vanilla
½ c. sugar   1 c. pastry flour
4 tbsp. cold water   1 tsp. baking powder
4 tbsp. cocoa   ½ tsp. salt

Sift together 3 times the flour, cocoa, baking powder and salt. Beat egg whites until stiff, adding sugar gradually, with constant beating. Beat egg yolks and water. Fold yolks into whites. Then fold in sifted dry ingredients. Bake in ungreased angel food pan in moderate oven (350° F.) 40–50 minutes. Cool in pan. Serve with sweetened whipped cream.

527

Who could resist sponge cake split and filled with sweetened fruit and topped with pastel icing or fruit whip?

CHOCOLATE FILLED SPONGE CAKE

Bake 6-egg sponge cake in angel food cake pan. When cool, cut it in 5 layers. On each layer spread the following filling:

4 sq. bitter chocolate	¾ c. sugar
1 c. water	2 tbsp. butter
1½ tbsp. cornstarch	1 tsp. vanilla
2 egg yolks, beaten	1 c. chopped nut meats
1 c. evaporated milk	

Put chocolate and water in top of double boiler. Heat until chocolate is melted. Mix cornstarch, sugar and milk and add to chocolate, stirring until smooth. Cook until mixture thickens, stirring constantly. Add egg yolks and butter. Remove from heat, cool and add vanilla and nuts.

Frost cake with the following icing:

1½ c. confectioners' sugar	1 sq. bitter chocolate
½ tsp. vanilla	1 egg white

Combine egg white, sugar and flavoring. Add melted chocolate. More sugar may be needed to make icing of spreading consistency.

528

GOLD CAKE

8 egg yolks
1¼ c. sugar
¾ c. butter
¾ c. milk

2½ c. pastry flour
2½ tsp. baking powder
½ tsp. flavoring

Cream butter and sugar together until fluffy. Sift flour and baking powder together 4 times. Beat the egg yolks until thick and light, and add to butter-sugar mixture, stirring in thoroughly. Add flour alternately with milk, a little at a time. Add flavoring. Bake in 3 greased layer cake pans in moderate oven (350° F.) 25 minutes. Put layers together with fruit filling and frost with marshmallow icing or apricot fruit whip.

EGG YOLK SPONGE CAKE

9 egg yolks
1 whole egg
2 c. sugar
1 c. hot water
2 c. pastry flour

½ tsp. salt
2 tsp. baking powder
1 tbsp. orange rind
1 tbsp. orange juice

Beat egg yolks and whole egg together until light and fluffy. Add sugar gradually, beating for about 10 minutes. When mixture becomes quite stiff, add a little hot water, beat it in thoroughly, then add a little more, until about ½ cup has been added. Sift flour, baking powder and salt together 4 times, and add it alternately with the remainder of the water. Fold in flavoring and bake in slow oven (325° F.) 60 minutes.

GOLDEN ANGEL CAKE

9 egg yolks
1½ c. sugar
¾ c. boiling water
¾ tsp. salt

3 tsp. baking powder
2¼ c. pastry flour
1 tsp. lemon juice

Beat eggs until thick and light. Add sugar, salt, water and lemon juice gradually, beating until sugar is dissolved. Fold in flour which has been sifted 4 times with baking powder. Bake in slow oven (300°325– F.) 50–60 minutes.

MOLASSES SPONGE CAKE

4 eggs, separated
1 c. sugar
½ c. molasses
1 tsp. vanilla
½ c. cold coffee

10 walnut meats, finely chopped
½ tsp. salt
1½ c. pastry flour
2 tsp. baking powder

Beat egg yolks until thick and light. Add gradually the sugar, coffee and molasses, beating thoroughly. Sift flour with salt and baking powder. Add to egg yolks. Fold in stiffly beaten whites. Last fold in vanilla and nut meats. Bake in ungreased cake pan in slow oven (325° F.) 35–40 minutes.

ICED CHOCOLATE SPONGE DROPS

3 egg yolks
½ c. sugar
¼ c. boiling water
1 tsp. vanilla

¾ c. pastry flour sifted with
1 tsp. baking powder
¼ tsp. salt
2 tbsp. cocoa

Beat egg yolks, gradually adding sugar. Continue beating until sugar is dissolved and eggs are lemon colored and thick. Gradually add boiling water, flavoring, mixing thoroughly. Fold in sifted dry ingredients. Drop by spoonfuls on ungreased cookie sheets and bake 20 minutes in moderate oven (350° F.). Ice lightly with chocolate icing.

GINGER SPONGE BALLS

5 eggs, beaten light
2 c. sugar
¼ tsp. salt
3½ c. flour

1 tsp. cinnamon
½ tsp. cloves, ground
2 tsp. baking powder
1 c. shredded crystallized ginger

Blend sugar and ginger thoroughly with eggs. Stir in 3 cups flour with which salt, spices and baking powder have been sifted, and beat well. Add enough more flour—usually ½ cup—so that mixture may be shaped into a long narrow roll, 1 inch in diameter. Let chill for several hours before cutting into ½-inch thick slices. Flatten these slightly before placing them on oiled baking sheet. Brush surface lightly with egg white, and center with red or green seedless raisins. Bake in moderately hot oven (400° F.) for 15 minutes. Store and allow to ripen for 3 or 4 days.

DAFFODIL CAKE

Yellow Mixture
3 egg yolks
⅛ tsp. salt
3 tbsp. sugar
1 tbsp. pastry flour

White Mixture
8 egg whites
¾ tsp. cream of tartar
⅛ tsp. salt
1 c. pastry flour
1 tsp. flavoring
1⅓ c. sugar

Prepare white batter as follows:
Beat egg whites with cream of tartar and salt until stiff. Beat in 1 cup sugar, adding gradually. Fold in 1 cup flour which has been sifted 4 times.
For the yellow mixture, beat the egg yolks until light and thick, and then beat in 3 tablespoons sugar. Fold in a tablespoon of flour and 4 tablespoons of the white mixture. Put half of the white batter into an ungreased angel food cake pan, leaving an open space around the tube. Pour the yellow mixture into this space around the tube, put remainder of white batter on top and bake in slow oven (300°–325° F.) 1¼ hours.

TEA TIME SPONGE CAKES

3 egg yolks
¾ c. sugar
3 tbsp. cold water
½ tsp. lemon rind
⅛ tsp. salt
½ tsp. lemon extract

¾ c. pastry flour
3 egg whites
¾ tsp. baking powder
2 cans crushed pineapple

Beat egg yolks until thick and lemon colored. Add sugar gradually, continuing beating. Combine water, rind and extract and beat into first mixture. Fold in flour. Beat egg whites until nearly stiff. Add baking powder and salt and beat until they peak. Fold into egg yolk mixture. Pour into ungreased muffin pans and bake in moderate oven (350° F.) 30 minutes. Cool by inverting pans, then remove from pans. When ready to serve, take out centers with a fork and fill with the following. Combine crushed pineapple, 1 cup cream whipped, and 1 cup marshmallows quartered. Chill ½ hour and use in sponge cake shells.

SPONGE DROP CAKES

3 egg yolks
½ c. sugar
¼ c. boiling water
½ tsp. lemon juice

¾ c. pastry flour
1 tsp. baking powder
¼ tsp. salt
¼ tsp. grated lemon rind

Beat egg yolks until thick and lemon colored. Add sugar, gradually and beat until thick, dissolving as much of the sugar as possible. Add the water, lemon juice and rind. Fold in the flour which has been sifted 3 times with the salt and baking powder. Drop by spoonfuls on ungreased cookie sheet and bake 15–20 minutes in moderate oven (350° F.).

SPONGE CAKE EASTER EGGS

1 c. sifted flour
1 tsp. baking powder
3 eggs
1 c. sugar

Pinch of salt
2 tsp. lemon juice
6 tbsp. hot milk

Sift flour, baking powder and salt together. Beat eggs until very light. Add sugar gradually, beating with an egg beater. Add lemon juice. Fold in flour alternating with milk, mixing quickly and lightly until mixture is smooth. Bake 45 minutes in moderate oven (350° F.).
To make an egg shape fill custard cups slightly less than ¼ full so that after the cakes have risen they will not more than half fill the custard cups. When the cakes are cool, put the flat sides of 2 of them together with icing between them. This makes the Easter egg shape.

531

APPLE SPONGE

2 eggs
1/4 c. sugar
1/4 c. milk
1/2 tsp. salt

1 c. pastry flour
2 tsp. baking powder
5 apples, sliced

Beat eggs until light and thick. Add sugar, beating it in thoroughly. Sift flour with baking powder and salt 4 times and fold into eggs. Fold in apples. Bake in buttered and sugared baking dish in moderate oven (350° F.) 1 hour. Serve with Italian Sauce.

ITALIAN SAUCE

2 tbsp. butter
3/4 c. confectioners' sugar
2 tsp. cornstarch
1/2 c. candied cherries

3 egg yolks, well beaten
1 lemon, juice and rind
1/2 c. boiling water

Cream butter. Add sugar and cornstarch. Blend well. Add boiling water, stirring constantly and cook 10 minutes. Remove from fire, add egg yolks and cook 1 minute longer. Add candied cherries and lemon juice.

PUFFBALL SPONGE CAKES

1 c. sugar
1/2 c. water
6 egg whites
6 egg yolks

1/2 tsp. vanilla
1 c. pastry flour
1/8 tsp. salt
1/4 tsp. almond extract

Boil sugar and water together until they spin a thread. Pour over the stiffly beaten whites. Beat until cool.
Beat the yolks and salt. Fold these into the whites and syrup mixture. Add flavoring. Fold in the flour which has been sifted 3 times. Bake in custard cups in slow oven (300°–325° F.) 30–45 minutes, depending on size of pans. Ice with plain icing of confectioner's sugar and warm water, flavored with vanilla.

POTATO FLOUR SPONGE

4 eggs, separated
1 c. powdered sugar
1/2 c. potato flour

2 tsp. baking powder
1/4 tsp. salt
1 tsp. flavoring

Beat yolks until light and thick, adding powdered sugar gradually. Add salt to whites and beat until stiff. Fold into yolks. Fold in a little at a time the potato flour which has been sifted twice with the baking powder. Add flavoring. Bake in 2 layers in moderate oven (350° F.) 15 minutes, or until toothpick inserted in center comes out dry.

532

UPSIDE-DOWN SPONGE

3-egg sponge cake, plus   ¼ c. nutmeats
½ c. butter   Sliced canned pineapple, prunes
1 c. brown sugar   or apricots

Melt butter in bottom of cake pan. Spread sugar over butter, then put in the nutmeats and fruit—pineapple slices, pitted prunes or stewed apricots. Pour sponge cake batter on fruit and bake in moderately fast oven (375° F.) 30–35 minutes. Let cake cool 5 minutes. Turn out and spread syrup over cake.

CARROT CAKE

1 c. mashed cooked carrots   1 c. nutmeats, finely chopped
6 eggs, separated   ¼ tsp. salt
1 c. powdered sugar

Beat yolks until light, adding sugar and salt gradually, and then the carrots. Fold in the stiffly beaten whites and then the nutmeats. Bake in moderate oven (350° F.) 45 minutes if in layers, or 60 minutes if in loaf. Serve with sweetened whipped cream.

GERMAN ALMOND TORTE

3 eggs, separated   4 large soda crackers, rolled fine
3 whole eggs   ½ tsp. vanilla
½ c. grated almonds

Beat 3 yolks with the whole eggs until light and thick. Gradually add the sugar, beating thoroughly. Mix the almonds and cracker crumbs and add to the yolk mixture. Fold in the stiffly beaten whites and the flavoring. Bake in a ring mold which has been greased and then dusted with cracker crumbs. Bake in slow oven (300° F.) an hour, or until done. The time will vary somewhat with the type of mold used. Serve with whipped cream. This batter may be baked in individual ring molds or shell pans.

PASTEL SURPRISE

Cut a loaf sponge cake in half lengthwise, as for a sandwich. Spread lower half thickly with pastel icing, then put on upper half of cake and ice all over with the remainder of the icing. This will keep nicely for 2 days. See Icings.

CRANBERRY TORTE

4 eggs, separated   2 tsp. baking powder
1 c. sugar   ½ c. water
1 c. chopped nut meats   Grated rind of ½ lemon
1 c. chopped dates   ¼ tsp. salt
1 c. pastry flour

Beat egg yolks with sugar until light, gradually adding water. Sift flour with baking powder, add nuts, dates and lemon rind. Fold into egg and sugar mixture. Fold in stiffly beaten whites. Bake in two layers in moderate oven (350° F.) 30–40 minutes. When cold spread with Cranberry Filling.   533

CRANBERRY FILLING

2 c. cranberries	1 tbsp. cornstarch
1 c. water	Grated rind of 1 orange
¾ c. sugar	

Boil sugar and water 5 minutes. Add cranberries and orange rind and cook until all of the berries have popped. Make paste of cornstarch with 1 tablespoon cold water. Cook 3 minutes. Cool and spread between layers of torte. Top with cranberry whip.

CRANBERRY WHIP

1 egg white	Pinch of salt
½ c. cranberry jelly	

Put all ingredients into bowl and whip until mixture holds its shape.

CHOCOLATE REFRIGERATOR TORTE

1 c. butter	1 sponge cake
1 lb. powdered sugar	3 eggs
½ lb. sweet chocolate	

Cream the butter, and add the powdered sugar gradually, and then the melted chocolate. Add the unbeaten eggs, one at a time, beating each egg in thoroughly before adding another. Line a spring form with slices of sponge cake, pour the chocolate mixture over the cake, cover with sponge cake, and chill in refrigerator 24 hours. If a pan other than a spring form is used, line the pan first with oiled paper so the torte may be removed without breaking.

DATE TORTE

6 eggs, separated	6 rolled crackers
1½ c. sugar	1 lb. dates, seeded and chopped
1 tsp. baking powder	½ lb. walnut meats, chopped

Beat egg yolks until thick and light. Add sugar gradually, beating thoroughly. Combine the dates, cracker crumbs, nuts and baking powder. Add yolk-sugar mixture. Fold in the stiffly beaten whites. Bake in spring form 1 hour in slow oven (300° F.). Cool in pan. To serve, top each piece with whipped cream. This cake shrinks from the pan as it cools.

LOG CABIN ROLL

1 c. flour	4 tbsp. cold water
4 tbsp. cocoa	½ tsp. vanilla
½ tsp. soda	1 c. coffee cream
4 eggs, separated	2 tbsp. confectioners' sugar
½ c. sugar	⅛ tsp. salt

Sift together three times flour, cocoa, soda and salt. Beat egg whites until stiff, adding sugar gradually with continuous beating. Beat egg yolks until light, adding water gradually. Fold into egg white mixture, then fold in dry ingredients. Pour batter into long shallow pan which has been lined with greased paper. Bake in a moderate oven (350° F.) 25–30 minutes. Turn out on damp cloth and cool slightly. Spread generously with marshmallow icing, roll jelly roll fashion and slice.

MACAROONS

¼ lb. almond paste
½ c. sugar
2 egg whites

3 tbsp. powdered sugar
1 tbsp. pastry flour

Break almond paste into bits. With the hands or with a pie crust mixer blend thoroughly the paste and egg whites, adding the granulated sugar gradually. When well mixed stir in the powdered sugar which has been sifted with the flour. Mix until stiff enough to hold its shape, adding more powdered sugar if necessary. Shape in rounds on cookie sheets covered with sheets of paper. Lay wet towel over top and let stand 4 or 5 hours, or over night. Bake in slow oven (300° F.) 30 minutes. Letting the macaroons stand before baking causes them to crack when they are baked. This is highly desirable since it adds to their attractiveness.

SPRINGERLE

2 lb. powdered sugar
1½ c. egg whites

2 lb. general purpose flour
1 oz. anise seed, pulverized

Put sugar and egg whites into the top of a double boiler and mix thoroughly. Set over hot water and whip briskly until light and frothy. Remove from hot bath and whip until the mixture becomes cool. Add the pulverized anise seed, and then the flour. Mix to a rather stiff paste. Put mixture through a cookie press on cookie sheets that have been slightly greased and then dusted with flour. Cover and allow to dry for 3 or 4 hours. Bake in moderate oven (350° F.).

BOHEMIAN CAKE

6 eggs
1 c. sugar

1 tsp. baking powder
½ lb. finely ground walnuts

Separate the eggs and beat well. Blend the nuts with the egg whites and combine with the sugar, yolks and baking powder. Bake in greased layer cake pans in slow oven (325° F.). Frost with butter frosting. It is important that the nuts be ground fine.

SWEDISH TORTE

5 eggs
1 c. sugar

½ c. potato flour
2 tsp. lemon juice

Beat egg yolks until light and thick. Add sugar, lemon juice and potato flour and beat thoroughly. Fold in the beaten whites carefully and bake in tube or layer pans in slow oven (325° F.) about 50 minutes. When cool, spread with egg filling.

Egg Filling

1 c. milk or cream	1 tsp. potato flour
2 egg yolks	1 tsp. lemon extract
2 tbsp. sugar	

Mix yolks, sugar and potato flour. Pour the hot cream or milk over the yolk mixture and cook in double boiler, with constant stirring, until it thickens. Cool and spread between layers of cake.

CAPUCIN BREAD

1 c. sugar	⅓ c. citron, chopped
7 eggs	½ c. flour
2 oz. chocolate	½ tsp. cinnamon
½ c. unblanched almonds, coarsely chopped	¼ tsp. cloves

Beat sugar and eggs with rotary beater until very light and fluffy. Blend in the melted chocolate. Sift together flour and spices, and add citron and nuts. Combine the flour mixture with the eggs and sugar and blend thoroughly. Pour into shallow greased pans. Bake in moderate oven (350° F.) 35–45 minutes. When cool cut into pieces 2 by 3 inches. Serve with coffee or tea.

BISCUIT SAVOY (French Cake)

1¼ c. granulated sugar	4 egg whites
4 egg yolks	Rind of 1 lemon
1 c. pastry flour	

Beat the egg yolks and the sugar with a rotary beater until the mixture is thick and light. Sift in the flour and beat well. Add the rind of a lemon. Fold in the beaten whites. Bake in an angel food cake pan in a slow oven (300° F.) for an hour. Let cake cool in pan. When cool, remove from pan and put cake into a slow oven for about 15 minutes to crisp the crust.

CINNAMON STICKS (Zimmetstangen—German)

4 egg whites	¾ lb. sugar
1 oz. cinnamon	14 oz. pounded almonds

Beat the whites of eggs and stir with the sugar for 15 minutes, or until sugar is practically dissolved. Then add the cinnamon and almonds to form a paste. Place little strips of this paste (about 3 inches long and ½ inch thick) on a buttered cookie sheet and bake in moderately hot oven (375°–400° F.).

TRIESTER TORTE (German)

½ lb. butter	½ lb. sugar
6 eggs	2 oz. grated dry roll or finely ground bread crumbs
¼ lb. unsweetened chocolate	
½ lb. unblanched grated almonds	

Cream the butter, add beaten yolks and sugar gradually, the almonds and the melted chocolate and finally the bread crumbs and whites of eggs, stiffly beaten. Fill a well buttered pan and bake in slow oven (325° F.) 55–60 minutes.

536

APRICOT WHIP CAKE

3 eggs, separated
¾ c. sugar
¼ c. apricot juice
½ tsp. lemon extract

1 c. pastry flour
1 tsp. baking powder
¼ tsp. salt

Beat the egg yolks until thick. Add the sugar gradually, combining thoroughly. Add the water and the lemon extract. Sift together the flour, baking powder and salt and blend with the liquid ingredients. Fold in the stiffly beaten whites. Bake in a shallow layer pan in a moderately hot oven (375° F.) 20 minutes. When cool spread thickly with apricot whip. Other fruit whips may be substituted.

WHITE CAKE WITH HICKORY NUTS

4 egg whites
½ c. butter
1½ c. sugar
1 c. chopped hickory nuts

1 c. cold water
2½ c. pastry flour
2 tsp. baking powder
1 tsp. almond extract

Cream the butter and sugar thoroughly. Alternately add the flour and the water, leaving out a small quantity of the flour to be sifted with the baking powder. Beat for 2 minutes, first adding the flavoring and then the mixed baking powder. Fold in the beaten whites of the eggs. Add one extra tablespoon flour sifted over 1 cup chopped hickory nut meats. Bake in a moderaet oven (350° F.).

POUND CAKE I

¾ c. butter
1 c. sugar
4 eggs
2 c. flour

½ tsp. salt
1 tsp. vanilla
1 tsp. lemon extract

Sift the sugar two or three times. Blend with the butter. Beat as light as possible. Separate the eggs. Beat the yolks until thick and lemon colored and the whites until stiff. Add the yolks to the butter-sugar mixture and beat hard. Fold in the beaten whites alternately with the flour previously sifted with the salt. Add the flavoring last. Pour into a paper lined loaf pan and bake in a moderate oven (350° F.).

BERKSHIRE CAKE

4 eggs, separated
¾ c. sugar
1 tsp. baking powder
1 tsp. flavoring

¾ c. flour, sifted 4 times with baking powder
¼ tsp. salt

Beat yolks until thick and lemon colored. Add salt and then gradually the sugar, beating constantly. Add flavoring. Fold in some of the flour (about ¼ cup), then about ⅛ of the beaten egg whites, then flour, and repeat until all the flour and egg whites have been added, adding some of the egg white last. Bake in 2 layer cake pans in moderately hot oven (375° F.) 20 minutes. When cool, put together and frost with chocolate filling.

Chocolate Filling

1/4 lb. sweet chocolate   1 c. cream or evaporated milk,
1 egg, slightly beaten   whipped

Melt chocolate over hot water. Add egg, mixing thoroughly. Fold into whipped cream or milk and spread on cake.

POUND CAKE II

1/2 c. butter   1/4 tsp. salt
1 c. sifted sugar   1 tsp. orange extract
6 eggs   Grated rind of 1 large orange
2 c. flour

Cream the butter thoroughly. Add the sugar and beat hard. Add well beaten yolks of eggs, then add the stiffly beaten whites. Sift the flour and the salt. Add flour to mixture gradually, and last the extract and grated rind. Bake in a loaf in a moderate oven (350° F.) 45–50 minutes.

EMERGENCY CAKE

4 1/3 c. sifted flour   1 c. butter
4 1/2 tsp. baking powder   2 c. sugar
1 1/2 c. milk   2 tsp. vanilla
4 eggs

Sift the flour, the baking powder and salt together at least three times. Cream butter, add sugar gradually and beat until light and fluffy. Add well beaten eggs. Beat briskly. Add dry ingredients alternately with the milk a little at a time and beat until smooth after each addition. Add vanilla. Divide into 3 equal parts and cover, place in refrigerator until ready to bake cakes. Batter can be kept a week if desired.

LEMON CREAM REFRIGERATOR CAKE

4 eggs   Juice of 2 lemons
1 1/3 c. condensed milk   2 tbsp. sugar
1 1/2 doz. lady fingers or small sponge cake

Beat egg yolks until lemon colored, add milk and lemon juice and cook over boiling water, stirring briskly until mixture thickens. Cool. Beat egg whites until stiff, add sugar and fold into first mixture. Line a loaf pan, bottom and sides with halves of lady fingers or slices of sponge cake. Pour in lemon cream, add layer of cake and then top with layer of lemon cream. Place in refrigerator over night and serve with topping of whipped cream.

Icings and Flavorings

QUICK FROSTING

1 egg white   2 1/2 c. sifted powdered sugar
2 tsp. hot water   1 tsp. flavoring

538   Add water to egg white, beat until stiff and add gradually the sugar until frosting is of proper consistency to spread. Add the flavoring and beat thoroughly.

BOILED ICING

2¼ c. sugar
¼ tsp. salt
2 egg whites

½ c. light corn syrup
½ c. water
1 tsp. flavoring

Cook sugar, syrup, salt and water together until the syrup forms a firm ball in cold water (248° F.). Pour hot syrup over stiffly beaten egg whites, beating thoroughly between additions. Beat until mixture holds its shape. Add flavoring. Spread on cake.

SEVEN MINUTE ICING

2 egg whites, unbeaten
1½ c. sugar
5 tbsp. cold water

¼ tsp. cream of tartar
1 tsp. vanilla
¼ tsp. salt

Put all ingredients except vanilla in upper part of double boiler. Beat with rotary beater until thoroughly mixed. Place over rapidly boiling water, beating constantly, and cook 7 minutes, or until icing will hold its shape. Remove from fire, add vanilla, and beat until cool and thick enough to spread.

DIVINITY FROSTING

3 c. sugar
1 tbsp. light corn syrup
1⅓ c. boiling water

4 egg whites, beaten
1 tsp. vanilla

Cook together the sugar, corn syrup and water until it forms a firm ball in water or spins a long thread (248° F.). Pour the hot syrup gradually over the beaten egg whites, beating constantly. Continue beating until cool and stiff enough to hold shape. Add flavoring.

DECORATIVE ICING

1 egg white
¼ tsp. cream of tartar

¼ tsp. vanilla
1⅓ c. confectioners' sugar

To the unbeaten egg white add cream of tartar, flavoring and ⅓ cup confectioner's sugar. Beat thoroughly and add gradually 1 cup sugar, beating until mixture is stiff enough to hold its shape. Shape with pastry tube.

HONEY FROSTING

2 c. sugar
2 tbsp. strained honey
½ c. water

⅛ tsp. salt
2 egg whites
1 tsp. vanilla

Cook sugar, honey, water and salt to firm ball stage (248° F.). Pour the hot syrup slowly over the stiffly beaten egg whites. Continue beating until the proper consistency for spreading. Add flavoring.

539

MOROCCO FROSTING

2 egg whites, unbeaten
1¼ c. sugar
¼ c. brown sugar

5 tbsp. cold water
1 sq. bitter chocolate

Put egg whites, sugars and water in top of double boiler. Beat with rotary beater until thoroughly mixed. Set pan over boiling water, and cook for 7 minutes, beating constantly with the rotary beater. The frosting should hold its shape when the beater is drawn through it. Remove from fire, fold in the melted chocolate thoroughly, and spread on cake.

BAKED ICING

1 egg white
½ c. brown sugar

¼ c. broken nut meats

Beat egg white until stiff. Add brown sugar gradually, beating it in. Spread the icing on top of batter, sprinkle on the nuts and bake icing and cake in moderate oven until done. This icing is best on cakes which contain fat, and must be baked at a moderate temperature (350° F.) for 35–45 minutes. It is especially good on spice cake.

REFRIGERATOR FROSTING

4 sq. unsweetened
  chocolate
2 tbsp. hot water

1 c. confectioners' sugar
½ c. butter
2 eggs, well beaten

Melt chocolate in double boiler over hot water. Add the hot water and blend. Add the beaten eggs and the sugar and remove from the fire, but allow the mixture to stand over hot water, stirring it constantly until it has thickened. Cool quickly until lukewarm. Add the butter, blending it thoroughly. This frosting may be kept in the refrigerator for several days, if stored in a tightly covered jar.

CHOCOLATE ICING

1 unbeaten egg white
1 tbsp. butter
1 tbsp. sweet cream

1¼ c. confectioners' sugar
1½ sq. bitter chocolate

Melt chocolate. Put egg white in shallow dish. Add sugar gradually, beating in with whip. Add butter, melted chocolate and beat until the right consistency to spread.

540

CREAMY CHOCOLATE FROSTING

1 tbsp. butter	¼ c. milk
1 c. sifted confectioners' sugar	½ tsp. vanilla
1 egg or 2 egg yolks	2–4 sq. unsweetened chocolate

Put butter in top of double boiler. When melted add confectioners' sugar and milk, mixing thoroughly. Let stand over hot water for several minutes. Remove from heat and add beaten egg, vanilla and melted chocolate. Set in a pan of very cold water or cracked ice and beat with rotary beater until proper consistency for spreading.

LEMON FROSTING

2 egg yolks, unbeaten	Grated rind of 1 lemon
4½ c. confectioners' sugar	4 tbsp. lemon juice

Add lemon rind and juice to egg yolks. Stir in the sugar until the mixture is of proper consistency for spreading.

PASTEL ICING

1 egg white	Pinch of salt
½ c. jelly	

Put all ingredients into bowl and beat until mixture holds shape. Spread on cake. This icing is best if used the day it is made.

COFFEE FROSTING

3 tbsp. butter	3 c. confectioners' sugar
¼ tsp. salt	¼ c. very strong coffee
1 egg yolk	

Cream butter and half the sugar. Add the beaten yolk and beat until fluffy. Add the remaining sugar alternately with coffee. Spread on cake and garnish with chopped pistachios.

APPLE CREAM TOPPING

1 c. grated fresh apple or unsweetened apple sauce	1 tbsp. lemon juice
1 egg white	¾ c. sugar

Beat all together until mixture holds shape. If used on spice cake a little cinnamon may first be blended with the sugar.

WHIPPED FRUIT FROSTING

1½ c. mashed or puréed fruit	1 tbsp. lemon juice
1½ c. powdered sugar	2 egg whites

Put all ingredients into a large bowl and beat with rotary or mechanical mixer until the mixture holds its shape. Spread on cake and serve. This frosting is best if served the day it is made.

541

CUSTARD CREAM FILLING

$\frac{1}{3}$ c. pastry flour	$\frac{7}{8}$ c. sugar
$\frac{1}{8}$ tsp. salt	2 eggs, or 4 yolks
2 c. scalded milk	1 tsp. vanilla

Mix the salt, sugar and flour. Add the eggs, slightly beaten. Add the hot milk gradually, stirring constantly. Cook in double boiler until smooth, stirring. When cool, add flavoring.

LADY BALTIMORE FROSTING AND FILLING

2 egg whites, stiffly beaten	1 tsp. light corn syrup
$1\frac{1}{2}$ c. sugar	1 tsp. vanilla
$\frac{1}{2}$ c. raisins, chopped	$\frac{1}{2}$ c. pecan meats
$\frac{2}{3}$ c. boiling water	6 figs, chopped

Combine sugar, corn syrup and water. Place over low heat and stir until mixture boils. Then boil rapidly until a small amount of syrup dropped in cold water forms a firm ball, or spins a long thread when dropped from the tip of a spoon (248° F.). Pour syrup slowly over beaten egg whites, beating constantly. Add vanilla. Continue beating with a rotary egg beater for 10–15 minutes, or until frosting is cool and of the consistency to spread. Use wooden spoon when too stiff for the egg beater. Add fruits and nuts to one-half the frosting. Spread between layers. Spread remaining frosting on top and sides of cake. Makes enough frosting to cover 2 nine inch layers.

LEMON BUTTER FILLING

2 eggs	2 lemons, juice and rind
1 c. sugar	2 tbsp. butter

Beat the eggs and sugar together. Add butter, the grated rind and juice of the lemons. Cook in double boiler until thick, stirring constantly. Cool before spreading.

WHIPPED CREAM PARFAIT TOPPING

1 egg white	3 tbsp. sugar
$\frac{1}{2}$ c. whipping cream	$\frac{1}{4}$ tsp. flavoring

Whip egg white until stiff. Gradually add sugar, beating after each addition. Whip cream stiff, and fold in the flavoring. Fold egg white mixture into whipped cream and spread on cake. Chopped nuts or candied fruit may be folded into the mixture. This is a good way to extend whipping cream.

Ethereal concoctions of egg white and sugar. Meringues, plain and fancy, to suit every taste.

The Three Kinds of Meringue

Meringues are ethereal concoctions of beaten egg whites and sugar, with or without flavoring added. Obviously, it is possible to have a wide variation in the proportions of the two chief ingredients, and this variation is the secret of the different kinds of meringues. A little sugar makes the meringue that rises fluffily on top of pies and puddings. A little more sugar makes the meringue, better known as frosting or icing, that makes a favorite cake doubly desirable. And a lot of sugar makes the confection-like meringue that crunches crisply and sweetly under strawberries in June, under peaches in September, and under ice cream the year around.

The first of these meringues, the one that is used on pies and puddings, usually contains two tablespoonfuls of granulated sugar for each egg white used. The sugar is either folded or beaten into the stiffly beaten egg whites. When it is beaten in there seems to be less tendency for syrupy beads to form on the surface of the meringue after it is baked. Perhaps the beating makes the sugar dissolve more thoroughly than folding it in can do.

When powdered or confectioners' sugar is used, two tablespoonfuls of powdered and one of granulated are allowed for each egg white. The powdered sugar is most easily blended with the beaten white if it is first thoroughly mixed with the granulated sugar.

543

There is a wide difference of opinion as to the proper temperature for baking meringues of this type. Some chefs prefer a very hot oven for a short time, while others insist the oven must be very slow, and the meringue cooked a longer time. For general household cookery, good results are obtained if the meringue is baked in a slow oven (325°–350° F.) for 12 to 15 minutes.

For frostings, the meringue is usually made by pouring a hot syrup over the beaten egg whites. This cooks the egg and takes the place of baking. Sweet meringues made by whipping the sugar into the uncooked egg white may be spread on cake batter and baked with the cake.

The sweet confection-like meringues which may be a dessert in themselves or the foundation of very special dishes, contain a large amount of sugar. This type of meringue is often called meringue glacé, or macaroons, or kisses. It has a crisp crust and a creamy interior, or it may be crisp all the way through, depending on the length of time it is baked.

What really happens in making this kind of meringue is that a large amount of sugar is first dissolved in the egg white by long beating. During the baking moisture evaporates and the sugar recrystallizes into tiny crystals, so tiny that they are imperceptible to the tongue. The egg white serves to keep these tiny crystals apart so they cannot cluster together to form a coarse grain. The smallness of the sugar crystals is what gives these meringues their melt-in-the-mouth quality.

An acid is sometimes added. It may be cream of tartar, vinegar or fruit juice. The acid does two things: it helps make the meringue mixture snowy white and it helps to make the sugar crystals small.

For these meringues the baking temperature must be low, about 250°–275° F., so that they keep their whiteness while the air in the egg white expands and gives them lightness as the water evaporates.

LIGHT MERINGUES

| 2 egg whites | ½ tsp. vanilla or other flavoring |
| 4 tbsp. sugar | |

Beat the egg whites until frothy. Add the sugar and continue beating until stiff. Add flavoring. Pile on pie or pudding and bake in a slow oven (325° F.) 15–18 minutes.

6 egg whites Pinch of salt
1½ tsp. vinegar Vanilla
2 c. sifted sugar

Beat egg whites until stiff. Sift about 2 tablespoons sugar over the whites and beat until sugar is thoroughly mixed, adding vinegar gradually. Repeat until all of the sugar has been whipped in. Bake on wet brown paper in slow oven (250° F.) until done.

MERINGUE KISSES

4 egg whites 1 c. finely granulated sugar
½ tsp. vanilla ⅛ tsp. salt

Beat egg whites and salt until stiff. Sift 3 tablespoons sugar over whites and beat thoroughly. Repeat until all of the sugar has been added. Fold in the flavoring. Drop mixture by spoonfuls or from pastry tube on wet paper and bake 30 minutes in slow oven (275°–300° F.). Chopped nut meats may be added before baking.

FRENCH MERINGUES

2 c. sugar 1 tsp. vanilla
¾ c. water Pinch of salt
5 egg whites

Cook the sugar and water together until syrup forms a soft ball in cold water (238° F.). Stir only until the sugar is completely dissolved. Pour gradually over the stiffly beaten egg whites, beating constantly. Continue beating until the mixture is cold. Add the flavoring. Cover and set aside for 15 minutes. Moisten sheets of clean paper and arrange them on cookie sheets or cake pans. On this arrange the meringues, shaping them with a pastry tube or with a spoon. Bake in a very slow oven (270° F.) for an hour or longer, depending on the size of the meringues. If desired, the soft inner portion may be scooped out after baking and the meringue shell filled with ice cream or fruit.

ITALIAN MERINGUE (Base for Sherbets)

4 egg whites ½ c. water
1¼ c. granulated sugar

Boil the water and 1 cup sugar to soft ball stage (240° F.). Beat the egg whites until stiff, and then beat in the remaining 4 tablespoons sugar. Pour the hot syrup over the egg whites in a thin stream, beating constantly. Beat until almost cool, and the meringue is ready to use.

CHOCOLATE MERINGUES

4 egg whites 1½ oz. chocolate, melted
1 c. sugar ½ tsp. vanilla

Beat egg whites until stiff. Add the sugar gradually, beating thoroughly after each addition. Stir in the chocolate and vanilla. Drop from spoon on cookie sheet covered with wet unglazed paper. Bake in a slow oven (275°–300° F.) 50 minutes.

545

ORANGE MERINGUES

2 egg whites   ⅔ c. powdered sugar
1 tbsp. orange juice

Beat egg whites until frothy. Add the orange juice and continue beating until stiff. Add the sugar gradually, beating thoroughly after each addition. Drop from spoon on wet paper and bake in slow oven (250°–275° F.) about 60 minutes. If desired, remove soft part of meringue with spoon and return the shells to oven to dry out thoroughly. When cool fill with ice cream and serve.

FAR EAST MERINGUES

1 c. confectioners' sugar   1¼ c. dates seeded and cut
2 cans moist cocoanut   ½ c. walnut meats, chopped
4 egg whites, stiffly beaten

Fold sugar gradually into egg whites. Fold in cocoanut, dates and nuts. Drop by spoonfuls on paper-lined baking sheet. Bake in moderate oven (325° F.) twenty minutes. Remove from oven. Invert paper, brush with water, let stand a few minutes and remove meringues.

ALMOND MACAROONS

1 egg white   1 c. finely chopped blanched
Pinch of salt   almonds
⅛ tsp. almond extract   1 c. powdered sugar

Beat egg whites until frothy. Add salt and continue beating until stiff. Add sugar gradually, beating thoroughly after each addition. Fold in the nuts and flavoring. Drop from spoon on greased cookie sheet and bake in slow oven (250°–275° F.) 25 minutes.

DATE MERINGUE CAKES

1 c. sugar   ⅛ tsp. salt
½ tsp. vanilla   1 plain sponge cake, baked in
1½ c. dates, seeded and cut   loaf pan
2 egg whites

Beat egg whites and salt until stiff, then gradually beat in sugar. Fold in flavoring and dates. Cut sponge cake into slices about ¾ inch thick, pile meringue on each slice, and bake in slow oven (325° F.) about 25 minutes.

CORN FLAKE MACAROONS

2 egg whites   2 c. corn flakes or other crisp
1 c. brown sugar   ready-to-eat cereal
½ tsp. flavoring   ½ c. chopped nut meats

Beat egg whites until stiff, add sugar gradually and continue beating until mixture is thick. Fold in flavoring, corn flakes and nuts. Drop by spoonfuls on greased baking sheet and bake in moderate oven (375° F.) until macaroons are delicately browned.

COCOANUT MACAROONS

1 egg white
¼ c. sugar
¼ c. light corn syrup

1¾ c. moist cocoanut (¼ lb. can)
½ c. flour

Mix the flour and sugar thoroughly. Gradually stir in the corn syrup, being careful to avoid lumps. Add the cocoanut to the beaten egg white, and add the flour and sugar mixture. Shape the mixture into little balls, place on slightly greased baking sheet, and flatten the balls with a spatula, making round, flat cakes of them. Bake in hot oven (410° F.) for 10 minutes. If not a rich brown at the end of this time, run them under the broiler flame for a moment.

COOKED HONEY MERINGUE

Heat 1 cup honey until it spins a thread (238° F.). Pour slowly over 2 stiffly beaten egg whites. Continue beating until icing is fluffy and will hold its shape.

SLICED PINEAPPLE MERINGUES

2 egg whites
5 tbsp. powdered sugar

6 slices pineapple

Drain slices of pineapple and place on a buttered baking sheet. Cover each slice with a meringue made by beating the egg whites and then adding powdered sugar. The meringue may be put on in design with a pastry tube if desired. Sprinkle with sugar. Put the pineapple with meringue in slow oven (300° F.) and bake until browned and crusty. Boil the pineapple juice with the juice of one lemon and ½ cup sugar until quite thick. Serve with the meringues.

PEACH SURPRISE

6 large peach halves
Italian meringue

6 slices sponge cake

Put each peach half on a slice of cake, cover with meringue and brown in quick oven (425°–450° F.).

BAKED ALASKA

1 qt. brick ice cream,
  frozen hard
4 egg whites
½ tsp. vanilla

8 slices sponge cake
7 tbsp. sugar
Pinch of salt

Cover a bread board or oven plank with white paper. On it arrange the slices of cake. The pieces of cake should be somewhat larger than the slices of ice cream. Make meringue by beating egg whites stiff, and then beating in the salt and sugar. Add flavoring. On each piece of cake put a slice of ice cream and cover completely with meringue. Brown quickly in hot oven (450° F.). Slip from paper to serving plate and serve at once.

APPLE MERINGUE

8 apples
3 eggs, separated
1/4 c. sugar
1/2 tsp. salt

2 c. milk
1 tsp. vanilla
3 tbsp. confectioners' sugar

Core apples and bake until tender. Make a custard of egg yolks, sugar, salt and milk. Put each baked apple into an individual baking dish and pour custard over apples. Make meringue of egg whites and confectioners' sugar and cover apples. Brown in quick oven (375° F.).

APPLE SAUCE MERINGUE

2 c. sweetened apple sauce
2 eggs, separated

1/2 c. confectioners' sugar

Beat yolks slightly and mix with the apple sauce. Put into buttered baking dish and bake 15 minutes in moderate oven (350° F.). Make a meringue of egg whites and the confectioners' sugar and spread on apple sauce. Brown in quick oven (375° F.).

STUFFED SWEET POTATOES WITH MERINGUE

Sweet potatoes
1/2 c. sugar

2 egg whites
Pinch salt

Bake sweet potatoes until tender. Cut into halves lengthwise, scoop out the center and mash. Season with butter and salt. Fill back into shells, top with meringue which has been made by beating egg whites, sugar and salt together. Brown in moderate oven (350° F.).

The Relation of Mayonnaise to Pastry

A drop of mayonnaise, under the magnifying lens of the microscope, becomes a mass of tiny bubbles closely packed together, yet each retaining its own identity. The little bubbles are in reality droplets of oil, each surrounded by a thin film of egg yolk and vinegar or lemon juice. The stiffer the mayonnaise, the smaller and the more tightly packed are the tiny globules of oil.

Another look into the microscope shows that each tiny drop has a sort of boundary line, a thin wall which keeps it separate from the oil in the neighboring drop. This thin wall goes by the prosaic name of emulsifying agent, and the collection of oil droplets we call mayonnaise is an emulsion.

Mayonnaise, says the food chemist, is a manufactured emulsion. Egg yolk is a natural one—the most nearly perfect one known. That is

548

CHICKEN SALAD DRESSING

1 c. chicken stock or clear
   canned chicken soup
½ c. vinegar
1½ tbsp. prepared mustard
¼ tsp. pepper

5 egg yolks, slightly beaten
1 tsp. salt
4 tbsp. butter
½ c. whipping cream

Combine all ingredients except butter and cream. Cook in top of double boiler, stirring constantly, until mixture coats spoon. Remove from heat at once, add butter and beat thoroughly. Cool. When ready to use, fold in whipped cream.

DRESSING FOR GREENS

2 hard cooked eggs
2 tbsp. salad oil
1 tsp. sugar
2 tbsp. vinegar, preferably tarragon

1 tbsp. cold water
1 tsp. salt
1 tsp. prepared mustard

Separate yolks from whites. Rub yolks through sieve. Add water, oil, salt, sugar and mustard and cream to a smooth mixture. Add vinegar last, blending thoroughly. Pour over greens. Cut whites into rings and use as garnish.

Candies That Melt in the Mouth

Millions of pounds of egg white are used each year in making fine confections. Smooth nougats, creamy chocolates and dainty divinity owe their rich creaminess to the egg white in them. Egg white gives these candies not only their whiteness and fluffiness, but their melt-in-the-mouth smoothness as well. The smoothness is responsible for what we call creaminess.

Years ago most candy manufacturers used dried egg white, as some of them still do today. It is easy to use and it gives excellent results. But it does have to be reconstituted before it can be used—that is, it has to be mixed with water and allowed to come back to its liquid form.

A few years ago some large candy makers wondered why, since frozen egg white gave such excellent results in the bakeshop, it would not do equally well in the candy shop. So they tried some of the frozen eggs, experimentally at first. The candy was a success. The frozen whites were so easy to use and gave such good results that gradually more and more of them were used, until today most leading confectioners prefer to use frozen egg whites.

Officially, egg white is known as an interfering agent in candy making. That sounds somewhat uncomplimentary, but egg white is a

553

Egg white gives candies individuality. The creams acquire a smoothness, and divinity a fluffiness.

kindly interferer, a sort of friendly policeman who sees that everything is in good order.

What egg white does in candy is really quite simple. When a sugar syrup of a given concentration is whipped or stirred, the sugar crystallizes out. That is why some types of candies are beaten. If the syrup is hot when it is beaten, the crystals form slowly, and they become large and the candy is grainy. If, on the other hand, the syrup is first thoroughly cooled and then beaten, the crystals form very quickly. Many crystals form at one time, and since there is only a certain amount of sugar from which they can form, each individual crystal gets only a little of the sugar, and consequently all of the crystals are small. The smaller the crystals the smoother the candy.

But sugar crystals have a great affinity for one another, and when candy stands for twenty-four hours or more the tiny crystals cluster together to form large crystals and the candy becomes grainy. Candy makers say the crystals "grow." But if something is added to keep the crystals apart, the candy remains smooth. Ingredients which do this are called "interfering agents," and egg white is one of them.

So when hot syrup is poured over stiffly beaten egg white and the

mixture is beaten until it holds its shape, the egg white forms a little protective layer around each crystal. When the candy cools and the tiny crystals try to get together to spoil things, there is the egg white to keep them in place. That is why divinity candy, creamy centers of chocolates, nougats, and similar candies keep their delicious smoothness until they are eaten, while fudge, most of which does not contain egg white, often becomes grainy on standing.

Temperatures for Candy Syrups

	Sea Level	High Altitude
Thread, or soft ball	236°–242° F.	217°–228° F.
Hard ball (long thread)	248°–254° F.	230°–240° F.
Crack	260°–275° F.	250°–260° F.
Hard crack	290°–298° F.	275°–280° F.
Caramel	305°	288°

DIVINITY

2 c. sugar	¼ tsp. salt
½ c. hot water	2 egg whites
½ c. light corn syrup	1 tsp. vanilla

Cook water, sugar and syrup together until they form a firm ball in cold water (248° F.). Pour gradually over egg whites which have been beaten stiff. Continue beating until mixture is stiff enough to hold its shape when dropped from spoon. Add flavoring and spread in buttered pan or on oiled paper.

DIVINITY VARIATIONS

For *Coffee Divinity* substitute coffee for the water in the recipe.
For *Mint Divinity* substitute a few drops of mint flavoring for vanilla. A light pink tint is attractive.

MAPLE DIVINITY

2 c. sugar	¼ tsp. salt
½ c. hot water	2 egg whites
½ c. maple syrup	⅛ tsp. cream of tartar

Cook sugar, water, maple syrup and cream of tartar until syrup forms a very firm ball (250° F.) when tested in cold water. Pour hot syrup over egg whites which have been beaten stiff with the salt. Continue beating until mixture holds shape when dropped from spoon. Spread in pan or drop from spoon on oiled paper. Nuts may be added if desired.

HONEY DIVINITY

2⅓ c. sugar
½ c. strained honey
1 c. water
½ tsp. vanilla

¼ tsp. salt
¾ c. shredded cocoanut
2 egg whites, beaten stiff

Cook together the sugar, water, salt and honey until the syrup spins a long thread (260° F.). Pour slowly over stiffly beaten egg whites, beating constantly. Beat until the candy is stiff enough to hold its shape when dropped from a spoon. Stir in the cocoanut and vanilla and drop by small spoonfuls on waxed paper or spread in buttered pan. Cocoanut may be omitted.

ORANGE DIVINITY

2½ c. sugar
½ c. water
½ c. light corn syrup or honey

2 egg whites
1 c. orange juice
Rind of 1 orange, grated

Cook sugar, water, orange juice and syrup until the mixture spins a long thread or forms a firm ball (250° F.) in cold water. Pour gradually over the stiffly beaten egg whites, beating constantly. Continue beating until the mixture holds its shape. Add the grated orange rind. Drop by spoonfuls on oiled paper or spread in a pan.

SEA FOAM

3 c. sugar
¾ c. white corn syrup
1 c. water
⅛ tsp. salt

¼ tsp. cream of tartar
1 egg white
⅓ c. nuts
½ tsp. vanilla

Cook sugar, water, syrup until it forms a firm ball (248° F.) in cold water. Beat the egg white and salt until stiff. Pour the syrup over the egg white slowly, beating constantly. Beat until the mixture holds its shape, fold in the nuts and flavoring and spread in buttered pan or drop by spoonfuls on waxed paper.

BROWN SUGAR SEA FOAM

2 c. brown sugar
1 c. water
1 egg white

¼ c. nut meats
½ tsp. vanilla

556   Use method for Sea Foam.

2 c. sugar	1 tsp. vanilla
1/3 c. light corn syrup	1 1/2 c. nut meats
1 c. water	1/2 c. candied cherries
4 egg whites	

Boil together half the sugar, half the water and half the corn syrup until a little of the syrup will form a hard ball in cold water (280° F.). Remove syrup from fire and pour it slowly over the beaten egg whites, beating constantly. Continue beating until cool. In the meantime, cook the remainder of the sugar, syrup and water to the same stage of hardness. Remove from fire and add at once to the first mixture, beating constantly. When cool, add the vanilla, nuts and candied cherries, and pour into buttered pans. Let stand over night in cool place, and then cut into small loaves and wrap in wax paper, or dip in chocolate.

HONEY NOUGAT

3/8 c. honey	1/2 c. brown sugar
1 lb. almonds	2 egg whites

Boil the honey and sugar together until a little of the mixture dropped into cold water holds its shape (250° F.). Add the whites of eggs, beaten stiff, and cook very slowly, stirring constantly, until a little of the mixture tested in water becomes brittle. Add the almonds, pour into buttered pan or on tray and cool under a weight.

UNCOOKED FUDGE

4 oz. sweet chocolate	1 tbsp. butter
1/2 c. confectioners' sugar	1 tsp. vanilla
1 egg, separated	Pinch of salt

Melt the chocolate over hot water, and add the butter, confectioners' sugar and the vanilla. Beat the egg yolk until thick and lemon colored and add to the chocolate mixture. Last add the stiffly beaten white. Shape into squares or balls. This fudge may be used as filling between layers of cakes.

ORIENTAL CANDY

Add to the white of an egg 3 tablespoons very strong black coffee. Then stir in as much confectioners' sugar as possible, keeping the mixture soft enough to mold. When it is a smooth paste, roll small bits between the palms, making little balls. Press between halves of English walnuts.

CUBAN ALMOND CANDY

1 lb. almonds, blanched and ground	1/3 tsp. salt
2 1/2 c. granulated sugar	12 egg yolks
	Cinnamon

Melt sugar slowly over low flame, add almond powder, stirring continually. Add beaten yolks slowly. Cook until well mixed and thickened. Pour into buttered pan in a thin layer, 1/4–1/2 inch thick, and dust lightly with cinnamon.

SPICED NUTS

½ lb. blanched almonds	½ c. cinnamon
1 egg white	2 tsp. ginger
1½ c. cold water	1 tbsp. ground cloves
1 c. confectioners' sugar	1 tsp. nutmeg
½ c. cornstarch	2 tsp. salt

Put the nuts in a slow oven to dry. Sift the sugar, cornstarch, salt and spices together 3 times. Add the cold water to the egg white and beat slightly to make a smooth liquid. Put the nuts into a coarse strainer and dip up and down in the egg white until each nut is thoroughly coated. Drain. Roll the nuts in a little of the spice mixture which has been placed on a sheet of waxed paper.

In shallow pans pat layers of the spiced sugar mixture to a depth of about ¼ inch. Drop the coated nuts into this, leaving spaces between them. Cover the nuts with the spiced sugar, and bake for 3 hours in a slow oven (250° F.). Remove the excess sugar, cool and serve.

DREAM CANDY

1 lb. sweet chocolate	2½ c. powdered sugar
1 tsp. butter	2 c. roasted peanuts, finely
1 tsp. peanut butter	ground
½ tsp. maple flavoring	½ tsp. walnut flavoring
3 eggs, well beaten	

Melt butter, peanut butter and chocolate over hot water. Blend thoroughly. Mix all the other ingredients and add to the chocolate mixture. Pour into buttered pan to cool and cut into small squares. Press a nut meat into the top of each piece, dip into melted chocolate and put on oiled paper to cool.

CRYSTALLIZED FRESH MINT LEAVES

Wash mint leaves thoroughly in cold water. Pick leaves off stems, preferably leaving them in groups of two or three. Dry by folding in a linen towel. Dip each leaf into unbeaten egg white and then into finely granulated sugar. Put into cool place to dry. These will keep several hours in a refrigerator. They are delightful served with tea and small cakes. Small flowers, such as violets and sweet peas may be treated in similar manner and used as garnish.

What Eggs Do in Ice Cream

In frozen dishes eggs do very nearly the same thing they do in confections, except that instead of sugar crystals there are tiny ice

Eggs give color, flavor, and nutritive value to ice cream.

crystals to be kept apart. And, of course, eggs add food value, too, especially when the yolk is used, as in custard ice creams.

Real sherbets always contain egg white, preferably in the form of Italian meringue, made by pouring hot syrup over beaten egg whites. The meringue is prepared first and then cooled, the flavoring, usually in the form of fruit juice, is added, and the sherbet is frozen, just a little past the mushy stage.

When desserts and salads are frozen in an ice cream freezer with paddles, the paddles beat air into the mixture during the freezing period. But when desserts or salads are frozen without stirring, as they usually are in mechanical refrigerators, the air must be incorporated in some other way. If this is not done, the mixture freezes into a solid block.

Whipped egg white, whipped cream, whipped evaporated milk, whipped gelatin may be used as air carriers. Eggs are always at hand, and they are easy to use. When the mixture to be frozen has reached the mushy stage, that is, when crystals have just begun to form, the stiffly beaten egg white is folded in and the mixture is allowed to freeze until it is as firm as desired.

Whole egg or egg yolk in ice cream gives color, flavor and nutritive value. It also makes possible the beating in of air in such a way that it stays in, giving smoothness and pleasant texture to the finished product. 559

FROZEN CREAM AND CUSTARD

1 c. milk, scalded	½ c. sugar
2 eggs	¼ tsp. salt
1 pt. coffee cream	1 tsp. vanilla

Make soft custard of milk, sugar, eggs, and salt. Cool, and add cream and vanilla. Freeze. If frozen in mechanical refrigerator, substitute whipping cream for coffee cream. Whip the cream and fold it into the cooled custard.

FROZEN CHOCOLATE CUSTARD

2 sq. bitter chocolate	3 eggs
1 c. sugar	½ tsp. vanilla
¼ tsp. salt	1 qt. milk

Melt chocolate over hot water. Add sugar and salt and then 2 cups hot milk, blending well. A rotary beater may be used to blend the chocolate smoothly. Pour over beaten eggs, return to double boiler and cook 2 minutes, stirring constantly. Add remaining milk, flavoring and cool. Freeze in ice cream freezer.

FROZEN HONEY NUT CUSTARD

1 tall can evaporated milk	2 c. boiling water
⅛ tsp. salt	1 c. honey
4 egg yolks	½ c. chopped nut meats

Scald milk in top of double boiler. Cool. Then chill in bowl surrounded by chipped ice. Add salt to beaten egg yolks. Pour water slowly over eggs, stirring constantly. Cook over hot water 2 minutes, stirring. Cool and add honey. Whip chilled milk with rotary beater until stiff. Fold into cold custard and add nuts. Freeze.

FRUIT SHERBET

4 c. fruit juice	½ c. lemon juice
4 tbsp. sweet cooking sherry	Italian meringue made with 4 egg whites

Combine all ingredients except meringue. Freeze until mixture reaches mushy stage. Fold in meringue and finish freezing. One cup crushed fruit may be added.

ITALIAN MERINGUE

4 egg whites	1¼ c. sugar
⅛ tsp. salt	½ c. water

Boil the water and 1 cup sugar until the syrup forms a thread. Beat egg whites stiff, then beat in the remaining ¼ cup sugar and the salt. Pour the hot syrup over whites, beating constantly. Continue beating until almost cool, when the meringue is ready to use.

Beaten egg white helps make frozen dishes pleasantly smooth.

SHERBET ESPAGNOL

1 qt. fairly soft vanilla ice cream
1 qt. brandy or whiskey

Italian meringue made from 4 egg whites

Mix the Italian meringue into the ice cream. Add the liquor the last minute before serving, so the sherbet will not become too thin.

THREE-OF-A-KIND SHERBET

½ c. orange juice
2 bananas
2 c. water
2 egg whites

3 tbsp. lemon juice
2 c. sugar
Pinch of salt

Put banana through sieve and mix with fruit juices. Add sugar, salt and water, stirring until sugar is dissolved. Freeze to mush, fold in stiffly beaten whites and continue freezing until firm.

GINGERALE SHERBET

1 qt. gingerale
½ c. orange juice

½ c. lemon juice
Italian meringue (4 egg whites)

Combine all ingredients and freeze.

561

HONEY NUT MOUSSE

½ c. honey
Pinch salt
½ c. chopped nut meats

3 eggs
2 c. whipping cream

Use same method as for Vanilla Mousse. Chocolate Shot may be added if desired.

CHOCOLATE MOUSSE

4 eggs, separated
¼ tsp. salt

6 bars sweet chocolate

Melt chocolate in double boiler. Beat yolks until thick. Add melted chocolate. Cool. Fold in stiffly beaten egg whites to which salt has been added. Pour into earthen jar and set on ice or in very cold place for 24 hours. ½ cup broken nut meats may be added before chilling.

BLACK WALNUT PARFAIT

1 c. sugar
½ c. water
3 egg whites

1 c. chopped black walnut meats
Pinch of salt
1 pt. whipping cream
1 tsp. vanilla

Cook sugar, salt and water until syrup spins a thread. Pour over stiffly beaten egg whites, beating constantly. Continue beating until cool. Then fold in nut meats, and then stiffly whipped cream. Freeze without stirring about 3½ hours.

DIVINITY PARFAIT

3 egg whites
1 tsp. vanilla
½ c. water
¼ lb. marshmallows

1 c. sugar
½ c. chopped nut meats
1 c. heavy cream

Cook sugar and water together until the syrup forms a long thread. Pour gradually over the stiffly beaten egg whites, beating constantly. Beat until light and fluffy. Add the marshmallows which have been cut up. Beat until cool. Then fold in the nuts, vanilla, and if desired, candied fruits. When thoroughly cold fold in the whipped cream and put mixture into refrigerator tray to freeze until firm.

FROZEN DATE PARFAIT

½ c. shredded, pitted dates
1½ c. water
4 tbsp. sugar
¼ tsp. salt

4 egg yolks, well beaten
½ c. orange juice
½ c. whipping cream

Cook dates in water 30 minutes. Add sugar and salt while cooking. Pour over beaten yolks. Return to double boiler and cook, stirring until well thickened. Cool and add orange juice and the whipped cream. Freeze without stirring, about 3 hours.

MOCHA PARFAIT

2 tbsp. coffee	2 eggs, separated
1 c. milk, scalded	½ c. sugar
1 tbsp. flour	1 c. whipping cream

Add coffee to ½ cup milk and put into double boiler. Cook 5 minutes, strain through cloth and cool. Mix flour and sugar, add milk-coffee mixture and remainder of milk and cook in top of double boiler until thick, about 15 minutes. Add beaten egg yolks and salt. Cook 5 minutes longer and remove from heat. Cool. Add stiffly beaten egg whites and then whipped cream. Freeze without stirring 3–4 hours.

CINNAMON PARFAIT

3 egg whites	4 tbsp. cinnamon candies
¾ c. sugar	Pinch of salt
½ c. water	1 pt. whipping cream
	1 tsp. vanilla

Boil together the sugar, water, salt and 2 tablespoons candy until syrup forms a thread. Pour over stiffly beaten egg whites. Beat until cool. Crush the remaining candies, and add to egg white mixture. Fold in stiffly beaten cream and freeze without stirring.

MAPLE NUT PARFAIT

¾ c. maple syrup	1 pt. whipping cream
3 egg whites	¼ c. nut meats, broken

Cook maple syrup until it spins a thread. Pour over stiffly beaten egg whites, beating constantly. Continue beating until cool. Whip cream and fold it into egg mixture. Fold in broken nut meats and freeze without stirring.

BUTTERSCOTCH PARFAIT

1¼ c. brown sugar	1 tsp. vanilla
½ c. water	½ c. chopped nut meats
2 tbsp. butter	1½ c. whipping cream
3 eggs	

Boil sugar and water five minutes. Remove from fire, add butter and stir till melted. Pour slowly over beaten egg yolks and beat until cool. Fold in stiffly beaten egg whites, vanilla, nut meats and whipped cream. Freeze.

GINGER PARFAIT

¼ c. sugar	3 tbsp. preserved ginger,
¼ c. water	chopped fine
2 egg whites	1 tbsp. ginger syrup
	1 c. heavy cream

Make a syrup of the sugar and water and 1 tablespoon syrup drained from a jar of Canton ginger. Have ready the stiffly beaten whites of eggs and when syrup spins a thread remove from the fire and pour slowly over the eggs, beating constantly until cool. When cool, chill thoroughly in refrigerator, then fold into the cream which has been whipped until it will hold its shape. Freeze for 3 hours.

LADY FINGER TORTE

2 doz. lady fingers	⅛ tsp. salt
1⅓ c. hot milk	3 eggs
1 sq. chocolate	1 tsp. vanilla
½ c. sugar	½ pt. whipping cream
3 tbsp. flour	

Line the bottom and sides of a bowl or baking dish with the lady fingers, which have been separated. Mix sugar and flour with the beaten egg yolks, then add to the hot milk. Melt chocolate and add to the flour mixture and cook in a double boiler until thickened. Beat egg whites stiff and fold into the mixture. Add salt and vanilla. Place layer of this over the lady fingers, then another layer of lady fingers and repeat until all the mixture has been used, having lady fingers on top. Let stand in the refrigerator over night. Turn out on dessert plate and cover with sweetened whipped cream to which chopped nuts and cherries have been added.

FROZEN FRUIT PUDDING

1 c. sugar	1 c. dry bread crumbs
1 c. water	1 c. mixed seeded raisins, cur-
3 eggs	rants, citron, candied cherries
2 tsp. gelatin	½ c. nut meats
	1 c. whipping cream

Boil sugar and water five minutes. Pour over beaten egg yolks, stirring constantly. Cook in double boiler until thick and add gelatin which has been soaked in 2 tablespoons cold water. Cool, add bread crumbs, fold in well beaten egg whites, then add fruits and nuts, lastly folding in the whipped cream. Freeze in individual paper cups placed in refrigerator tray.

FROZEN STRAWBERRY OMELET

1 pt. strawberries   6 tbsp. confectioners' sugar
1 tbsp. granulated sugar   3 eggs

Mash strawberries and add granulated sugar. Let stand to draw off juice. Separate eggs and beat yolks until thick and lemon colored and whites until stiff. Drain juice from berries, and add berries to egg yolks. Fold confectioners' sugar into stiffly beaten egg whites and combine the two mixtures. Add about 4 tablespoons of the strawberry juice. Pile lightly in refrigerator tray and freeze.

UNCOOKED ICE CREAM

6 eggs, beaten   ½ gal. milk
2 c. sugar   2 tsp. vanilla extract
1 pt. cream   ¼ tsp. lemon extract

Combine, being sure sugar is completely dissolved. Freeze.

UNCOOKED CHOCOLATE ICE CREAM

Omit sugar from uncooked ice cream and add chocolate syrup made by cooking together ½ cup cocoa, or 2 squares bitter chocolate, 1 tablespoon cornstarch, 2 cups sugar and ¾ cup water. Cook, stirring constantly for 10 minutes. Add to cold milk and cream. Add eggs, flavoring and freeze.

GRAPE MALLOBET

1 c. grape juice   1 tbsp. sugar
¼ c. orange juice   20 marshmallows
2 tbsp. lemon juice   ¼ c. egg whites (2–3 whites)

Melt marshmallows in grape juice over hot water. Add other fruit juices and let cool until it begins to congeal. Beat together the egg whites and sugar, beat until stiff and fold into fruit juice mixture.

CIDER MALLOBET

1½ c. sweet cider   23 marshmallows
2 tbsp. lemon juice   ¼ c. egg whites
2 tbsp. sugar   Pinch of salt

Melt marshmallows in ¾ cup cider over hot water, stirring frequently. Remove from heat, add remaining cider, lemon juice and 1 tablespoon sugar. Cool until mixture begins to congeal. Add remaining sugar and the salt to egg whites and beat stiff. Fold egg whites into fruit juices and freeze.

STRAWBERRY MALLOBET

21 marshmallows	2 tbsp. lemon juice
½ c. water	2 tbsp. orange juice
1⅓ c. finely crushed strawberries	¼ c. egg whites
2 tbsp. sugar	Pinch of salt

Melt marshmallows with water in top of double boiler. Remove from heat, add berries, fruit juices and 1 tablespoon sugar. Let cool until mixture begins to congeal slightly. Beat egg whites until stiff with 1 tablespoon sugar. Fold into fruit mixture and freeze without stirring.

GRAPEFRUIT MALLOBET

1 c. grapefruit juice	20 marshmallows
¼ c. water	2 tbsp. sugar
4 tbsp. orange juice	¼ c. egg whites
1 tsp. lemon juice	Pinch of salt

Put grapefruit juice, water and marshmallows over hot water and steam until liquified. Add other fruit juices and half the sugar. Cool. Add remaining sugar and salt to egg whites and beat until stiff. Fold into cold fruit juice mixture and freeze without stirring.

FROZEN RICE AND APRICOT PUDDING

½ c. rice	4 eggs, separated
1 qt. milk	½ c. minced apricots
1 c. sugar	1 tbsp. lemon juice

Cook washed rice 5 minutes in boiling water. Drain, and add to milk and ½ cup sugar in top of double boiler. Cook 50 minutes, covered. Add beaten egg yolks and cook 3 minutes longer. Cool. Whip egg whites, lemon juice, apricots and ½ cup sugar until mixture holds shape and fold into cooled rice. Freeze.

BANANA APRICOT FLUFF

1 medium banana	½ c. canned apricots
½ tbsp. lemon juice	⅓ c. confectioners' sugar
3 egg whites	Pinch of salt

Put bananas through sieve. Mince apricots. Beat egg whites until stiff, and then beat in salt and sugar. Combine banana pulp, lemon juice and apricots, and fold into egg whites. Freeze without stirring.

FROZEN HEAVENLY HASH

2 bananas   ⅔ c. sugar
2 oranges   ⅓ c. water
½ c. crushed pineapple   3 eggs, separated
1 c. white grapes   1 lemon

Peel and dice oranges and bananas. Cut grapes into halves. Chill. Boil sugar and water together 5 minutes. Pour over beaten egg yolks, return to heat and cook until mixture thickens, stirring. Add lemon juice, cool and add fruits. Fold in stiffly beaten egg whites. Freeze.

SOUFFLÉ GLACÉ

4 eggs, separated   ¼ c. wine jelly
1 lemon, rind   ¼ c. hot water
1 tbsp. lemon juice   Pinch of salt
⅔ c. sugar   ¾ c. whipping cream

Beat egg yolks, add lemon juice, rind, jelly, water, sugar and salt and cook until mixture thickens, stirring constantly. Cool. Fold in stiffly beaten whites. Last fold in whipped cream and freeze.

BISCUIT TORTONI

1 c. sugar   1 tsp. gelatin softened in
½ c. water   1 tbsp. cold water
6 egg yolks   ¾ c. chopped blanched almonds
¾ c. crushed macaroons 1 tsp. vanilla
½ c. chopped nut meats   1 pt. whipping cream
¼ tsp. salt

Boil sugar, water and salt until syrup spins thread. Pour over beaten yolks, stirring constantly. Add softened gelatin and stir until completely dissolved. Cool. Fold in macaroons and nut meats, and then whipped cream. Put into individual paper serving cups, set into refrigerator tray and freeze.

FROZEN SURPRISE

Small loaf sponge cake 1 egg white
1 pt. ice cream   ½ c. jelly

Put jelly and egg white into mixing bowl, beating with a rotary beater until mixture holds its shape. Split the sponge cake lengthwise, sandwich fashion. On the lower half arrange the ice cream and cover with upper half. Ice all over with the jelly-egg white mixture. Candied flowers and a wreath of crystallized fresh mint leaves make an attractive garnish. Custard or some of the jelly whip may be put between the layers instead of ice cream.

The Delectable Custard

In custards eggs are the thickener, the ingredient that gives body and texture and character. True custards contain only eggs and milk with seasoning. Sweet custards have sugar and flavoring added, while those used to serve with meat courses and in soups are slightly salted and sometimes highly seasoned. The proportion of egg to milk is usually about the same, one whole egg or two egg yolks to one cup of milk.

From the point of view of texture there are two general types of custards: stirred and baked. The only difference between them is in the method of cooking.

The soft custard is most often served as a sauce or garnish for puddings or other dishes. Its name describes it. The custard mixture is cooked in the top of a double boiler, with constant stirring until the mixture coats the spoon. Then the upper part of the double boiler, the part containing the custard, must be quickly taken from the lower part, so that the cooking is stopped at once. If cooking continues, the egg becomes overcooked, and the custard curdles or separates. If there is any tendency to curdle, it may be prevented or at least lessened by setting the pan at once into cold water and beating the custard with an egg beater. The cold water reduces the temperature and the beating breaks up any small curds that may have formed. Slow cooking lessens the danger of curdling, too, for the custard thickens more slowly, and the danger point is more easily observed.

For baked custard the uncooked mixture is put into baking dishes that have been rinsed with cold water. The dishes are set into a pan of hot water and baked in a moderate oven (325°–350° F.) until the custard sets. How long this takes depends on how large the dish is, how much custard there is in it, how sweet the custard is. Usually, however, about forty-five minutes is necessary for a larger custard and thirty minutes for small individual ones.

If custards contain such ingredients as fruits, vegetables, rice, cocoanut or other solids that might have a tendency to sink to the bottom of the dish before the custard has time to set, this settling out can sometimes be lessened by putting the mixture into a baking dish which has been thoroughly warmed by letting boiling water stand in it while the mixture is being prepared. Then the custard begins to set as soon as it is put into the oven, and the suspended foods remain distributed throughout the entire dish.

The classic test for judging the doneness of baked custards is to insert a knife into the center. If the knife comes out clean the custard

Proper baking makes smooth, creamy custards.

is done. Overcooking causes the egg to separate out, and the custard "weeps" when it is cut. When properly baked, custard has about the consistency of clabbered milk and cuts down as smoothly as soft butter, though it holds its shape when it is unmolded. A custard unmolds most easily when it is still somewhat warm, though it tastes best when it has been chilled.

Custards made with only the yolks are richer in color than those made with the whole egg. An attractive, economical thing to do is to use the yolks in the custard mixture and then make a meringue of the whites to use as a garnish on the finished dish.

Custards seasoned with bouillon cubes, or made with equal parts of milk and meat broth or vegetable liquor and then cut into small cubes when baked are delicious in soups.

Swedish cooks use custards as a sort of vehicle for other foods, just as gelatin is used. When anchovies, fried ham, salted fish or lobster are used in this way the dish is called *lada*. Vegetables com- 571 bined with custard not only make excellent main dishes for luncheon or dinner, but they offer excellent means for including in the menu at least three of the chief protective foods: eggs, milk and vegetables.

Frozen Custard

The sweetened custard mixture makes an excellent base for a wholesome ice cream. The custard may first be cooked or it may be frozen without previous cooking. A small quantity of the milk may be scalded and added to the beaten eggs. This cooks them slightly. For children a most wholesome dessert is made by cooking a thin custard, cooling, adding a little thin cream, and freezing.

Custard Salad Dressing

When eggs are used as the thickener in salad dressings, the mixture is cooked like a stirred custard. This type of dressing, when mixed with whipped cream, is especially good on fruit salads.

PLAIN CUSTARD

2 eggs or 4 yolks	2 c. scalded milk
1/4 c. sugar	1/2 tsp. vanilla
1/4 tsp. salt	

Beat eggs slightly, add sugar and salt. Add the hot milk slowly, stirring constantly. Cook over hot water, in top of double boiler, stirring constantly until mixture coats spoon.

BAKED CUSTARD

Use ingredients for plain custard. Pour into custard cup or molds, set into pan of hot water, and bake in slow oven (325° F.) for 40 minutes. Test by inserting a sharp knife in center. When custard is done, knife comes out clean.

MOCK CUSTARD

3 tbsp. flour	2 eggs
2 cups milk, scalded	2 tbsp. sugar
Dash of nutmeg	1/4 tsp. salt

Mix flour, sugar and salt thoroughly. Add to hot milk in top of double boiler, stirring constantly until thickened. Set top of double boiler over hot water and cook mixture 10 minutes. Add the beaten yolks, stirring constantly. Remove from fire and fold in the egg whites which have been beaten with 2 tablespoons sugar. Cool and serve.

An up-side-down custard with caramel on the down side.

HONEY NUT CUSTARD

1 c. cream or evaporated milk
1 c. boiling water
1 whole egg
1 egg yolk
⅛ tsp. salt
½ c. honey
1 egg white
¼ c. chopped nuts

Combine cream, whole egg, egg yolk and salt. Blend thoroughly. Combine honey and boiling water and bring to boil. Pour hot syrup over stiffly beaten egg white. Fold in the first mixture and the nuts and freeze.

ANGEL CUSTARD

¼ c. sugar
⅛ tsp. salt
1¼ c. scalded milk
3 egg whites
½ tsp. flavoring

Combine the milk, sugar and salt, stirring until sugar is dissolved. Beat the egg whites slightly, but not until they are light. Pour milk over egg whites, add flavoring, and pour mixture into custard cups. Set the cups in a pan of hot water and bake in a slow oven (325° F.) about 30 minutes, or until a knife inserted comes out clean. Serve with crushed fruit or custard sauce.

573

FRENCH FRUIT CUSTARD

2 eggs	2 c. scalded milk
1/3 c. sugar	1/4 tsp. vanilla
1 pt. strawberries	

Beat the eggs slightly with the sugar, and over them pour the milk which has been scalded, cooking in top of double boiler and stirring constantly until mixture coats a spoon. Cool. Add vanilla and chill. Hull the strawberries and cut in halves. Chill. Arrange fruit in sherbet glasses, pour custard over and serve.

DATE CUSTARD

To plain custard recipe add 6 dates, stoned and cut. Add to the custard before baking.

PRUNE FILLED CUSTARD

1 1/2 c. milk	2 eggs
3 tbsp. sugar	1/4 tsp. salt
	1/2 tsp. vanilla

Heat milk in top of double boiler. Beat eggs with sugar and salt. Add milk gradually to eggs, stirring constantly. Return mixture to double boiler and cook, stirring constantly, until mixture coats spoon. Remove at once from double boiler. Add flavoring. Pour into sherbet glasses. Chill thoroughly. When ready to serve, top with a generous tablespoonful of Prune Filling.

PRUNE FILLING

1 4 oz. can or 1/2 c.	1 tsp. lemon juice
strained prunes	3 tbsp. sugar

Blend thoroughly. An excellent variation of this dish is to use 1 egg yolk and 1 whole egg in the custard, saving the other egg white to make a prune whip with which to top the dessert.

FLOATING ISLAND

4 eggs	Pinch salt
1/2 c. sugar	1 tsp. vanilla
2 c. milk	

Put the egg yolks into a bowl with the sugar, milk, salt and vanilla. Beat thoroughly and turn into a double boiler. Cook slowly for 10 minutes to form a creamy custard. Remove from the flame and cool. Chill. Beat the egg whites stiff, gradually adding the powdered sugar. The whites must be stiff enough to stand alone. Spread a little jam over the custard and then put on the egg white to resemble islands. For chocolate floating island, add two squares of chocolate to the milk when hot.

DIVINITY CUSTARD

Use ingredients for plain custard substituting ⅛ cup honey for the sugar. Cook milk, yolks and salt until the mixture coats spoon. Add flavoring and chill. Heat the honey and pour gradually over stiffly beaten whites, beating constantly. Fold into the yolk mixture and chill in freezer.

MAPLE CUSTARD

1½ c. maple syrup	4 eggs
2½ c. milk	Pinch of salt

Beat the eggs slightly, add the syrup, salt, and blend thoroughly. Scald the milk and add it to the eggs and syrup, stirring constantly. Pour into custard cups, set in pan of hot water and bake in moderate oven (350° F.) for 30–40 minutes. If baked in one large dish, bake for 45–50 minutes.

CHOCOLATE CUSTARD MERINGUE

1 sq. bitter chocolate, chipped	2 c. milk
	⅓ c. sugar
3 eggs	½ tsp. vanilla
⅛ tsp. salt	Cocoanut or nut meats

Heat chocolate and milk in top of double boiler. Stir occasionally until chocolate is melted. Beat with egg beater to blend thoroughly. Beat the eggs (saving one white for meringue) and add sugar, salt and vanilla. Pour the hot chocolate milk over the egg mixture, stirring constantly. Pour into custard cups, set in pan of hot water and bake in slow oven (325° F.) until firm, 25–30 minutes. For meringue, beat egg white until stiff and then beat in 4 tablespoons sugar. Add ¼ teaspoon vanilla. Top each custard with a heaping spoonful of the meringue, sprinkle with cocoanut or nut meats and serve.

TIPSY TRIFLE

Line custard cups with slices of dry sponge cake. Cover with a soft custard, which has been cooled and flavored with cooking sherry. Top with meringue and brown in the oven.

MOCHA PUFF

3 eggs, separated	¾ c. hot coffee
¾ c. milk, scalded	½ tsp. vanilla
½ c. sugar	½ c. whipping cream
⅛ tsp. salt	

Beat yolks with sugar and salt. Mix scalded milk and coffee and pour gradually over yolks, stirring constantly. Cook in double boiler until mixture coats spoon. Cool and fold in the egg whites which have been beaten stiff with 4 tablespoons sugar. Put into parfait or sherbet glasses. Chill. Top with whipped cream.

575

COFFEE FROTH

3 egg yolks	1 tbsp. cold water
¾ c. sugar	1 c. strong hot coffee
1 c. milk, scalded	Few grains salt
1 tbsp. cornstarch	

Beat egg yolks with sugar until light and thick. Add scalded milk and coffee slowly. Mix cornstarch and salt to paste with the cold water. Add to the coffee mixture. Cook in double boiler until mixture coats spoon. Pour into sherbet glasses and chill. Garnish with the following meringue:

1 c. sugar	3 egg whites
½ c. water	¼ tsp. vanilla extract
Pinch of salt	

Boil sugar and water together until syrup spins a thread. Beat the egg whites and the salt until stiff. Pour hot syrup slowly over beaten whites, beating continually until thick enough to hold shape. Add vanilla.

APRICOT COCOANUT ISLANDS

4 c. plain soft custard	6 tsp. shredded cocoanut or
1 c. whipped cream	chopped nut meats
1 can apricot halves	

Pour custard into deep sherbet glasses. Top each with 3 apricot halves, cut side up. Fill center of each half with whipped cream and sprinkle with cocoanut or nuts.

ORANGE FLUFF

2 eggs	3 tbsp. sugar
Grated rind of ½ lemon	Grated rind of ½ orange
1 tbsp. hot water	3 tbsp. orange juice
2 tbsp. lemon juice	20 lady fingers

Separate eggs. Beat yolks with 2 tablespoons sugar. Add grated rind and the fruit juices. Add hot water, beating continually. Cook mixture in top of double boiler until it coats spoon, stirring constantly. Pour over egg whites which have been beaten stiff with remaining tablespoon of sugar. Pile into glasses which have been lined with lady fingers. Chill and serve. May also be served as topping for sponge cake.

FOUNDATION CUSTARD FOR SWEDISH EGG DISHES

3 eggs	2 c. milk
Salt	Sugar

Beat the eggs slightly, add the milk and seasonings. The amount of salt required depends on the type of food which is to be combined with the custard. If chopped ham, anchovies or other salty food is used, about ½ teaspoon salt is sufficient. If fresh flaked fish or lobster is used, a teaspoon of salt is desirable. For some dishes ½ to 1 teaspoon sugar added to the custard gives a delicious flavor, especially if vegetables are cooked with the custard. The vegetables or meat are put into a baking dish, the custard is poured over and the dish is set into a pan of warm water and baked until the custard is set.

CARROT CUSTARD

2 eggs
½ c. milk
Pinch of celery salt
2 tsp. lemon juice
1 tbsp. sugar

2 tsp. melted butter
2 cans or 1 c. strained carrots
1 tsp. salt
2 tsp. grated onion

Beat eggs. Add other ingredients and blend thoroughly. Pour into individual custard cups and set in pan of water. Bake 35-45 minutes in slow oven (325° F.). If a fluffier product is desired, the egg whites may be beaten separately and folded in last.

PASTEL OF EGGS

4 eggs
¼ lb. grated cheese

4 tbsp. butter
½ tsp. salt

Beat the eggs with the salt, add the cheese. Melt the butter in a pan, and in it cook the egg-cheese mixture, stirring until thickened like custard. Serve on buttered toast.

ROYAL CUSTARD

3 eggs
1 tsp. sugar
½ tsp. salt

¾ c. milk
Dash white pepper

To the beaten eggs add the milk, gradually, and then the seasonings. Strain into a buttered flat dish. Set dish in pan of water and bake about 30 minutes in slow oven (275° F.) When cold, remove to board and cut into cubes or fancy shapes to use as garnish.

CORN PUDDING

2 eggs, slightly beaten
1 c. milk
2 c. corn, cut from cob

2 tbsp. melted butter
Salt and pepper to taste

Combine all ingredients and pour into buttered baking dish. Set into pan of hot water and bake in moderate oven (350° F.) for 35-45 minutes, or until set.

NOODLE CHICKEN CUSTARD (With Pineapple-Butter Sauce)

¼ lb. noodles
1 c. chopped chicken
½ c. milk

1 egg
4 slices pineapple
Salt and pepper

Cook noodles in boiling salted water until tender. Drain. Add the chopped chicken, milk and slightly beaten egg. Season. Put into buttered ring molds or custard cups and bake in a pan of water in a slow oven (325° F.) until the custard is set. Remove each custard from mold and place it on a ring of pineapple which has been fried in butter until brown. Serve with pineapple butter sauce.

577

PINEAPPLE BUTTER SAUCE

1 tbsp. butter	1 tbsp. flour
½ c. pineapple juice	Salt

Brown the butter. Blend in the flour and add slowly the pineapple juice and then a dash of salt. Cook the mixture, stirring until it thickens.

BACHELOR'S SPECIAL

1 c. cooked, chopped spaghetti	6 eggs, beaten
1 tbsp. butter	1 tsp. salt
1 c. fresh mushrooms	1 tsp. chopped parsley
1 c. milk	Pepper
	Toast points

Melt the butter in a saucepan, add the mushrooms and cook for 5 minutes. Pour in the milk and spaghetti and heat slowly. When beginning to simmer add the eggs, salt and a dash of pepper. Stir slowly until the eggs thicken, and then add the parsley and turn into a hot dish. Garnish with toast points.

CHICKEN CUSTARD

2 eggs	½ c. cooked mushrooms
2 c. milk	Salt and pepper
1 c. diced cooked chicken	

Beat eggs slightly, add milk, then other ingredients. Season to taste. Pour into hot buttered baking dish, set into pan of hot water. Bake in moderate oven (350° F.) until custard is set. Serve with fruit salad.

CHEESE EGG NOODLES

¾ lb. noodles	½ c. sour cream
1 lb. cottage cheese	½ tsp. salt
3 eggs	1 tsp. cinnamon

Boil noodles in salt water till tender; drain. Mix cheese, eggs, sour cream, salt and cinnamon. Line casserole alternately with noodles, then with cheese mixture until full. Bake in moderate oven (350° F.) till light brown. Garnish with browned bread crumbs. Serve hot.

NOODLE EGG YO-YO

¼ lb. noodles	1 small onion, minced
2 c. chopped celery	2 tsp. salt
1 c. sieved cream cheese	1 tsp. pepper
1 green pepper, minced	½ c. butter, fat or oil
6 eggs	

Cook noodles in boiling water until tender. Drain. Chill. Chop slightly. Add celery, sieved cheese, green pepper, onion and seasoning. Mix well. Melt butter in frying pan. Add mixture, simmer about 10 minutes or until noodles have absorbed fat. Cover with well-beaten eggs, brown slowly, as in making omelet. Turn out on hot platter. Serve with white sauce into which salted almonds or peanuts have been sprinkled.

Chicken Yo-Yo may be made by adding 1 cup cooked chicken to the above recipe.

MACARONI EGG LUNCHEON

6 eggs	½ lb. macaroni
2 tbsp. butter	2 tbsp. chopped onion
1 small can mushrooms	1 c. tomatoes, strained
2 tbsp. green peppers	1 tbsp. capers

Cook macaroni in boiling, salted water until tender, drain and place in baking dish. Let onions and peppers simmer a few minutes in butter. Add the mushrooms, capers and tomatoes. Heat thoroughly. Beat the whole eggs well and add to the other ingredients, quickly stirring the whole into the macaroni. Put into moderate oven (350° F.) for 5 minutes or in a double boiler until eggs have set. Serve immediately.

POLISH EGGS

3 eggs, beaten	½ tsp. salt
¼ c. grated cheese	⅛ tsp. pepper
1 tsp. minced parsley	4 tbsp. butter
1 tsp. minced onion	½ c. bread cubes
½ tbsp. cream	

Fry bread cubes in butter until brown. Blend the eggs, cheese, parsley, onions, cream and seasonings. Add egg mixture to bread cubes in skillet. Cook, stirring until thick enough to spread. Drop by tablespoonfuls into hot deep fat (350° F.) and fry light brown, about 2 minutes. Serve with tomato or tartar sauce.

The Trick of Custard Pie

Custard pie is simply a custard baked in a pastry shell instead of in a baking dish. The trick lies in having the custard filling smooth and jelly-like, but at the same time firm enough so that it will just hold its shape nicely when the pie is cut. The crust must be nicely browned, and moist without being soggy.

For a nine-inch pie three cups of milk are required, for a really good pie must have a fairly thick filling. One and a half eggs per cup makes a custard of good consistency, but if a firmer texture is desired another egg may be added.

In order to insure a crust that is not soggy, a stiffer pastry than that ordinarily used gives best results. Rolling the crust and chilling it for about an hour in the refrigerator also helps. Some cooks have 579

Lemon meringue pie seems too prosaic a name for such a dish as this.

good results when they bake the crust before putting in the custard mixture. Experimental work, however, indicates that the stiffer pastry, chilled, gives more consistent good results than the pre-baking.

If the pastry is brushed with raw egg white and then baked before putting the custard mixture into it, the egg white cooks and makes the pastry shell somewhat more resistant to the absorption of moisture. Still another helpful thing to do is to use warm milk in making the custard (the milk being scalded in making the custard) so that the filling starts to cook at once.

The temperature at which to bake custard pie offers an interesting problem. There are two things to consider: the baking of the pastry and the baking of the custard. According to all cookery rules, pastry should be baked at a high temperature. But high temperatures are exactly the thing that custards cannot stand if they are to be creamy and smooth. The solution is to bake the pie for fifteen minutes in a hot oven (450° F.) to cook the pastry, and then to finish it in a slow or moderate oven (325° F.) for twenty-five minutes more to set the filling. Incidentally, a trick to get the pie into the oven without spilling the thin filling is to set the pie shell on the oven shelf and then pour the custard into it.

Folded into the filling or piled on top, meringues are literally the finishing touch to many a dessert.

Custard-like Pies

Pie fillings in which egg is used as a thickening and fruit juices for the liquid are not, in the strictest sense, custards. The principles of cookery are similar, however. In one type of such custard-like pies, the egg yolks are used in the filling and the whites make the meringue. In other types, the beaten egg whites are folded into the cooked filling to make fluffy pies known as chiffon pies. After the filling is poured into the baked shell it is browned for a few minutes in a hot oven or under a broiler flame.

CUSTARD PIE

Plain pastry (for 1 crust)	¼ tsp. salt
4 eggs	3 c. milk, scalded
½ c. sugar	½ tsp. vanilla

Roll out pastry and chill for an hour.
Beat eggs, sugar and salt slightly. Add hot milk gradually, stirring until sugar is dissolved. Add flavoring. Set pie pan containing crust on shelf in oven, pour in the custard and bake for 15 minutes in a hot oven (450° F.) and then finish in a slow oven (325° F.) for 25 minutes.

COCOANUT CUSTARD PIE

To recipe for custard pie add ¾ cup shredded cocoanut before pouring mixture into pastry shell.

581

CUSTARD FRUIT PIE

1 large or 4 individual pastry shells, baked

3 eggs	½ c. sugar
⅛ tsp. salt	2 c. milk
2 c. halved strawberries, sweetened	½ c. whipping cream

Scald milk in double boiler. Beat eggs slightly, add sugar and salt and add gradually to milk, stirring constantly. Pour into pastry shell and bake 30 minutes in slow oven (325° F.). When pie is cool arrange strawberries over the custard, top with sweetened whipped cream.

ORANGE CUSTARD PIE

1 pkg. orange flavored gelatin	¼ c. sugar
	½ tsp. salt
1¾ c. boiling water	¼ c. cream
3 eggs	1 baked pastry shell

Dissolve gelatin in boiling water. Separate eggs, beat yolks with sugar and salt until thick. Pour on hot gelatin mixture slowly, beating continually. Add cream. Chill until mixture begins to thicken, then whip with egg beater until frothy. Fold in stiffly beaten egg whites. Pour into cold baked pastry shell and chill until firm. Before serving garnish with orange sections.

CRANBERRY CUSTARD PIE

2½ c. cranberry sauce	¼ tsp. salt
1 c. milk	½ tsp. lemon extract
3 eggs, separated	3 tbsp. confectioners' sugar
½ c. sugar	Pie paste
1 tbsp. cornstarch	

Line pie pan with pie paste. Cover with cold cranberry sauce. Mix sugar, cornstarch, salt, milk and beaten egg yolks. Pour over cranberries. Bake in hot oven (425° F.) 10 minutes, then reduce heat and bake in slow oven (325° F.) 35 minutes longer. Make meringue of egg whites and confectioners' sugar. Spread over pie and brown in slow oven (325° F.).

LEMON MERINGUE PIE

3 eggs	⅓ c. lemon juice
¾ c. sugar	2 tbsp. water
Grated rind of ½ lemon	1 baked pie crust

Beat eggs slightly, add the sugar, lemon rind, lemon juice and water. Cook in top of double boiler until thick stirring constantly. Pour into baked shell. Cool slightly and spread with meringue and brown.

ORANGE MERINGUE PIE

1 c. orange juice
2 tsp. grated orange rind
1 c. sugar
2 c. rich milk

3 tbsp. flour
1 tsp. butter
¼ tsp. salt
3 egg yolks

Put the grated rind and sugar into the orange juice and let stand 15 minutes
Mix the flour and ½ cup milk to a smooth paste. Scald the remaining milk in
the top of a double boiler. While hot, add to it the flour paste and stir
until the mixture thickens. Add the butter, salt and orange juice mixture.
Beat the egg yolks slightly and add them, stirring. Cook for one minute.
Cool and put into baked pastry shell. Cover with the following meringue:

3 egg whites
8 tbsp. powdered sugar

½ tsp. lemon or orange extract

Beat egg whites until stiff. Add ⅓ of the sugar gradually and beat thoroughly.
Fold in the remaining sugar, add flavoring and spread on pie. Bake in moderate oven (350° F.) for 8–12 minutes.

LEMON CHIFFON PIE

1 c. sugar
3 eggs, separated
3 tbsp. cold water

Juice of 1 lemon and rind of ½
¼ tsp. salt

Beat yolks, add water, ½ cup sugar and lemon juice and cook in double boiler
until thick, stirring constantly. Add the grated rind, cool. Beat egg whites
stiff, adding salt and the rest of the sugar. Fold the egg yolk mixture into
the beaten whites. Pour into a baked pastry shell and brown in a quick oven.
A little of the white may be reserved to spread thinly over the top of the pie.

FRUIT WHIP PIE

1 c. fruit pulp (prune,
   apricot or banana)
¾ c. sugar
¾ c. fruit (such as stewed prunes, apricots or sliced bananas)
1 large or 6 individual pastry shells, baked

2 tbsp. lemon juice
2 egg whites
Pinch of salt

Put fruit pulp, sugar, egg whites, lemon juice and salt into bowl and beat
until mixture holds shape. Spread fruit over bottom of pastry shell, fill with
fruit whip, chill and serve.

HONEY PECAN PIE

¾ c. to 1 c. honey (de-
   pending on richness
   and sweetness desired)

3 eggs
¼ tsp. salt
1 c. broken pecans

Beat eggs slightly. Add honey, pecans and salt. Mix well, put in partly
baked pie shell and bake in a slow oven (325° F.) 40 minutes.

CHOCOLATE CREAM PIE

¾ c. sugar
2 tbsp. cornstarch
⅛ tsp. salt
2 c. milk, scalded

1 tsp. vanilla
1 sq. chocolate, chipped
3 eggs
Baked pastry shell

Heat milk and chocolate in top of double boiler. Beat with egg beater to blend thoroughly. Mix sugar, cornstarch and salt. Add to hot milk. Cook 15 minutes in top of double boiler, stirring constantly until thick, and occasionally after that. Remove from fire and add egg yolks and 1 whole egg, which have been beaten slightly. Return to heat and cook for 1 minute, stirring. Add flavoring and cool. Pour into pastry shell, top with meringue made from 2 egg whites, ⅛ teaspoon salt and 4 tablespoons sugar. Brown 12 minutes in moderate oven (350° F.).

SOUR CREAM PIE

3 eggs
⅓ c. honey
2 tbsp. flour

1 tsp. cinnamon
1 c. sour cream
3 tbsp. honey

Separate the eggs and beat the yolks; add ⅓ cup honey which has been blended with the flour and cinnamon. Add the sour cream. One cupful chopped raisins or dates may be added. Cook until thick. Pour into baked shell. Beat the egg whites to a stiff froth and add 3 tablespoons honey. Spread on top of the pie and brown lightly in a slow oven (325° F.).

PINEAPPLE CUSTARD TARTS

6 pastry shells
2 c. milk
3 eggs

¼ c. sugar
⅛ tsp. salt
2 c. pineapple tidbits

Partly fill pastry shells with custard made by scalding 2 cups milk, adding 3 eggs beaten with ¼ cup sugar, a pinch of salt and then straining. Bake in a moderate oven (375° F.) for 5 minutes. Reduce heat to slow (300° F.) and bake until a knife inserted in the custard comes out clean. Cool. Cover the custard with tidbits and glaze. To make the glaze cook the pineapple juice from the can with ¼ cup sugar until thick. Cool and cover the tarts, letting the glaze fill spaces between the pineapple and cover the tops of the tarts.

ANGEL FLUFF PIE

1 lemon, juice and rind
⅛ tsp. salt
1 c. sugar

6 eggs, separated
Baked pastry shell

Beat egg yolks, add lemon juice, grated rind, ½ cup sugar and salt. Cook in top of double boiler, stirring constantly, until thickened. Beat 3 egg whites stiff, add ¼ cup sugar and beat again. Fold into yolk mixture and pour into pastry shell. Beat remaining 3 egg whites, add sugar, beat again and spread on top of filling. Brown in moderately hot oven (375° F.) 8–10 minutes.

584

LEMON CHIFFON PIE II

1 tsp. gelatin
¼ c. cold water
1 c. sugar
1 tsp. grated lemon rind

4 eggs
½ c. lemon juice
½ tsp. salt

Soak gelatin in water for five minutes. Add ½ cup sugar, lemon juice and salt to well-beaten egg yolks and cook over boiling water until of custard consistency. To this mixture add grated lemon rind and the softened gelatin. Stir thoroughly. When mixture begins to thicken fold in stiffly beaten egg whites to which the remaining sugar has been added. Fill baked pie shell and chill in refrigerator. Just before serving spread with a thin layer of whipped cream.

CURRANT MERINGUE PIE

1 qt. currants
3 tbsp. flour

1½ c. sugar
2 eggs, separated

Wash currants. Add beaten egg yolks. Mix flour and sugar and combine with currants. Pour into uncooked pie crust and bake in moderate oven (350° F.) 35 minutes. When done, top with meringue made by beating the 2 egg whites with 4 tablespoons sugar. Brown.

The Popular Cookie

Eggs are used in cookies in many ways. They are especially useful as a binder in the drop varieties made from rough flours such as whole-wheat or oatmeal. In the rolled varieties eggs contribute a smoothness of texture, and yolk brushed over the top gives a golden glaze. Both the decorative and adhesive functions of eggs are displayed when plain cookies are dipped into the slightly beaten white and sprinkled with sugar, cocoanut or chopped nuts. Cookies derive much of their pleasing flavor and general goodness from eggs, and their nutritive value assures them a prominent place on the pantry shelf.

NORMANDY WAFERS

½ c. butter
½ c. sugar
1½ c. pastry flour

¾ tsp. lemon extract
4 egg whites

Cream butter and sugar until light and fluffy. Add flour gradually, creaming it in. Stir in the flavoring. Fold in the stiffly beaten egg whites. Drop by small spoonfuls on greased cookie sheet, or with a pastry tube shape batter into lady fingers. Bake 8–10 minutes in hot oven (400° F.). Remove at once from baking sheet.

585

GROUND OATMEAL COOKIES

¾ c. lard	2 c. quick oatmeal, ground
1 c. brown sugar	1 tsp. soda, dissolved in
2 eggs, beaten	1 tbsp. hot water
1 c. flour	¼ tsp. salt

Cream fat and sugar. Add eggs. Combine all dry ingredients and add to creamed mixture, adding soda last. This makes a very soft dough. Chill. Roll out to ⅛ inch thickness on lightly floured board and cut with small round cookie cutter. Bake in moderate oven (350° F.). Spread date filling between cookies.

Date Filling

½ pkg. dates, stoned and ground
1 c. granulated sugar
½ c. water

Combine all ingredients and cook until mixture forms a paste, stirring constantly. Cool and spread on cookies.

REFRIGERATOR COOKIES

1½ c. butter	½ tsp. soda
1½ c. brown sugar	2 tsp. baking powder
3 eggs, beaten	¾ tsp. salt
2 tsp. vanilla	4 c. pastry flour (more to roll)

Cream butter, adding sugar gradually and creaming until mixture is fluffy. Add eggs and vanilla. Sift soda, salt and baking powder with four cups of flour. Add to butter-sugar-egg mixture. Add enough more flour to make a firm dough. Shape into two rolls two or three inches thick. Wrap in waxed paper and chill. When firm, slice thinly and bake about 8 minutes in moderate oven (375° F.).

CHOCOLATE DROP COOKIES

½ c. butter	2 c. flour
1 c. sugar	1 tsp. vanilla
2 eggs, separated	3 sq. chocolate
½ c. milk	1 c. raisins and nuts
1 tsp. soda	

Cream butter and sugar until fluffy. Add beaten egg yolks and then the melted chocolate. Sift soda with flour. Add alternately with milk. Stir in the raisins and nuts and then fold in the stiffly beaten egg whites and the vanilla. Drop from spoon on greased cookie sheet and bake in moderate oven (350° F.) 12–15 minutes. Frost with fudge frosting.

586

KRIS KRINGLES

½ c. butter
½ c. sugar
1 egg, separated
3 hard cooked egg yolks

½ tsp. cardamon seed
2 c. pastry flour
Grated rind of ½ lemon
1 c. coarsely chopped blanched
almonds

Cream butter and sugar. Put hard cooked egg yolks through sieve, add beaten uncooked yolk and mix thoroughly. Add to butter and sugar mixture. Mix cardamon seed and grated rind with flour and add, kneading well to make a smooth dough. Roll out to ⅛ inch thickness on lightly floured board. Cut with small doughnut cutter. Dip each cookie into slightly beaten egg white and then into chopped almonds which have been mixed with granulated sugar. Place on waxed paper on cookie sheet and bake in moderate oven (350° F.) until delicately brown.

Holly wreaths are made by brushing the unbaked cookies with egg white and sprinkling them with chopped pistachios. Tiny red candies represent holly berries.

PRUNE CRUMBLES

2 c. bread crumbs
1½ c. cooked prunes,
pitted and chopped
1 c. sugar
½ c. butter

2 eggs, separated
½ c. flour
½ tsp. baking powder
½ tsp. vanilla

Brown the bread crumbs lightly in the oven. Spread them over the bottom of a buttered pan and cover them with the chopped prunes. Cream the sugar and butter. Add the beaten egg yolks, mixing thoroughly. Add the flour which has been sifted with the baking powder. Add the vanilla and last fold in the stiffly beaten egg whites. Pour the batter over the prunes and crumbs in the pan and bake about 45 minutes in a slow oven (300° F.). Remove from pan while warm, turning the bottom side up. When cool, cut into strips.

OATMEAL DROPS

2 tbsp. butter
1 c. sugar
2 eggs, separated
2½ c. rolled oats

2 tsp. baking powder
½ tsp. salt
¾ tsp. flavoring

Melt butter and add sugar. Stir in the beaten egg yolks and flavoring. Thoroughly mix the dry ingredients and add to the first mixture. Fold in the stiffly beaten egg whites. The batter is quite stiff. Drop a teaspoonful at a time on a greased cookie sheet, allowing room for macaroons to spread during baking. Bake 10 minutes in moderate oven (350° F.).

587

Abbreviations used in the Recipes

lb. = pound
qt. = quart
pt. = pint
oz. = ounce
c. = cup

tbsp. = tablespoon
tsp. = teaspoon
pch. = pinch
° F. = degrees Fahrenheit

About Eggs

A dozen of eggs weigh, on the average, 1½ pounds.
Eight eggs, with shells, equal one pound.
Ten eggs, without shells, equal one pound.
A cupful of egg white equals 8–10 whites.
A cupful of yolks equal 16–18 yolks.
A case of eggs contains 30 dozen eggs.
One carload (American) contains 400–500 cases.
A pound of dried whole egg represents 34.2 liquid eggs.
A pound of dried albumen represents the whites of 101.2 eggs.
A pound of dried yolk represents the yolks of 50.6 eggs.
Whole egg coagulates at 149°–158° F.
Egg white coagulates at 140°–149° F.
Egg yolk coagulates at 149°–158° F.

About Poultry

A 5 pound chicken, purchasing weight, yields 3 cups of diced cooked chicken meat.

A 3½ pound fowl, purchasing weight, makes about 10 salads.

A 3–4 pound roaster requires 4 cups of stuffing.

A 14 pound turkey, purchasing weight, yields about 12 cups of diced cooked meat.

A 14 pound turkey requires 9–10 cups of stuffing.

Amount of Poultry to Buy

Broilers—½–1 bird per person, depending on size of broilers.
Fryers—¾–1 pound per person.
Roasters—½–¾ pound per person.
Fowl—⅓–½ pound per person.

How to Carve a Bird

The carving is almost as important a part of the chicken, turkey, goose or duck dinner as the eating. The skillful carver deftly removes piece after juicy piece of meat, leaving the left-over portion somewhat undressed looking, perhaps, but neat nevertheless. In days long ago, when dining and its attendant ceremonies were looked upon as something of an art, an ambitious host wrote a book called, "The Book of Carving," wherein he described the various steps in the process of carving whatever kind of roast might be set before the host. The carving was so skillfully done that the pieces could be put back together to make a whole bird.

The modern host does not take carving so seriously today, but the head of the table still takes pride in his skill.

Second in importance only to the bird to be carved is the carving equipment, consisting of a long, stout fork and a. sharp-pointed knife of suitable size. It is worth while to have a steel at hand, too, for as the joints of the bird are separated, the tip of the knife may become slightly dulled. Only the sharpest knife will cut the tender, juicy slices so that they look their smooth best.

For carving, the bird is placed before the carver so that the breast is toward his left. It is convenient to have a small platter at hand, to which the carver may transfer the pieces as he removes them from the bird.

Insert the fork firmly about midway of the breast. Remove the leg at the hip joint, making a cut through the skin between the body and the thigh. Cut through the skin and flesh all around the joint, and 589 with the tip of the knife find the socket and separate the parts of the joint. Transfer the piece to the smaller platter, separate the drumstick from the thigh at the joint. If the bird is large, such as a capon or a turkey, cut the thigh into thin slices. Remove the wing next, being careful to separate it at the joint. Slice the meat from the breast, cutting parallel to the breast bone. Serve a slice of the white and one of the dark on each plate. To serve the dressing, remove it from the body cavity with a spoon.

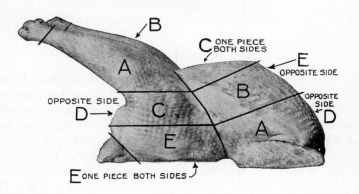

Carving five portions of roast chicken—dark and light meat equally divided

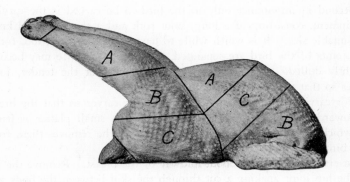

Carving six portions of roast chicken—dark and light meat equally divided

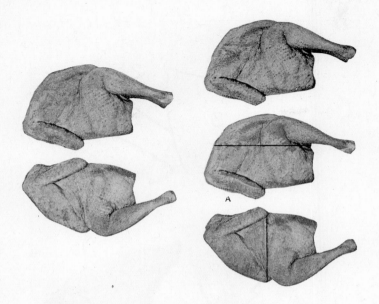

A

The standard method for cutting up chickens for broiling is to split them down the back, making two portions. This practical method divides the light and dark meat into equal portions, and makes attractive pieces for serving.

Broilers which yield halves that are too large to serve easily may be divided into four pieces. Diagrams to the right above show two methods of cutting. In one method, after the broiler has been split into halves lengthwise, each half is divided into two pieces as shown in the middle picture at the right. This divides the light and dark meat into almost equal portions. The other method is to divide each half as shown in the lower right diagram, yielding one serving of almost all light meat and one serving of almost all dark meat.

Very small broilers, stuffed and trussed, are baked and served whole.

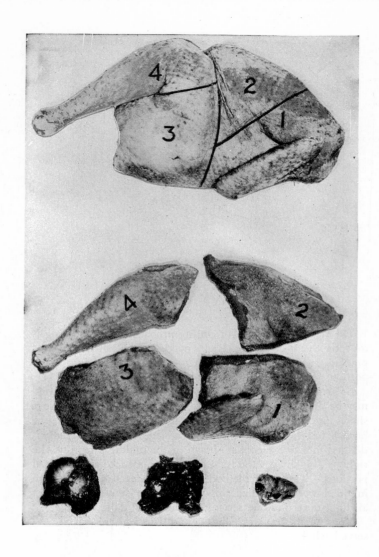

Cutting a chicken into four parts for frying or stewing: 1—
upper breast, wings and upper back; 2—breast and side;
3—upper portion of thigh and lower back; 4—leg and part of
thigh; gizzard, liver, heart.

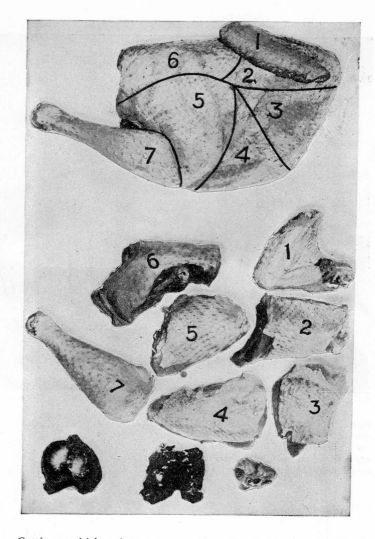

Cutting a chicken into seven portions for frying or stewing:
1—wing; 2—side back; 3—upper breast; 4—lower breast;
5—thigh; 6—lower back; 7—leg; gizzard, liver, heart.

Eggs. By Jean Baptiste Simeon Chardin 1699–1779. A painting in the collection of the Art Institute of Chicago, shown in the Century of Progress Exhibit of Art.

RECIPES CURIOUS
AND HISTORICAL

Rare old cookbooks and fascinating historical treatises on cookery give insight into the esteem with which famous cooks and gourmets of bygone days regarded eggs and poultry.

In home medication as well as in cookery both eggs and poultry were indispensable. "Restoratives" almost invariably included eggs, and often both eggs and chicken broth, or essence of chicken. From the recipes and formulas "Collected and Practised by the Right Honourable, the Countess of Kent," published in 1708, come these recipes for restoratives.

Restorative
(1708)

"Take a well flesht Capon from the Barn door, and pluck out his Intrails, then wash it within with a little white wine, then flay off all the skin, and take out his bones, and take the flesh, only cut it in little pieces, and put it into a little stone bottle, and put to it one ounce of white Sugar candy, six Dates slit, with the stones and piths taken out, one large Mace, then stop the bottle up fast, and set it in a chafer of water, and let it boil three hours; then take it out, and pour the juice from the meat, and put to it one spoonful of red rose-water, and take the better part for your breakfast four hours before dinner, and the other part at three a clock in the afternoon, being blood warm."

Another Restorative
(1708)

"Take two new-laid Eggs, and take the whites clean from them, and put the yolks both in one shell; then put in two spoonfuls of Claret wine, seven grains of Ambergriece small bruised, and a little Sugar-Candy; stir all these together, and make them blood-warm, and sup them up for a breakfast three or four hours before Dinner."

A Restoring Breakfast
(1708)

"Take the Brawn of a Capon, or Pullet, twelve Jordan almonds blanched, beat them together, and strain out the juice with a draught of strong Broth, and take it for Breakfast, or to bedward."

The wish of Henry of Navarre (1553–1610), later King Henry IV of France, that every peasant might have a chicken in his pot on Sunday has become popular history. King Henry not only made the wish but he actually gave the recipe for stewing the fowl. Babet writes that "in spite of its apparent simplicity, the poule-au-pot of good King Henry was a choice morsel." He gives the directions for cooking it as follows:

Poule-au-pot
(16th century)

"Get a good, fat hen and buy it alive if possible, or at least not drawn. Put aside the liver, gizzard, heart, lungs, head, neck and wings, and mince the whole with ham, lard, bread crumbs dipped in milk, salt, pepper, spices, sweet herbs, parsley, garlic, for we must remember that Henry IV was a Bernaise, and that garlic is found in all the cooking in that part of the country.

"When the hash is ready, add the yolks of eggs and put the stuffing into the fowl. Sew the opening, tie with string and cook as follows:

"All is in readiness for the pot-au-feu. Skim it, add the vegetables, and put in the chicken, which you allow to cook slowly. Withdraw it before the flesh loosens from the bones, which would occur very quickly in the case of a young bird. From time to time lift it on a skimmer and prick it with a knife to ascertain the degree to which it has been cooked.

"Prepare upon a bed of parsley, or better yet, upon a bed of cress. Take the hen from the pot, remove the strings, and lay it on the platter, sprinkling fine salt over it. It should be eaten very hot. The stuffing should be firm enough to cut in slices. The bouillon obtained by this process is exquisite, and the fowl loses none of its flavor. Taste it, and become convinced of King Henry IV's solicitude for the peasants of France."

"Food and raiment is all the portion that a man hath in this life," wrote Will Rabisha in 1661 in the introduction to his book *Cookery*. The book, he says, represents "the whole body of cookery dissected, Taught and fully manifested, Methodically, Artificially, and according to the best Tradition of the English, French, Italian, Dutch,—or, a Sympathie of all varieties in Natural compounds in that Mysterie." Then he invites the reader in verse to "read his book and judge his pains, his is the labour, yours the gains."

Among the most fascinating of Rabisha's recipes are these:

To Fry Primrose Leaves in March with Eggs
(1661)

"Take a handful or two of Primrose leaves, mince them very small, beat them into a dozen eggs; your pan being very hot, cool it a little, and put in a piece of butter, so put in your eggs, fry them very soberly; when it is enough on that side, turn it, and lay it in again on the other side; when it is enough, scrape on Sugar, scruise on the juice of a Lemmon or two."

How to Bake a Goose
(1661)

"Break the bones of your Goose and parboil him; then season him with Pepper and Salt, a little Cloves or Mace; if you please, you may bake a Rabbet or two with it, because your stubble-Geese are very fat, and your Rabbets dry, you need not lard either. Bake it in good hot butter paste. This is the

Goodwyfe's pye upon the season, or against a good time, by the same Rules as aforesaid, you may bake other goose flesh or fowl, according to its nature or quality."

A little later came *The Compleat Cook's Guide* (1683) with its directions for making a Chicken Pye.

To Make a Chicken Pye
(1683)

"After you have trust your chickens, then break their Legs and Breast-bones, and raise your crust of the best Paste, lay them in a Coffin close together, with their bodies full of butter, then lay upon and underneath them, currans, great Raisins, Pruans, Cinnamon, Sugar, whole Mace and Sugar, whole Mace and Salt, then cover all with good store of butter, and so bake it; then pour into it the white-wine, rosewater, sugar, cinnamon, and vinegar mixt together, with Yolks of two or three Eggs beaten amongst it, and so serve it."

A sort of sweetened egg whip called a "Whip Syllabub" is mentioned in many rare old cookbooks, but none of them gives more entertainingly the recipe for making it than does the quaintly named *The Closet of the Eminently Learned Sir Keneline Digby, Kt., Opened.* Even in 1669, cooks were interested in the secrets of other cooks, especially those from great houses.

To Make a Whip Syllabub
(1669)

"Take the whites of two Eggs, and a pint of cream, six spoonfuls of Sack, as much sugar as will sweeten it; then take a Birchen rod and whip it; as it riseth with froth, skim it, and put it into the Syllabub pot; so continue it with whipping and skimming, till your Syllabub-pot be full."

Many of the recipes are accompanied by anecdotes and elaborate explanations, such as these directions for preparing tea with eggs.

Tea with Eggs

"The Jesuite that came from China, Ann. 1664, told Mr. Waller, That there they use sometimes in this manner. To near a pint of the infusion, take two yolks of new laid eggs, and beat them very well with as much fine Sugar as is sufficient for this quantity of Liquor, when they are very well incorporated, pour your Tea upon the Eggs and Sugar, and stir them well together. So drink it hot. This is when you come home from attending business abroad, and are very hungry, and yet have not conveniency to eat presently a competent meal. This presently discusseth and satisfieth all rawness and indigence of the stomack, flyeth suddainly over the whole body and into the veins, and strengthneth exceedingly, and preserves one a good while from necessity of eating. Mr. Waller findeth all those effects of it thus with Eggs. In these parts, He saith, we let the hot water remain too long soaking upon the Tea, which makes it extract into itself the earthy parts of the herb. The water is to remain upon it, no longer that whiles you can say the *Miserere* Psalm very leisurely. Then pour it upon the sugar, or sugar and Eggs."

Nor were hard-cooked eggs overlooked. In the earliest book on salads, *Acetaria, a Discourse of Sallets* (1706), Alexis Soyer gives as one of the rules of salad making "That there be the Yolks of fresh and new-laid Eggs, boiled moderately hard, to be mingl'd and mash'd with the Mustard, Oyl, and Vinegar; and part to cut into quarters, and eat with the Herbs."

In *The True Gentlewoman's Delight,* the Countess of Kent tells how to make a "fool", which seems to have been a sort of custard pudding.

To Make a Fool

(1708)

"Take two quarts of cream, set it over the fire and let it boil, then take the yolks of twelve Eggs, and beat them very well with three or four spoonfuls of cold Cream; before you put the Eggs into the hot Cream, take three or four spoonfuls of the Cream out of the Skillet, and pour it into the Eggs, and stir it together, and then strain the Eggs into the Skillet of hot Cream, stirring it all the time to keep it from burning, then set it on the fire, and let it boil a little while, but keep it still stirring for fear of burning, then take it off, and let it stand and cool, then take two or three spoonfuls of Sack, and put in the dish, and some four or five Sippets, and put them in the dish, set the dish and the sippets a drying, and when they be dry that they hang to the dish, sweeten with Cream, and pour it in the dish softly, because the Sippets shall not rise up, this will make three dishes, when it is cold it is fit to be eaten."

And here are some other recipes recommended by the Countess whose reputation as a good cook seems to have been unquestionable.

To Make Yellow Tart-fluff

(1708)

"Take four and twenty Eggs, and beat them with Salt together, and put it into a quart of seething Milk, stirring until it caudles, then take it off, and put it into a Napkin hanging it up till all the Whay be run through; when it is cold, take it and grind it in a stone Mortar with Sack and Sugar to your taste; and otherwise to make it look white, leave the yolks, and instead of Sack put in Rose-water."

How to Make a very good Tansie

(1708)

"Take fifteen eggs, and six of the whites, beat them very well, then put in some Sugar, and a little Sack, beat them again, then put about a pint or a little more of Cream, then beat them again, then put in the juice of Spinnage or of Primrose-leaves to make it green, then put in some more Sugar if it be not sweet enough, then beat it again a little, and so let it stand till you fry it, when the first course is in, then fry it with a little sweet Butter; it must be stirred and fryed very tender; when it fryed enough, then put it in a dish, and strew some Sugar upon it, and serve it in."

What the modern cook would probably call a caramel custard, *The Frugal Housewife* (1730) calls Burnt Cream.

Burnt Cream

(1730)

"Boil a stick of cinnamon in a pint of cream, four eggs well beat, leaving out the whites; boil the cream and thicken it with eggs as for custard; then put in your dish and put over it half a pound of loaf sugar beat and seared; heat a fire-shovel red hot and hold it over the top till the sugar be brown. So serve it up."

The anonymous author of *The Modern Cook* includes both simple and elaborate recipes for egg and poultry dishes. Written with painstaking neatness in the careful hand of eighteenth century scribes, the cooking directions are given with many a fine flourish about the capital letters. Eggs were recommended as a meat substitute in the diet of the poor.

A sort of Pottage which the Poor may make instead of Meat Broth

(18th century)

"The Poor may make a wholesome Pottage by mixing one or two yolks of eggs in a pint of boiling water, with a little Honey or Sugar, and two or three spoonsfull of Wine."

Compare this version of a chicken pie with the modern one.

Pottage a la Houzarde

(18th century)

"Take two chickens, pick them very clean, truss them, and put them in the Broth Pot for half an hour, then take them out and cut them in pieces as for a Fricasee, and put them into a Stew-pan with some melted Butter, season'd with Pepper, Salt, sweet Herbs, and fine spices, and rasp Bread and Parmesan cheese upon them one after another, as you do Smolts, or fry'd Gudgeons; then put them handsomely in a Pastry-pan, and let them take a fine colour in the Oven. Take a French Rowl, cut it in slices; make a layer of Bread in your Soop-dish, and another of Parmesan Cheese, another of boil'd Cabbage, and one of Bread over all, that the Cabbage may not appear; put your Dish on the Stove, with some good Broth in it; let it simmer till the Bread be almost dry, then drudge it with Parmesan Cheese, and brown it with the cover of a Pastry-pan: Then shove a thin Skimmer under your Bread in the dish, and put in some Broth till your Bread swims in it. When it is ready to serve, lay your chickens on handsomely, and serve it hot."

France seems to have a special claim on historic chicken dishes. In addition to the recipe for Henry IV's stewed chicken, the directions for preparing chicken à la Marengo has been preserved for us by some forgotten chef. This is the way the chicken is said to have been prepared for Napoleon Bonaparte the evening before the Battle of Marengo (1800). This is the modern form of the recipe.

599

Chicken a la Marengo

1 stewing chicken	1 bay leaf
4 tbsp. olive oil	Thyme to suit taste
2 c. chicken stock	Parsley
4 tbsp. flour	Salt
1 egg yolk	Pepper to suit taste

Cut stewing chicken in desired pieces. Cover with water, simmer until tender. Remove and fry in olive oil with parsley and a bit of thyme. Remove chicken from pan. Stir flour into the drippings in the pan, add the chicken stock and then the beaten egg yolk. Cook until thick, stirring constantly. Strain and pour over the chicken. To serve it as it was served to Napoleon, arrange a border of poached eggs on strips of toast for garnish.

Almost all of the authors of old cookbooks stress economy, or what was considered economy in their day. John Farley, for many years chief cook at the London Tavern, was no exception. His recipes, especially that for the Yorkshire Goose Pie, will enable the reader to compare nineteenth and twentieth century ideas of economy.

Broiled Eggs

"Having cut a toast round a quartern loaf, brown it, lay it on your dish, butter it and very carefully break six or eight eggs on the toast. Take a red hot shovel, and hold it over them. When done, squeeze a Seville orange over them, grate a little nutmeg over it, and serve it up for a side-plate. Or you may poach your eggs, and lay them on a toast, or toast your bread crisp, and pour a little boiling water over it. Season it with a little salt, and then lay your poached eggs on it."

Duck Stewed

"You may lard it or not, as you like. Half roast it, and then put it into a stewpan, with a pint or more of good gravy, a quarter of a pint of red wine, onion chopped small, a spoonful of eschalot vinegar, a piece of lemon-peel, cayenne and salt. Stew it gently, close cover it till tender. Take out the duck from the sauce, boil it up quick, strain and pour over the duck; add truffles and morels, if agreeable."

Icing for Tarts

"Beat the white of an egg to strong froth, and put in, by degrees, four ounces of double refined sugar, with as much gum as will lie on a sixpence, beat and sifted fine. Beat them half an hour, and then lay it thin on the tarts."

Yorkshire Goose Pie

"Split a large fat goose down the back, and take out all the bones; treat a turkey and two ducks the same way, and season them well with salt and pepper, and also six woodcocks. Lay the goose down on a clean dish, with the skin-side down, and lay the turkey into the goose in the same manner. Have ready a large hare, well cleaned, and cut in pieces, and stewed in the

600

oven, with a pound of butter, a quarter of an ounce of mace beat fine, the same of white pepper, and salt to the taste. Stew it till the meat leaves the bones, and skim the butter off the gravy. Pick the meat clean off, and beat it very fine in a marble mortar with the butter taken off, and then lay it on the turkey. Take twenty-four pounds of the finest flour, six pounds of butter, and half a pound of fresh rendered suet. Make the paste pretty thick, and raise the pie in an oval form. Roll out a lump of paste, and cut it into vine-leaves, or any other form; then rub the pie with the yolks of eggs, and put the ornaments on the walls; turn the hare, turkey, and goose, upside down, and lay them in the pie, with the ducks at each end, and the woodcocks at the sides; make the lid pretty thick, and put it on. Ornament the lid, but make a hole in the middle of it, and make the walls of the pie an inch and a half higher than the lid. Then rub it all over with the yolks of eggs, and bind it round with three fold paper, and lay the same over the top. Bake it four hours; and when it comes out, melt two pounds of butter in the gravy that comes from the hare, and pour it hot into the pie through a funnel. Close it well up, and do not cut it in less than eight or ten days. If the pie is to be sent to any distance, it will be necessary, in order to prevent the air getting to it, to stop up the hole in the middle of the lid with cold butter."

Yorkshire Giblet Pie

"Put a tea-cup full of grots into the blood of the goose while it is warm, in order to swell them. Grate the crumb of a penny loaf, and pour on it a gill of boiling milk. Shred half a pound of beef suet very fine, chop four or five leaves of sage and two leeks very small, put three yolks of eggs, and season it to the taste with pepper, salt and nutmeg. Mix them all up together, and have ready the giblets well seasoned with pepper and salt. Lay them round a deep dish, and put a pound of fat beef over the pudding in the middle of the dish. Pour in half a pint of gravy, lay on a good paste, and bake it in an oven moderately heated."

Pompadour Cream

"Take the whites of five eggs, and beat them to a strong froth; put them into a tossing pan, with two spoonfuls of orange-flower water, and two ounces of sugar; stir it gently for three or four minutes, then pour it into a dish, and pour good melted butter over it. This is a pretty corner dish for a second course at dinner, and must be served up hot."

One of the most elaborate of all poultry dishes is said to have been first prepared by the French Prince Soubise. The prince was a soldier, who seems not to have distinguished himself on the battlefield. An English philosopher-historian, who signs himself "An Old Bohemian" describes the dish as it was prepared for Madame Pompadour, mistress of Louis XV. The Bohemian remarks acidly that had the prince been as diligent in his soldiering as he was in concocting fanciful dishes he might not have lost so many battles.

Saucisses Soubisse aux Pommes Pompadour

"Roast at a brisk, clear fire a fine turkey, a plump duck, two fat capons, and six good-sized pigeons. When half done, carve out the breasts, and chop them with the hearts and livers very fine, together with two pounds of lean pork

601

chops, half broiled; add a pound of sound fat bacon cut into very small pieces, with two ounces each of sweet herbs, parsley, truffles, mushrooms, and sultanas, the peel of a lemon, and ten grains of garlic, all chopped very fine. Work and need the mass well together; season with four ounces fine salt, one ounce each of ground pepper and pimento, and two nutmegs grated; add an ounce and a half of fresh lemon-juice and a wineglassful of Malaga, and thoroughly mix the whole mass once more; then fill in very thin small chitterlings, and make into sausages three inches long, about twelve to fifteen to the pound. Pare, mash, and dry six pounds of mealy potatoes, and boil them in new milk; when thoroughly done and soft, mash and pass through a fine sieve; chop two ounces each of parsley and shalots very fine, and fry eight to ten minutes in six ounces fresh butter; mix with this a pint of cream and the yolks of four eggs, and add the mixture to the mash. Season with an ounce and a half of fine salt, a quarter ounce of ground white pepper, and a little mace. Put the whole in an earthenware dish and heat in a brisk oven until the crust turns yellow; melt a pound of fresh butter in a saucepan over a charcoal fire, and add a teacupful of water; when boiling put in the sausages, cover close, and keep for six or eight minutes in the fire. Serve hot on the mashed potatoes."

The same author gives the recipe for Arrack, a cream and egg punch.

Arrack
(1887)

"Beat the yolks of four fresh eggs with two ounces of finely pounded sugar-candy; add a quartern of new milk, and half a nutmeg grated. Heat a quart of sweet cream to boiling; take the pot off the fire, and add to the hot cream the eggs, sugar, milk, and nutmeg. Stir, then add half a pint of arrack or rum, mix thoroughly, and serve hot in tumblers."

Credit for inventing pâté de foie gras goes to Strasburg, where it was first prepared in one of the princely houses. Later on the preparation of these special goose livers in small earthern jars called tureens became a leading industry of the city. The Old Bohemian tells how French pastry-cooks prepared pâté.

"The pastrycook divides the liver into two parts, at the spot where the lobes join. He cuts out the part that has been in immediate contact with the gall bladder, which is generally marked by a yellowish tint, and washes the cut surfaces with new milk. For a tureen that will fetch from a guinea to twenty-five shillings in the market, he takes three livers, one and a quarter to one and a half pound each. This gives six parts, of which he selects the four finest for the body of the tureen. He pares about a pound of truffles, and cuts three-fourths of them into thin and narrow strips, about the length of a little finger. With these he sticks the four half-livers all over. The remaining two halves he cuts into very thin slices, which he pounds in a mortar. He boils about two pounds of bacon for an hour, lets them get cold, and cuts them up very fine. He adds to the pounded liver one ounce and a half each of shalots, mushrooms, and capers, the remainder of the truffles chopped fine, four anchovies, boned, washed and chopped, a teaspoonful of fine salt, and one of white pepper and grated nutmeg, and the bacon. He pounds and triturates the whole, and rubs the mass through the tamis. He annoints the tureen all over with fresh butter, and proceeds to fill it, putting in first a layer of the stuffing or lining, then a half liver; sprinkled with salt and pepper; then another layer of stuffing and another half liver, and so on a third and a fourth, with a layer of the lining to finish up. He now puts on the top a pound of fresh butter, mixed with half an ounce of fine salt and white pepper, spreading it out all over the top. He finishes up with some slices of fat bacon, puts on the cover, pastes paper all around, and bakes the pâté about two hours in a slow oven. When done, he takes off the cover, and pours a layer of hog's lard over the mass, to shield it from the air."

"Then," adds the philosopher, "the tureens are sent forth on their dyspeptic mission to all parts of the world."

And through all the books, from earliest to latest, run recipes for galantines, forerunner of today's jellied chicken. Galantines are mentioned as early as the fourteenth century. The early galantines, such a one perhaps as Chaucer mentions, were elaborate affairs. A turkey, known in those days as the cock of India, was boned so as to keep the meat in one large piece. The boned bird was spread out flat, skin side down, and seasoned. Then a goose similarly boned was laid on the turkey, a boned hen on the goose, a pigeon on the hen, a squab on the pigeon, and a tiny bird, perhaps a lark, on top of all. The whole was then rolled up tightly, tied and put into a huge iron pot. It was covered with water, seasonings were added and the roll was simmered gently for a whole day, or even longer. When the meat was done the pot was set in a cool place. As the broth cooled it formed a jelly around the roll. When cold the whole was sliced and served.

Early American Recipes

Cookery in early America was as varied as the traditions of the cooks who came to this country. But not always were customary supplies available, and it was necessary to make the best of the materials at hand. So there developed, especially in New England and in the South, special types of cooking. Many of the recipes have been preserved.

A number of these recipes are named Shirley, after the home of Robert Carter to whom the king gave enormous grants of land along the James River. From this home, famous for its hospitality, and presided over by a succession of seven wives, came the Shirley recipes.

Creamed Chicken Shirley

1 lb. cold chicken, cut as for salad
2 hard cooked eggs, chopped

4 tbsp. butter
2 tbsp. flour

Cover the chicken with 1½ cups milk. Heat. Stir in the butter and flour, worked together. Season with salt, red and black pepper to taste. Just before serving add a glass of sherry and the eggs.

Coquilles de Volaille is a French recipe that was transplanted to Philadelphia in the early nineteenth century.

Coquilles de Volaille

1 fowl, boiled and diced	1 c. fat-covered stock

Put into a pan with a chopped challot. Mix 2 teaspoons flour with a little water and add. Stir until sauce is thick. Add 1 cup butter, ½ cup mushrooms, sliced and fried, 1 cup heavy cream. When this grows cold, add a large cup of good sherry. Place in shells, sprinkle with crumbs and brown.

The Famous Winston Potato Pudding
(1799)

2 lbs. potatoes (after they are boiled and mashed)	8 eggs
	Nutmeg to taste
½ lb. butter	½ pt. sweet corn
1 lb. white sugar	½ tumbler brandy

Boil and mash the potatoes. Cream the butter and add it. Beat the eggs and beat into them the sugar.
When the potatoes are cool, add sugar and egg, then cream, brandy and nutmeg. Pour into a pie crust and bake.

Simple Potato Pudding

6 large potatoes, boiled and mashed	6 eggs
	1 saucer sugar

Beat the egg yolks yellow. Beat in the sugar, and add the potato. Beat egg whites to a froth, and add them, folding in carefully. Put into buttered baking dish and bake in moderate oven 15 minutes.

Yellow Chicken Fricassee

1 stewing hen	2 egg yolks, beaten
1 slice bacon	½ c. water
½ onion	1 tsp. lemon juice
Pinch of nutmeg	1 tsp. vinegar
2 tbsp. butter	1 c. thick cream

Cut up hen and put into heavy pan with the bacon. Add the onion, nutmeg, butter and water. Cover and steam until chicken is tender, about 1½ hours. Remove chicken from broth.
Combine egg yolks, cream, lemon juice and vinegar. Pour into the drippings in the pan, stirring until it thickens. This makes a custard to serve over the chicken.

From *Mrs. Howland's New England Cookbook* (1846), "compiled with regard to the most economical mode of preparing dishes," and "recommended particularly to the attention of those who would cook well at moderate expense," come these recipes.

604

Sponge Cake

"The weight of six eggs in sugar, the weight of four eggs in flour, a little rose water. The whites and yolks of ten eggs should be beaten thoroughly and separately. The eggs and sugar should be well beaten together; but after the flour is sprinkled, it should not be stirred a moment longer than is necessary to mix it well; it should be poured into the pan, and got into the oven with all possible expedition. Twenty minutes is about long enough to bake it."

Cheap Sponge Cake

"Four eggs, three cups of sugar, one cup of milk, one tea-spoonful of saleratus, flour enough to make it a good stiff batter, a little salt and spice, quick oven. Bake it twenty minutes."

Rice Flour Sponge Cake

"It is made like other sponge cake, except that you use three quarters of a pound of rice flour, thirteen eggs, leaving out four whites, and a little salt."

Wedding Cake

"Four pounds of flour, four pounds of sugar, three of butter, forty eggs, five pounds of stoned raisins, three pounds of currants, one ounce of mace, half an ounce of nutmeg, six tea-spoonfuls of rose-water, four tea-spoonfuls of cream of tartar, stirred in the flour, two tea-spoonfuls of saleratus well dissolved. Beat the butter and sugar to a cream; beat the yolks and whites separate, add the flour gradually, then the spice and saleratus. Bake it two hours and a half."

Frosting for Cake

"Three and a half pounds of loaf sugar, the whites of twelve eggs, lemon juice, and a little potato starch."

Custard Pudding

"Mix by degrees a pint of milk with a large spoonful of flour, the yolks of five eggs, and some grated lemon. Butter a basin that will exactly hold it; pour the batter in, and tie a floured cloth over. Put it in boiling water over the fire, and turn it about a few minutes to prevent the eggs from going to one side. Half an hour will boil it. Serve it with sweet sauce."

To Boil a Turkey

"Prepare and stuff the turkey, the same as for roasting; boil it two hours, with a piece of striped pork, a nice head of cabbage, flat turnips and potatoes. Serve up with butter gravy."

To Hannah Widdifield, famous in Philadelphia for the fine food she made, goes credit for the recipe for what she called a Homeopathic Sponge Cake, as well as for Mock Cream.

Homeopathic Sponge Cake

Twelve eggs   Three quarters of a pound of flour
One pound of sugar   Three tablespoonsful of water

Separate the eggs, beat the yolks, sugar and water together until very thick and light; then whisk the whites until stiff and dry, which stir in lightly with the flour, half of each at a time. Butter and line your pan with white paper, put in the batter, and bake in a moderate oven.

Mock Cream

"Take two quarts of new milk, then whisk the whites of five eggs and the yolk of one, just sufficiently to incorporate them, which stir into the milk gradually; place it on the fire and let it come to a slight boil, observing to stir it all the time; then take it off and continue stirring until it cools; then strain it through a fine sieve and place it on ice to get cold.

"This is very nice, and when carefully made cannot be detected from the richest cream."

Frickasie a la Grandmother

"Take ye fowls, cut them in pieces and clean them. Season with pepper and salt, a little mace, nutmeg, cloves, some parsley, a little bit of onion. Let them lay two hours, then flour them well, fry in sweet butter hott before you put them in. Fry fine brown. Wash ye pan and put them in again with a pint of gravy. Let them symmer in ye gravy. Take the yolks of three eggs with a little grated nutmeg and a little juice of lemon, and two spoonfuls of wine. Shake it over the fire until it is as thick as cream, pour over ye frickasie, and so serve it to ye table hott."

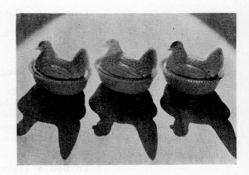

MY OWN RECIPES

MY OWN RECIPES

INDEX TO RECIPES

611

614

615

618

619

621

623

624

625

626

627

628

629

Games and Game Bantams

Games
  Modern Black-Breasted Red
  Modern Brown-Red
  Modern Golden Duckwing
  Modern Silver Duckwing
  Modern Birchen
  Modern Red Pyle
  Modern White
  Modern Black
Game Bantams
  Modern Black-Breasted Red
  Modern Brown-Red
  Modern Golden Duckwing
  Modern Silver Duckwing
  Modern Birchen
  Modern Red Pyle
  Modern White
  Modern Black
  Old English Black-Red
  Old English Spangled

Fancy Bantams

Polish
  White-Crested Black
  Non-Bearded Golden
  Non-Bearded Silver
  Non-Bearded White
  Buff-Laced
  Bearded Golden
  Bearded Silver
  Bearded White
Mille Fleur
  Booted
Silkies
Wyandotte
  Buff
  Black
  Columbian
  Partridge
  Silver Penciled
  White
Sebrights
  Golden
  Silver

Fancy Bantams —Con.

Rose-Comb
  White
  Black
Booted
  White
Brahmas
  Light
  Dark
Cornish
  Dark
Cochin
  Buff
  Partridge
  White
  Black
Japanese
  Black-Tailed
  White
  Black
  Gray

Oriental Class

Sumtras
  Black
Malays
  Black-Breasted Red
Malay Bantams
  Black-Breasted Red

Continental Class

Campines
  Silver
  Golden

Special Class

Sultans
Frizzles

Turkeys

Bronze
Narragansett
White Holland
Black
Slate
Bourbon Red

Ducks

Pekin
  White
Aylesbury
  White
Rouen
  Colored
Cayuga
  Black
Call
  Gray
  White
East India
  Black
Muscovy
  Colored
  White
Swedish
  Blue
  Buff
Buff
Crested
  White
Runner
  Fawn and White
  White
  Penciled

Geese

Toulouse
  Gray
Embden
  White
African
  Gray
Chinese
  Brown
  White
Egyptian
  Gray
Canada
  Colored

GENERAL INDEX

iv

V